THE CHRIST OF EVERY ROAD

A Study in Pentecost

BY
E. STANLEY JONES

THE ABINGDON PRESS
NEW YORK   CINCINNATI   CHICAGO

Copyright, 1930, by
E. STANLEY JONES

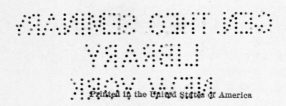
Printed in the United States of America

First Edition Printed January, 1930
Second Printing, January, 1930
Third Printing, January, 1930

CONTENTS

PREFACE

AFTER the publication of my last book, *Christ at the Round Table,* I determined that I would not write another for a number of years. The decision seemed wise.

On a recent evangelistic trip to South America, in the quiet hours of meditation on shipboard, this book in outline, if not in essence, came to me. When I returned to the United States the very first request I received was from the publishers asking me, in view of the forthcoming celebration of the nineteen hundredth anniversary of Pentecost throughout Christendom, to write a book on Pentecost. Ordinarily, it would have been the last thing to which I would or could have acceded. One cannot produce such a book by request. But when the gift of the quiet hours and the request of the publishers spoke the same thing the combination seemed a compulsion. This book is the result.

E. STANLEY JONES.

Mission House, Sitapur, U. P. India.

CHAPTER I

ON THE VERGE OF A SPIRITUAL AWAKENING?

THE world-ground is being prepared, I am persuaded, for a spiritual awakening on a very extensive scale. I do not say this lightly—it is a growing conviction, forced upon me by the facts. The factors that compose the preparing of this world-ground seem to me to be these:

First, the scientific attitude toward life, which seemed in the beginning to be inimical to the gospel, is creating a soil upon which that gospel can come to its own. The scientific attitude is a frank, open demand for facts. Its sphere seemed at first to be in the realm of physical fact. Now it is penetrating into all realms and is sifting all facts—physical, mental, and spiritual. Some have attempted to reconcile science and religion by saying that science has as its sphere the province of physical facts and religion the province of values. This division seems to me to be artificial. The method of science will go over, is going over, into all realms. Can our gospel stand up under this search for fact? Not if it is a system dogmatically and arbitrarily imposed on life which we must obey or be lost. It can, if it turns out to be, not something imposed on life, but something coming up out of life, necessary to life, completing life. Someone has said that the gospel found congenial soil among the Greeks in their cry of "a return to nature." The gospel was something that fitted into human nature and completed human nature. It broke the shackles that made a man less than a man and restored him to normal, symmetrical, harmonious human living.

On this soil of a return to the facts the gospel will come into its own. It is founded on fact, the Fact of Christ. I am not afraid that men will be too scientific, I am afraid they will not be scientific enough. I am persuaded that if we go far enough with the facts, they will lead us to the central fact of our moral and spiritual universe—Christ.

His gospel is not a theory spun out of the brain of a philosopher apart from life, unchecked by the facts of life. It came out of life and it speaks to life. A great English schoolmaster once cried, "My creed is life . . . blessed be life, the King!" Under the searching scrutiny of the moral facts and under the testing of the ways of human living, I am persuaded that it is turning out that Christ, our gospel, is "not a mere way of life, nor even the medicine of life, but Life itself," so that we can cry, "My creed is Life . . . blessed be Life, the King!"

The Hebrew word was Goodness, the Greek word was Light, the Hindu word is Devotion, the Christian word is Life. The Christian word is Life because our gospel is founded on life and it imparts life. Blessed be Life, the King!

In the train one day I was talking with a famous Orientalist. He was going fifteen hundred miles across the burning plains of India to fill up a single gap in his knowledge of Buddhism. Three thousand miles to verify a single point of knowledge! I was reverent in the face of such demand for truth. He said to me in very earnest tones, "We in Europe are looking for a new religion." I asked him what he wanted in the new religion. He replied, "First of all we want religion to take the open, frank attitude toward life; in other words, the scientific attitude; and, second, we want it to take the human attitude toward people, really to care for and love people. If we could get these two things in the new religion, we would be satisfied."

How the gospel had been overlaid and obscured by ecclesiasticism! So overlaid that even this discerning professor could not see it. I asked him to go back beyond the obscuring centuries and stand face to face with Christ and then make his two demands and see if they are answered. Out of the heart of the account come these decisive words of the Master, "Ye shall know the truth, and the truth shall make you free." Those words could be written over

[11]

the portals of any Hall of Science and exactly express the scientific attitude and spirit. I pointed this out to him. Very thoughtfully he replied, "If that expresses the attitude and mind of Christ, then no statement could more adequately and beautifully express our spirit." As to the second demand I said that to ask the question of Christ's real interest in and care for people was to answer it. He loved people—not merely their souls—he loved them. Then we traced out together this human strain in the gospel. At the close we were face to face with the inescapable fact of Christ and of his mind and saw that what we needed was not a new religion, but a new discovery of Christ, who is Religion.

It is remarkable that Jesus used two names for the Spirit, which would imply that he meets and more than meets the two demands of the professor: "The Paraclete, . . . even the Spirit of Truth." The Spirit of Truth—could any name more perfectly designate that which science is dimly groping after in its search for truth? Here is the very Spirit of Truth. And the Paraclete (*para*, "beside," and *kaleo*, "I call")—the One who stands alongside of men, counseling, consoling, inspiring, giving power by which to live—could anything more adequately express the passionate human interest of the Divine? The passion of science for truth and

[12]

the human interest are more than met in the gospel.

"Our civilization is passing into a new phase, the scientific," says Dean Inge, "and the whole framework of our Christianity belongs to the old phase, the classic. It is no wonder that the results just at present are so discouraging." Note that he says "the framework of our Christianity belongs to the old phase"—the framework, but not the facts. The facts of our gospel belong to Life itself. Any return to the facts will only bring us nearer to that gospel.

We therefore welcome this frank facing of life and its facts and believe that it is helping to prepare the world-ground for a spiritual awakening.

The second factor that is preparing the world-ground is the trend toward experience. It is part of the above but sufficiently definite to be noted separately. The trend is away from abstract ideas to ideas that life will back. How does it work in experience? is the searching test.

It can be seen at a glance that this is an atmosphere in which the gospel is at home. For, as Matthew Arnold says, "Jesus based himself always on experience, never on theory." If there is one note that sounds through the whole of the gospel, it is the note of experience: "That which we have seen and heard declare we unto you."

In the pages of the New Testament men did

not speculate about God—they shared him. They said little about the Beyond of salvation, they were so sure of its immediacy. They were sure of heaven because they had it—had it in immediate experience. Their souls sang to the music of things.

It is often said that only those elements in Christianity which are expressible in and through human experience are likely to influence an age which openly revolts against dogma. True, but there is little in the New Testament that these Christians were not finding in experience. God? They knew him! Miracles? They themselves were miracles! Resurrection? They had gone through it! Heaven? They were living in it! Hell? They had escaped it! Reconciliation? They rejoiced in it! Eternal life? They possessed it!

The demand of this age for experience leads straight toward Christ, for the whole of his gospel is founded upon experience.

The third factor in the world-ground is an undertone of deep spiritual craving. No one can get close to the soul of this age without feeling that in spite of its materialism and its lack of discipline there is an honest wistfulness running through it. Touch it in Latin America and you will find that the intelligentsia are standing between two worlds—one, the world of dogmatic authority, dead; the other, the world of spiritual experience, not yet born. Into that vacuum is rushing every cult of ancient and modern times, from the worship of Psyche and Cupid to Theosophy and Vedantism. It all witnesses to the vast thirst that is upon their spirits. "I can go to my work in the law courts at any time," said one of the outstanding lawyers of Latin America after he had been four hours in our Round Table Conference during the middle of a busy day, "but I cannot get this every day." A leading editor expressed his feeling in even more forceful language: "That was the happiest day of my life. I had lost my faith through wide reading and had been trying to regain it, but there I opened my life to Christ and he came into it. I have been living in a new world ever since. This is what Latin America needs." "Had I known this was the gospel, I should never have gone to these cults," said another brilliant, but thirsty mind. Their agnosticism is not irreligion, so much as it is a protest against hollow, unthinking dogmatism.

Get in touch with the students of the United States and under blasé or cynical attitudes you will find a heart-hunger that is appalling. It is there *if you can get to it*. When speaking to them it is a question as to whether they will mentally kick you out or fall at your feet. They are terribly hard on cant, on unreality, on words, but they rise like a trout to a fly when confronted with sincerity and a gospel that challenges the depths. A young thing of the flapper type marched up to me at the close of a meeting and said: "Gee, but you walked all over my needs this morning. Say, you got me, boy!" Slangy? Yes, but sincere. In her slangy words there was running the same sort of sincerity and spiritual craving as that voiced by a modern philosopher in these strong and stately words: "The fact of religious vision and its history of persistent expansion is our one ground for optimism. Apart from it, human life is a flash of occasional enjoyments lighting up a mass of pain and misery, a bagatelle of transient experience."[1] Or when Bradley says: "There is nothing more real than that which comes in religion. To compare facts such as these with what is given to us in outward existence would be to trifle with the subject. The man who demands a reality more solid than that of the religious consciousness seeks he knows not what" (Bradley, *Appearance and Reality,* p. 449). It seems that, as Dr. Wheeler Robinson says, "philosophers are now prepared in greater measure than formerly to consider religious experience as among the most significant of their data."

When we turn to the scientists they tell us that they are abandoning the idea of a universe

---

[1] Whitehead, *Science and the Modern World,* p. 276.

whose basic constituency is atoms, hard, like billiard balls, in favor of electrons, or organized force or energy centers. This new conception seems to be turning the scientific mind of the age from a materialistic conception and explanation of our universe to a spiritual interpretation. "Materialism as a philosophy is vanishing, for matter itself is vanishing." It is easier to step up from force centers to an immanent God than it was to posit a Creator of a hard material world out of nothing. It is no wonder, then, that, as Doctor Milligan tells us, there is a definite turn of the tide of scientific thinking away from agnostic materialism to God.

When we look at the group supposed to be apostles of modern materialism, the modern men of big business, I find they are not. No groups of people impress me more with their simplicity, frankness, and longing for a spiritual basis for human living than the groups of wealthy business men. As one faces these groups one finds the spiritual hunger appalling. It is often covered up, but it is there if we can get to it. "Don't talk to this crowd of business men about religion," said the head of a large business men's association. "They are hardboiled and will not take it." I didn't know how to talk about anything else, took for granted that they were folks just like myself, and wanted something, and so poured out my soul to them. At the close the

[17]

chairman said: "I take it all back. I am glad
you talked to us this way. We are men as well
as business men." Fundamentally, all men are
men. When we get down to that fundamental
manhood we find it has a fundamental need—
God.

When I turn to the East I find it changing
from center to circumference. The unchanging
East? The most changing portion of the globe
to-day. The tension is terrific and terrifying.
In this state of tension comes the consciousness,
sometimes only dimly realized, that the old sanctions of life are giving way, that they cannot
stand up under the modern pressure. The brilliant editor of an Indian weekly, conscious that
things are somehow going wrong, lashes out
against what he calls "the dead-set against Hinduism." Many have rushed into print to assure
him that there is no dead-set against Hinduism,
that new attitudes of sympathy and understanding have taken the place of the older attitude of
iconoclasm. But the editor is right. There is a
dead-set against Hinduism, though not in the
way he thinks. He picks out certain writers as
symptomatic of this dead-set against Hinduism.
His diagnosis is wrong. It is far deeper than
that. The dead-set against Hinduism comes
from the whole pressure of the scientific attitude toward life. He calls it Westernism. It is
deeper than Westernism and far more decisive.

The East can withstand Westernism, but this pressure is deep and all-inclusive. This facing of life frankly and openly and asking for the facts is undermining the religious sanctions of the East. The youth goes to his sacred books, which are nearly all based upon the a priori; he goes to the university, where all is based on the a posteriori. His soul becomes a seething mass of conflicting claims. Tradition and the scientific attitude struggle for mastery within him. Ten years ago I threw out the remark that the non-Christian systems are nestling up under the British Government, that the strain of modern conditions is not falling upon these systems as yet, but that when Self-Government begins, and the British Government is taken away, the pressure will rest directly on these systems. They will then be called upon to furnish a basis for modern living and to sustain the progressive reforms of modern life. When that pressure falls full upon them it will crack them to pieces. That is taking place before our very eyes. "All our customs are in the cooking pot," said a Hindu to a friend of mine one day. He meant the melting pot, but it didn't matter. "If we change all these customs, what happens to the authority of our sacred books wherein these customs are rooted and approved?" asked a discerning Hindu in Gandhiji's paper, Young India. The whole thing is summed up in the words of

[19]

the head of an orthodox Hindu college, spoken to me rather pathetically one day: "The intellectuals of South America are not the only ones who have found tradition losing its hold with nothing to take its place. Some of the rest of us would like to find new sanctions in the place of the decaying old."

There seem to be four alternatives before the soul of the East: First, the old religions, reconstituted and modified, providing sanctions for a progressive future. Second, secular civilization, the method that Turkey is trying. Third, Bolshevism, anti-religious and iconoclastic of the whole present order. Fourth, Jesus Christ, furnishing a basis of human living adequate to stand up under the modern stress and providing a moral and spiritual dynamic for personal redemption and for human progress.

I dismiss the first three as unworkable. I do not dismiss them lightly, but I am compelled to do so after looking into the soul of the East in our Round Table Conferences. Nowhere, except in Jesus Christ, did life seem to catch its rhythm, its harmony, its way to live. Outside of him there were left only the weird and the wistful: the weird was unthinkable, the wistful was unsatisfied. The future of religion is bound up with this Man. If we cannot be religious after the mind and Spirit of Christ, we cannot be religious at all. The lines in the East are converging upon this alternative: Christ or secular civilization. But the soul of the East is too spiritually inclined to be utterly secular, and we have reason to hope that the ultimate issue will be Christ. "We are now face to face with Him," said a thoughtful Hindu doctor to me one day.

That leads me to the last reason for thinking that we are on the verge of a spiritual awakening —religion is now becoming Christ-centric. As long as religion was denominational-centric God could not trust us with power. Had he done so, it would have run into a denominational megalomania. Nor could he trust us with power so long as religion was bound up with Westernism and its supremacies. Had he done that, it would have run into religious imperialism. But if religion is Christ-centric, if to be a Christian is to be Christlike, to catch his mind and Spirit, then I think God can back that with power to the utmost. We do not "step on the gas" if the car is turned toward the ditch. We apply power only when the road is open before us. Religion has an open road in Christ, and power applied will issue in good will, in self-abandoning service, in human brotherhood, in making individuals and society Christlike. God can trust us with power here.

To sum up:

My reasons for believing that the world-ground is being prepared for a spiritual awakening on a widespread scale are these:

The scientific attitude, with its demand for fact, is a soil upon which our gospel can come to its own, for it is founded upon fact and appeals to and produces fact;

The trend toward experience leads us straight toward the heart of the gospel, for the genesis and genius of that gospel is experience;

Underneath the agnosticism and materialism of our day runs a note of wistfulness that will burst into a seeking for God if we can bring to it a gospel that is adequate;

Every other way of life is breaking down, except Christ's way; this is seen especially in the East, where the entire foundations of life are giving way under modern pressure;

The issues are now being cleared, religion is becoming more and more Christ-centric and God can trust us with power to the utmost if it is to be used to make us Christlike.

If this is anywhere near a correct statement, we can see at a glance that the center of that situation is a demand for experience. If that be true, then it heads us straight toward Pentecost, where experience becomes immediate, living, morally and spiritually transforming, God-filled, aflame and adequate to meet life. At Pentecost Jesus' announcement of the central purpose of his coming was fulfilled: "I am come

[22]

that they might have life, and that they might have it more abundantly." They had life and they had it abundantly. And life is the one thing a seemingly living world needs.

> " 'Tis life of which my nerves are scant,
> More life and fuller that I want."

The first Hindu youth I talked to after my return to India said, very thoughtfully: "India has everything but life. You Christians have it."

But have we? Potentially, yes. Actually? I question.

At Pentecost potential life and actual life were fused into a living whole. As I believe that to be the dominant need of our age the theme and purpose of this book will be: Pentecost, the meeting and fusing of potential and actual life.

CHAPTER II

THE CHURCH BEHIND CLOSED DOORS

THERE is nothing new in saying that we live in an age of transition. Someone has facetiously said that when Adam and Eve were going out of the garden of Eden Adam turned to Eve and said, "My dear, this is an age of transition." The oldest known bit of writing in the world is a piece of papyrus in a Constantinople Museum. On it is written: "Alas, times are not what they used to be. Children no longer obey their parents and everyone wants to write a book." "We are suffering from transition," said a Bengali youth. He felt that we were suffering from it as one does from measles. Transition does seem to be as recurring as measles, and every age suffers.

Nevertheless, no one can get down amid the currents of this age without feeling that the thoughts and ideas and tendencies flowing there are not ripples on the surface, but something that is changing the whole fundamental outlook on life. We are in the throes of a passing from traditionalism to life based upon the authority of facts, of truth, of experience. This whole tendency sends life straight to the doors of the Christian Church, and there it stands waiting for some clear word of guidance, some note of certain experience of God, of the way to live, of power over evil and self, of victorious human living, of a human brotherhood.

Can the church speak that word out of the depths of its own radiant sense of God, out of its own experience of victory in life, out of its deep sense of sureness amid a world of clashing change?

I wish I could answer that with a clear-ringing "Yes," but my intimate contact with thousands of ministers in our Retreats, with the general church life in East and West, compels me to say that the church is largely unready for this hour. If the whole demand for experience heads us straight toward Pentecost, candor compels me to say that the church is not living in Pentecost.

It is living between Easter and Pentecost. Easter stands for life wrought out, offered; Pentecost stands for life appropriated, lived to its full, unafraid and clearly and powerfully witnessing to an adequate way of human living.

The church stands hesitant between the two. Hesitant, hence comparatively impotent. Something big has dawned on its thinking—Christ has lived, taught, died and risen again and has commissioned the church with the amazing Good News. But something big has yet to dawn in the very structure, make-up, and temper of the

life of the church—Pentecost. Easter has
dawned; Pentecost has not. If the church
would move up from that between-state to Pentecost, nothing could stop it—nothing!!

Now it is stopping itself by its own ponderous
machinery. Whenever we have been troubled in
conscience about our spiritual impotence we
have added a new wheel—a new committee or
commission, a new plan or program, and in the
end we have found that we have added one more
wheel, but with little or no power to run the old
or the new. We become busy—devastatingly
busy—turning old and new wheels by hand-
power, by sheer hand-power instead of lighting
central fires. So much of this is forced, nerve-
wearing, instead of spontaneous and healing.
Pentecost is not a living fact with us.

Hence we worship machinery instead of winning men. I once came down from Almora over
one of the worst winding roads of the world.
The driver of the bus had never driven in the
Himalayas before, and it happened that on his
first trip the previous day he had almost gone
over one of those terrifyingly precipitous cliffs.
He was nervous, so before starting back he came
around in front of the engine and stood with
folded hands saying his prayers to the machine.
That done, we started off, but had not gone far
when the engine began to overheat. There was
no water in the radiator! This was remedied.

But when we were still many miles from
our destination the machine stopped while going
up a hill. There was no petrol in the tank!
There we stayed until rescued. The driver said
his prayers to the machine, but put no water in
the radiator, and no petrol in the tank. We ran
on left-overs—and stopped. How often we worship the machinery of our ecclesiasticisms, depend on left-overs that have come down to us
from the sacrifices of our fathers, neglect the
sources of power, and then stop dead!

Imagine the early church with Pentecost eliminated! Imagine those men going out to interpret that wonderful message, but themselves not
inwardly corresponding with that message!
That hiatus would have been their paralysis. It
is ours. Pentecost made the men and the message one, hence their power. We cannot imagine
the church with Pentecost eliminated. For
there would have been no church. Here the
church was born. True, there had been the
period of gestation, for this holy thing lay within
the womb of the purpose of God and was nour-
ished by the life and teachings of Christ; the
cross was the birth-pain; Easter heralded the
coming birth, but Pentecost was the birthday.
On that day was born the New Humanity. A
new type of human being came into existence as
different from ordinary humanity as ordinary
humanity is different from the animal.

[27]

But suppose for a moment there had been no Pentecost. The situation would have been impossible for them. Here were men commissioned to proclaim a crucified Jesus as Saviour and Master; they were to replace the present world-order with a new world-order, the kingdom of God, and all this in face of a deep hostility—with their pre-Pentecost resources an impossible task. Without this inner transformation and moral re-enforcement we would expect to find them just where we do find them: It was evening on that day, "the first day of the week, when the doors were shut where the disciples were assembled for fear of the Jews." A church behind closed doors! A church living between Easter and Pentecost is always behind closed doors.

They had ringing in their ears the most gracious word that ever broke into human life—the gospel; they had seen the most perfect exhibition of living that this planet has known—His life; they had witnessed earth's most terrific and decisive moral struggle—his death; they had found their sadness turned into joy over the most transforming and astonishing fact in history—his resurrection; they had seen wounds that would heal wounds, a death that would banish death, a resurrection that would raise a world into new life; they had looked into that Face, so tender, so triumphant, and had heard him commission them to go share this with the world, and what had they done? With all of this back of them, what had they done? They had shut themselves up behind closed doors for fear. They had the message the world needed and awaited, the one message that would heal the sin-hurt of the world, and yet that message was shut up behind closed doors.

The only power that could and did get them out from behind those closed doors and loose them and their message upon the world was Pentecost. It was not enough for them to see Him and to hear him say, "Peace be unto you: As my Father hath sent me, even so send I you." His presence and his commission were not enough, for a week later we find them still behind closed doors. His assurances and his commission did not get them out. Only Pentecost got them out. For up to Pentecost the whole thing was on the outside of them, objective, something spoken, acted before them. It wasn't *in* them. At Pentecost this gospel came within them, became identical with them—what they had heard and seen and what they were became one, hence they became irresistible apostles of a mighty passion.

The church to-day is behind closed doors for fear. Pentecost has not closed the hiatus between its message and what it is, so with resources too inadequate to face life it closes the doors for fear.

The church has often stayed behind closed
systems of thought for fear of the scientist.
Afraid that the scientist will explain away
things that have become precious to us, we clasp
our faith to our bosoms to protect it, forgetting
that our faith does not need protection—it needs
proclamation. If it is real, it is its own protection. If it is not real, then the sooner we find it
out the better. "Ye shall know the truth, and
the truth shall make you free." There is only
one refuge in life and that is in truth and reality. If our faith can be broken, the sooner it is
broken the better. So I have taken my faith and
have put it out these years before the non-Christian world and have said: "There it is, brothers;
break it, if it can be broken. Only the truth can
make me free." It is glorious to watch your
faith rise out of the stress, resplendent, shining,
shining the brighter the more it is smitten. The
truth does make us free.

In Buenos Aires I saw a beautiful monument.
It was erected to Christopher Columbus, whose
statue stood upon the top. In front at the base
stood a figure of Liberty—her torch aloft; on
one side of her stood Youth looking with eager
face toward the dawn; on the other was Learning, her face thoughtful, an open book before
her; below these figures were strong muscular
men pushing at the prow of a boat, depicting the
boat of human progress; this whole side of the

monument evidently designed to show progress.
It was all eager, and faced toward the dawn. On
another side were two men caught in the coils of
serpents. One had succumbed, his face was
upon his hands, a broken, defeated soul; but the
other was putting up a great battle. He was
uncoiling the serpent about him and there was a
look of hope in his face as he looked toward the
rising sun. This side showed the fierce moral
struggle that men undergo. On the opposite
side was a pagan figure with the world in his
hand. At the back of the monument, faced toward the setting sun, was the figure of Faith, a
palm branch in one hand, an anchor in the other,
her face placid and calm, *her eyes blindfolded*.

I said to myself: "Faith, what are you doing
here, faced toward the setting sun? Why aren't
you around on the other side of this monument
facing the rising sun? You should be the soul
of liberty, the inspiration of youth, the heart of
learning, and strength and courage to those men
who push the boat of human progress into the
future. And, Faith, what are you doing to help
those men in their moral struggle as they battle
with the serpents of passion and lusts too strong
for them? And why are those eyes blindfolded?" This is not Faith, this is credulity.
Credulity is blindfolded. Faith is open-eyed,
eager to know the truth that shall set men free.
No wonder paganism holds that world on the

other side. Faith might seem superficially to rule men, but a submerged paganism will really rule unless Faith ceases to be afraid and looks at life open-eyed and frank, comes around in front and assumes the moral leadership, because Faith thinks beyond, experiences beyond, and goes beyond all human life.

In Valparaiso, which means "the Vale of Paradise," I saw the beautiful harbor strewn with the hulks of wrecked ships. I wondered why there was so much wreckage in this Vale of Paradise. I was told that the harbor though beautiful is subject to terrific storms which break in from the sea, and that the only safe thing to do in a storm is to weigh anchor and make for the open ocean. Ships that hug the safety of the harbor are almost invariably wrecked. Safety comes in the open sea.

If religion hugs its safe harbors and gazes upon its entrancing vales of paradise, the wreckage of the future will be terrible. Had I not seen the wreckage of faith in that very Vale of Paradise? The whole of the intellectuals were estranged from religion, turning to arid agnosticism or blindly groping amid cults that promised a way to live, because the church had imposed its authority instead of teaching men to find the authority of truth through experience. The only safety is in the open sea, where we have inward resources that can outride any storm of criticism or any search for reality. The open sea is our home. Our gospel came out of life and it speaks to life. But it does more—it triumphs over life. "Faith is not belief in spite of evidence, but life lived in scorn of consequences." "I am afraid of safety," said Paul in *Dawn* when they asked him to flee for safety. Both physically and spiritually his inner surety was his safety. But the church to-day has not realized that fact, so it is, in large measure, behind closed systems of thought, clamped down, hard and fast, for fear of thinkers and scientists.

The church is behind closed economic systems, fearing to offend wealthy contributors.

Modern life is organized on behalf of those who have and against those who have not. In an acquisitive society money is the golden key that unlocks privileges, education, position, and power. We know in our heart of hearts that this is wrong and unchristian. It cuts straight across Christ's mind. Yet the church is so dependent on that acquisitive society for its economic maintenance that it locks itself behind a closed economic system. Concerning any looking toward justice and fairness, say the one word "Bolshevik" and most of us take to cover. We are afraid, so we close the doors.

The church is behind closed doors of race exclusiveness for fear of losing white prestige.

A new kind of religion has been evolved: the

[33]

religion of being white. Yet our own Master was probably not white. A friend made this statement in a public address and a lady came up at the close pale and trembling with emotion. Jesus not white! The bottom had dropped out of her religion. I repeated this statement before a group of ministers, and a friend at the rear heard an excited and involuntary exclamation come from the lips of a minister: "That's a lie." But it is probably the truth. We liken Jesus to the modern Jew, who is white. But the modern Jew has been two thousand years or more under cover and has been bleached out. To see the farmer Jew of that day we must see the modern nomad Arab. The Arab is decidedly colored. The Roman officer took Paul for an Egyptian (Acts 21. 38), and the Egyptian, ancient and modern, is colored. "I am black, but comely, O ye daughters of Jerusalem," said an ancient Jewish biblical writer.

Huntington, in *The Character of Races,* says that the European and consequently the American is made up of three strains: the Caucasian, the Mediterranean, and the Negroid. The cold winters have bleached out the Negroid color, but this strain has left its traces in the curly hair. (Let me hasten to say that my own mother had beautiful curly hair, and I'm proud of it!) Whether this statement of Huntington be true or not, we may be certain that the races

[34]

are mixed—beneficially so. We may also be reasonably sure that Jesus was not white. Yet many hold to what virtually amounts to the religion of being white. It certainly is not the religion of Jesus.

The church has not fearlessly and uncompromisingly taken its stand against race snobbery. Unless it does it cannot lead in a world where the superstition of blood will surely fade and the fact of character take its place. For the most part we are now behind closed doors for fear of white prestige and supremacy.

As we are behind the closed doors of race exclusiveness so we are behind the closed doors of national isolation for fear of being called unpatriotic.

We have the feeling that "above all nations is humanity," that narrow patriotisms are behind international uneasinesses, that it is this spirit that blocks disarmament, that fans trivial sparks into national flames and into international conflagrations. We know that this is the thing that is bedeviling the world situation today—we know this, and yet we haven't the moral courage to speak out against it lest we be accused of committing the modern unpardonable sin—being unpatriotic.

The world situation is crying to high Heaven for someone to lead out of the narrow, vicious circles in which we have become entangled to a human brotherhood, and the church could do it. But it is afraid of being called unpatriotic, and shuts the doors.

The church is behind closed doors of mere routine of ritual for fear of breakdown.

The early church was spontaneous. No one knew what it was going to do next. Now you can anticipate what the church will do. It is in ruts, and "a rut is a grave with both ends knocked out." But ruts are so safe! When life ceases to be spontaneous we groove it in order to be sure we have something. We do have something, but whether it is life is a question.

On my trip to America I was struck by the growing grandeur of the houses of worship and the increasing ornateness of ritual and liturgy. The feeling seemed to be that the millennium lay just on the other side of an elaborate new church building, a vested choir, and stately processions. If life lay along this line, then Roman Catholicism would have it, for it makes Protestantism seem amateurish in this realm. Europe is filled with stately cathedrals and stale Christianity, with religious processions and with religious paralysis. No, this is not the way to life; and yet, feeling the emptiness within, we add to the outer, hoping that the appearance of life will make life appear. History says it does not. Nevertheless, we close our doors behind "safe" ritual for fear of breakdown.

Akin to this is the fact that the church is behind closed doors of unshared personal experience for fear of failure.

How few in the church share their personal spiritual experience with others! And yet that was the basis upon which the whole method of evangelism was founded in the early church. "There is no doubt," says Harnack, "that the early church won all its victories by informal missionaries." They were spiritually contagious. They infected others with God.

But to-day we find it easier to pay the minister to be our proxy. It is easier—and more deadly. The church becomes a field instead of a force for evangelism. And that field soon becomes dry and dead, for it is a law of the mind that that which is not expressed dies. All expression deepens impression. As someone has put it, "Impression minus expression equals depression." Our churches are filled with spiritual depression because there is so little spiritual expression. "No virtue is safe that is not enthusiastic, no heart is pure that is not passionate," no Christianity is Christian that is not Christianizing.

I heard Woodrow Wilson end a speech with this climactic sentence: "We must loose American business upon the world." I inwardly commented, "We must loose the gospel upon the world." But we shut it within our hearts, afraid. "I was afraid, and went and hid my talent," said the man in the parable. Fear had paralyzed him. He remained an undeveloped spiritual being because his spiritual life was unshared. Our churches are filled with spiritual dwarfs for the same reason. We call it reticence; its real name is barrenness. We need nothing so much as we need a passionate personal evangelism that will take men out from behind closed doors and impel "each one to reach one."

Nothing will be more tragic to the church and to the world than for the church to close itself up, encase itself in its own inner activities, while the great stream of the world's life flows past it and the church is not at its center. Our one problem is to loose our gospel upon the world.

CHAPTER III

Do not take the edge off my cry by telling me that some have moved out from behind closed doors, that there are brilliant and blessed exceptions, that there are those who have moved up from that between-state to Pentecost and are illustrating its meaning. I know it. And I am so deeply impressed by it that I would see the whole church there. Those brilliant exceptions only make the shadows darker by contrast. The church has not moved up.

It is quite true that some have moved out from behind closed doors. For instance, many religious thinkers to-day do take fearless attitudes toward truth. They are frank and open. Nevertheless, one cannot escape the feeling that while they have come out from behind closed doors many of them have stopped this side of Pentecost. They are frank and wistful, but not full and winsome. They lack the clarion certainties of Pentecost.

Someone looked at a well-executed painting and thoughtfully said, "Its perspective is good, its colorings are brilliant and correct, its conception is splendid, but it lacks *that,*" snapping his fingers. It lacked life. A correct picture but—*flat.* It is one thing to have truth; it

[39]

is another thing to have living truth. The modern thinker may have discovered truths—he lacks the fire of living truth.

Someone has said that the modern church is suffering from "the paralysis of analysis." It can dissect life, but cannot give it. It knows everything, except how to live and to live abundantly. It has learned to deny; it has not yet learned to affirm. It knows how to ask searching questions, but knows not yet how to send men on a quest for certainty.

> "The centipede was happy quite
>   Until the frog for fun
> Asked, 'Which leg comes after which?'
>   It threw him into such a fright
> And raised his mind to such a pitch
> That he lay distracted in a ditch,
>   Not knowing how to run."

Many modern religious thinkers are in a ditch, and they know it. Many can tell the processes by which they slid there. A mechanistic psychology undertakes to explain life in terms of mechanics. It seems so plausible. Many listen, question; and then the creeping paralysis and the ditch. Much of modernism has discovered processes, but not power; it knows biology, but lacks life; it has found truths, but is not possessed by the Truth; it is penetrating, but not Pentecostal; it has found right attitudes, but insufficient altitudes. It lacks sky.

"For a year I lost my sky," said a very dear earnest Christian friend. "I was so eager to have the church accept a plan for a more vital Christian life that when they turned a cold shoulder to it something withered within me and I lost my sky. For a year I grubbed in the drab earth without a sky. And then I got it back." His face showed that he had.

I will not say that the church has lost its sky, and yet—and yet I fear sometimes that if there is sky, it is small and overcast. And sometimes it is not there. Then we grub amid duties, we plod amid tasks, we fumble and grumble—something has gone wrong. We have no sky. We have no sky into which we can grow, and into which we can stretch strong hands of prayer, and, listening, catch the music of the spheres. Hence we sigh when we might sing.

Before Pentecost the disciples had little or no sky. They were bound and bounded by self-interest. A step or two outside themselves and they had reached their horizons. And "then there arose a reasoning among them, which of them should be greatest," and this took place as Jesus was offering them a limitless sky—the kingdom of God. As if one could discuss his own greatness while he gazed into a limitless Sky! In that hour, if you really see it, only the Sky is great. The way to get rid of your own self-importance is to get under and be in fellowship with a Sky so big that you are "lost in wonder, love, and praise."

Pentecost did that for the disciples. It hasn't yet done it for us, hence we are still taken up with trivialities, such trivialities as our own position and place and power. In the Federated Malay States you can see men, grown men, sitting on the ridges of the rice fields and fishing in a foot of water. Within sight of them the great ocean rolls, but there they sit and fish in rice fields. I have sat in great conferences and have heard the ponderous debates on trivialities, and involuntarily the thought has forced itself upon me—"Fishing in rice fields." And all the time the great world problems were roaring in our ears: the demand for God, for healing from sin-hurt, for human brotherhood, for social and economic reconstruction, for world evangelization. There is where we should be fishing. It is dangerous, but worth while.

One could not listen in at the Lausanne Conference without feeling that often in these solemn debates they were fishing in the shallow waters of ecclesiastical tradition and catching little minnows of polite and pious wishes for reunion while dodging the supreme issue of losing one's life to find it—and all the time before Christendom a war-torn world, suspiciously armed to the teeth, with another conflict in the offing. The whole situation demands a healing word, coming from the depths of reality, but the church cannot say it, for it is taken up with prestige as the nations are. The nations know it, shrug their shoulders, and set their brains to work upon more poison gases and upon more appalling weapons.

Fishing in rice fields! It is true that some interesting little fish are caught in those rice fields. They are called "the fighting fish." I saw some of these militant little fellows in glass bowls. When one bowl was set up against another the very color of the fish would immediately change. They would turn red with anger and would back off and fiercely charge the other fish, bumping against the side of the bowl. This warfare would go on until one was defeated, in which case he would turn black and sink to the bottom of the bowl in despondency. Fishing in rice fields means that we have not only caught a lot of *little* fish, but a lot of *fighting* fish. Each in his ecclesiastical bowl reddens with importance and pugnacity and we fight our battles over what? Orders, rituals, rites, and prestiges! And when we settle them we settle no more than those little fish settled in their mimic warfare.

Pentecost saved the disciples from the trivial, the marginal, the irrelevant. Henceforth they saw real issues, they had "a sense of what was vital," they knew where the real battle lay.

In the early days of Jaipur the city was situated on a hill within a fort. There was the Raja's palace and there were the temples. In the meantime the city has moved some miles away, down on the plains. But if you go to the hill, you can see ragged sentinels standing with rusty swords before empty palaces and priests sacrificing goats before deserted altars. The city has moved on and has left sentinels guarding emptiness; has left religion standing beside deserted altars offering meaningless sacrifices. Down in the city the throbbing problems lie and religion is out of touch, high and dry.

We desperately need something to bring us to where the real battles lie. We may be militantly guarding emptiness and pompously sacrificing on dead altars, while all the time the battle center has moved on. The damnation and elimination of the Pharisees lay in this: they were earnest religious men, but they tithed mint and anise and cummin while a world of human need demanded justice and mercy. If religion is eliminated from the thinking of many, it will not be because it is bad but because it is not worth while.

Again and again I have said that if I had one gift to give to myself and to the church, I would give the gift of courage. Nothing, it seemed to me, was so desperately necessary as to get the church out from behind the closed doors of its routine, out into those streams of life where issues throb and where battles mean something. Again and again I have seen an ounce of courage bring forth a pound of result. Courage was the need, so it seemed to me. But I have changed my mind. I have come to believe that courage is a by-product of something deeper. The reason we fear is that we haven't sufficient inner resources to meet life. Life with its demands is too great for us. We lose our moral nerve. It is useless to try to get rid of that fear by saying that there is nothing to be afraid of. A Hindu student, who was urged by a friend of mine not to be afraid of the idol which he was about to remove, replied, "My mind tells me there is nothing there, but my heart is very afraid." You might have told that band of disciples, behind closed doors for fear, that since Jesus had arisen from the dead there was nothing to be afraid of. But that would not have taken them out from behind those closed doors. There was only one way to get them out and that was to raise the tone of the inner life so that they were inwardly a match for outer circumstances. Pentecost gave them that inner adequacy. Inner life became adequate for outer life. Henceforth nothing could stop them. Fears fell away as irrelevancies. Out of that Upper Room which had been the place of fears they burst with the glad Good News. They smiled at poverty, rejoiced under stripes, were elated at their humiliations, sang in midnight prisons, courted death and shared with every man, everywhere, their own abundant life. God had matched them against that need and they were spiritually adequate.

I see nothing, absolutely nothing, that will get the church of to-day out from behind closed doors except it be this one thing—Pentecost. Increase the ornateness of its ritual as you will, improve the quality and quantity of its religious education as you may, raise the standards of qualifications of the ministry as high as you can, pour money without stint into the coffers of the church—give it everything—everything except this one thing that Pentecost gave, and you are merely ornamenting the dead. Until this sacred Fact takes place, preaching is only lecturing, praying is only repeating formulas, services cease to be service—it all remains earth-bound, circumscribed, inadequate, dead.

These penetrating words are true: "When the Holy Ghost departs from any set of opinions, or form of character, they wither like a sapless tree." (Ed. Ewing, in Mrs. Oliphant's *Life,* p. 178.)

But the church has shied away from Pentecost. It is afraid of it. The teaching concerning the Spirit is the most vague and uncertain thing in the life of the church.

"It is the undiscovered country of Christianity, the dark continent of the Christian life," says Arthur Hurd, "the land where our spiritual resources lie, but lie undeveloped."

There was a time when the Christian Church celebrated Whitsunday, the anniversary of the coming of the Spirit, more than it did Christmas, the anniversary of the coming of Christ. Now Whitsunday has largely dropped out. Did we find it was easier to celebrate Christ's birth than it was to be born again? Was it easier to commemorate his coming into the world than it was for us to go with his message into the world? Did it cost less to give gifts at Christmas than to give ourselves at Pentecost? Christmas is the festival of God with us. Pentecost is the festival of God in us. Is he more with us than in us?

Go through Palestine and you will find that the Christian Church has fastened on almost every important event in the Old and New Testaments and has commemorated them by the erection of a Christian shrine. But none has been erected in commemoration of its own birthday, Pentecost. Did it seem too remote to commemorate?

At any rate, whatever the cause, there is, in Christianity, a lost chord, and that lost chord haunts us. Until we get it back our spiritual lives will be more wistful than winsome, more plaintive than passionate.

That lost chord is Pentecost.

CHAPTER IV

WHAT HAPPENED AT PENTECOST?

WHAT is it that has made the church shy away from Pentecost? Why is it, when you speak to the modern church about Pentecost, that cold shivers go up and down the spines of cultured people?

I announced the theme of Pentecost before a group of highly trained ministers, and at the close one of them, the head of an examining board for young ministers, said to me, "When I heard you announce that subject I said to myself, 'Good gracious, are we going to have some more rant?'" The head of the examining board for young ministers looks on Pentecost as rant! What has happened?

Well, for one thing, Pentecostalism has hurt Pentecost very badly. The queer have "queered" Pentecost for us. So much so that one is tempted to leave out the word altogether. But words as well as people need to be redeemed. The church is largely responsible for this situation, for in neglecting this most essential part of the gospel the hungry-hearted have gone off into irresponsible groups. Here rampant emotionalism has often been identified with Pentecost. And the thinking mind of this age is rather hard on religion as rampant emotionalism. They ask the searching questions, "What is the emotion worth?" "How does it issue in character?"

The tragedy of all this is that we cannot do without emotion in religion. Emotion is the wind that fills the sails of the soul and drives it to its destination. I am not afraid of the winds of heaven filling the sails of my soul, provided there is a Hand on the rudder—provided He has my will and my intelligence as well as my emotion. But an overemphasis upon emotion in these groups has made the church react against a religion in terms of emotion. This reaction has brought on an appalling sterility and spiritual deadness in the church. Spiritual anæmia has set in.

There is no doubt that the divine purpose was and is that Pentecost should be normal Christianity. But we are largely subnormal. When one is physically subnormal he is much more susceptible and more easily succumbs to disease germs which he would normally throw off. Many things are upsetting us—trivialities about our own position and power; pettinesses in the church life harass minister and people. We are spiritually below par, hence these things that we would normally throw off as irrelevant are upsetting us. It is true that in the name of this beautiful fact of Pentecost some have gone up above normal into fever. And when one goes into fever he often talks irrationally, sometimes deliriously. And because some have gone into fever it has frightened the most of us into an anæmic condition. Because some have gone above, we have been frightened into living below. The sane, wise Christian thing to do would be for those who are below and those who are above to return to normal—that normal, Pentecost. For Pentecost, as I shall endeavor to show, is sane, normal, spiritually healthy human living.

The second thing that makes Pentecost difficult for our thinking is that the framework in which the Gift came at Pentecost seems very remote and out of harmony with the thinking of this age. Cloven tongues like as of fire, the sound as of a rushing mighty wind, the place being shaken, speaking in other tongues—how remote all this seems from an age of culture and scientific training! What has all this to do with finding God, with the business of living ethically, brotherly, of bringing the kingdom of God on earth? And is God to be found in the aberrations of nature and not in its dependablenesses? Tell an audience of average cultured Christians that they would hear the sound of a rushing mighty wind, would find the place shaken, that cloven tongues like as of fire would sit upon the head of each and that they would speak in tongues, and that audience would probably ask,

"Well, what's the use of all this?" They probably would, all except the type that usually dabbles in the occult or in spiritism, and that type does not seriously count.

The wrappings of the Gift that came at Pentecost have seriously affected its wide acceptance. They seem to have called the attention away from the central fact—finding God in transforming intimacy and power. The Jews at the time of Christ fastened upon the lowly wrappings in which he came and lost sight of his central moral and spiritual significances, and there ensued national disaster and spiritual bankruptcy. The church to-day is losing sight of or rejecting the fact of Pentecost because of its framework; and the consequent moral and spiritual disaster and bankruptcy is the greatest tragedy of the Christian centuries. I know of no call so urgent as the call to get down beneath the phenomena to the fact at Pentecost. What is that fact?

One very interesting book on Pentecost says, "Just what was implied by the expression 'the gift of the Holy Spirit' we cannot say with certainty." Cannot say with certainty? And this after two thousand years? Doctor McGiffert, in his book, *The Apostolic Age,* says: "Pentecost was the inauguration of the evangelistic activity of the Christian Church, when the disciples began the work to which they believed themselves

[51]

called by the risen Lord, the work of witness-
bearing. . . . It was not the coming of the
Spirit, but the testimony of the disciples, that
constituted the great central fact of the day, the
fact that makes the day historic." But this
seems to me to take one element and make Pentecost mean that. Had not the disciples witnessed to Christ before Pentecost? And the
seventy also? True, after Pentecost there was
a quality and power in their witness that had
never been there before, but their mighty witness at Pentecost and the subsequent days was
the result of a deeper fact. The witness was a
by-product. The witness they gave was the result of the witness they received, that witness a
sense of God in immediate experience.

Scott, in his able book, *The Spirit,* answering
the question, "What happened at Pentecost?"
says that it was "the creation of The Fellowship," the Fellowship where walls between Jew
and Gentile were broken down. This Fellowship,
"called into being by the Holy Spirit, was prior
to the organized Ecclesia: it was related to it
as the life to the organization." The creation of
"The Fellowship" was indeed one of the outstanding things, if not the outstanding thing,
that emerged from Pentecost. But certainly
this is not what happened at Pentecost. This
Fellowship was the result of something deeper.
That deeper something was that they had found

God. And God not as a fleeting idea, but as a living fact of experience; God, "no longer marginal and vague, but focal and dynamic"; God, no longer coming to them in awful Sinais and in stern prophetic word, but God tender, intimate, face-to-face. The exquisite sense of the Divine Presence spread healing and freedom into every portion of their being. The long quest was over, they were now at home in the home of the soul—God.

Another fact merged with this one. Christ, their Master, had gone away. He had left them alone. But he hadn't; he was with them! More intimate, more real than they had ever known him—he was with them! There had always been that moral and physical barrier between him and them; now it was gone. In the intimacies of a fellowship almost too deep for words they could whisper "Saviour," for the dark ugliness of sin had been purified away in the fire of his presence.

There was the merging of the sense of God and of Christ in experience. In their experience they could not tell where one ended and the other began. They found they could turn as easily to one as to the other. Moreover, God was no longer localized at Sinai—in national epochs, in being the God of a chosen people. In their experience he was universalized. The same was true of Christ. They could no longer think of him merely as the Teacher who taught them on the hillsides and companioned with them along the shores of Galilee. He too was universalized. Did they not commune with him along all ways now? And did not their hearts burn within them on every road now? He was no longer merely the Christ of the Galilæan Road, nor even the Christ of Emmaus Road—he was THE CHRIST OF EVERY ROAD. He was there! He was everywhere! He was within!

God and Christ were both merged and both were universalized in their experience, so they said, "The Spirit." They knew God and Christ through and in the Spirit. "The Spirit is the method of Christ's presence," says Moberley. The Spirit is also the method of God's presence. The Spirit is thus the method of the presence of the Christlike God with human spirits.

They could think of God no longer except in terms of Christ. Christ had put a new content into God—he was now a Christlike God. And they could think of Christ no longer except in terms of God—he was now a Godlike Christ. They could think of neither Christ nor God except in terms universal and experimental, hence the Spirit.

Sometimes they said, "The Spirit of God," sometimes "The Spirit of Christ," sometimes "The Holy Spirit," sometimes "The Spirit." As Robinson says: "The Spirit of God had become so blended with the person of Christ that there is practically no difference for Paul between the indwelling Spirit and the indwelling Christ and he can indeed speak of the Lord the Spirit."[1] Thus a doctrine of the Trinity grew up, not out of formal thought, but out of the realities of experience. They were trying to express the inexpressible—the inexpressible, but the knowable and the realizable.

The localized and far-off God and the limited and absent Christ were now universalized and available in experience—the experience of the Spirit.

The greatest hour of human history had dawned. God was utterly available to human need. The barriers were all down.

[1] *The Christian Experience of the Holy Spirit*, p. 135. Reprinted by permission of the author and James Nisbet & Co., Ltd., publishers, London.

CHAPTER V

IN WHICH WE SEE LIFE

WHY was the Spirit given at this particular period of human history and under these particular circumstances? He seemed to come with abandon, as if pent up for ages awaiting this particular moment. True, there were touches and intimations of the Spirit in all ages and in all nations. But at Pentecost there was not intimation, there was inundation. Why could he now come with utter abandon?

The reason is not hard to find. He could not come until the Norm had been fixed in the minds of men—the Norm that would tell them what the Spirit is like and what moral content could be put into the term. For what God is like determines what we should be like. "Show me your gods and I will show you your men." If our ideas of God hold a moral misconception, then the whole of life is under moral misdirection. It will, therefore, be better to have no idea of God than to have a false one. In all ages God has been thought of in terms utterly misleading and false.

"Why do you Christians raise the question about the moral character of Krishna? Look at his power," said a Theosophist to me one day.

I could answer that I was not interested in power as such. The day of irresponsible power is over. The moral character of power is the all-important.

I once came from a great meeting in a Hindu theater where I had poured out my heart to the non-Christian audience about the cross. In that hour we faced the self-giving, redeeming God. Our hearts were moved and melted before this Love Divine. I went straight from the meeting to the train. As I came to our compartment, I saw a great crowd surrounding it. The center of attraction was a Swami and his chela, or disciple. The crowd surged into the compartment and kissed the Swami's feet. I turned to his chela and asked who he was. He replied: "He is God. He can tell you anything you want to know." I listened with astonishment, for I could see at a glance that the Swami lacked physical co-ordination. He dragged himself into the compartment, his arms jerked convulsively, his eyes rolled, and he paid no heed to the crowd that bowed and touched his feet. After the train had pulled out amid cries of, "Swami ji ki jai" ("Hail to the Swami"), I asked the Swami to tell me certain obvious things. He replied in a painfully disconnected way, for his speech was unco-ordinated, that his head was tired. I called a well-educated Hindu to my side and said: "My heart is sinking within me. If this man were normal, you wouldn't look at him twice. But because he is abnormal you fall at his feet as God. This strikes me like a blow, for what hope can I have of the future of the country that I love if you run after the weird in this fashion?" My educated friend agreed that these superstitions must be cleansed. I tried to sleep, but could not. The scene was haunting me. The lights were out in the compartment, but I could see the Swami seated opposite, puffing cigarette after cigarette. After midnight my educated friend got up and sat beside the Swami. I could see them silhouetted against the night sky. The educated man's face was all eagerness. All his education had dropped away and he too was under the spell of the uncanny. All through those night hours I could not rid my mind of the thought: Here is God conceived as the Weird.

I once went to call on one of the famous devotees of India. He is a highly educated man, the center of an influential cult. I asked if I might see him. I was told that I could not, for he had not been seen by anyone for eight months, except for two minutes on his birthday. I asked what the purpose was and received the reply, "He is realizing himself as Divine." I asked further whether it had been accomplished. The reply was that "it would be," that "he was on the verge." As I went away I could not help feel-

[58]

ing that here was the Divine conceived as the Great Silence, the Vast Aloof.

I went at midnight to see a festival of god-realization. One man fantastically dressed was being carried on the shoulders of others before an idol shrine, which was also carried on the backs of men. He would maneuver before the idol, going back and forth, and at the moment when the spirit of the idol entered him he would shake from head to foot and a shout would go up from the crowd. A goat would be sacrificed and a cup of its hot blood passed up to the now god-possessed man, who would drink it to satisfy the spirit of the god within him. The god could only be satisfied with blood. I turned away sick at heart—here was God conceived as the Terrible, the Blood-thirsty.

Again, a Hindu friend writes to me: "When one comes into that Nirvana state, where no mood exerts any influence on him, the Jiva [lower life] unites with the Supreme Divinity and they are one. Then he is in that stage which is *sans* care, *sans* thought, *sans* everything, where pure essence only prevails." Here is God, so emptied of attributes and relationships that he is conceived of as the Supreme Indifference, almost the Supreme Emptiness.

And think how men misconceived God even in the history of Israel, where the highest conception of God was found among men. A mother was explaining to her little girl about the murder of the Amalekites. She said that revelation was progressive, and that now in Jesus we were told to love our enemies and to do good to them that despitefully use us. The little girl thought a moment and then her face lighted up and she said, "Now I understand—this back here was before God was a Christian."

Think how partial, limited, racial we have made God. A man stood on one of the peaks of the Alps and when the sun went down below him it threw a huge shadow of him against the sky. Very often man has projected an enlarged shadow of himself into the heavens and has called that God.

Among the Greeks, Meander said that "sheer fluke was probably God," and Aristotle said that "to love God would be improper." Neither would have said that had they caught the meaning of Christ.

It is obvious that God could not give himself fully to men until the Norm had been fixed. Suppose he had done so while distorted and false ideas of himself were in the minds of the seekers. What would have been the result? In giving himself in those circumstances there would have been fixed in the mind of the seeker the belief that God is like the image the seeker has in mind. This would have made God stand back of the false, would have created a false universe, would have set up false standards of human living. Divine Love must withhold until Divine Love can fully reveal.

What do we really want to know about God? His omnipotence? It would frighten us out of our senses to realize that. His omniscience? We could not understand it even if he showed it. His omnipresence? The wings of our imagination falter and fall limp in following such a conception. It would do us no good to know any of these even if God could reveal them to us. Then what do we want to know? We want to know what his character is like, for what he is like we, his children, must be like. The revelation we need is the revelation of the moral character of our Father. If this is our central need, how could this be done? There is only one way it could be done and that is to live it out in the same circumstances in which our characters are made and lived out. It must be Lips like our lips that shall speak the word, a Life like our life that shall show us Life, and Hands like our hands that shall throw open the gates of life to us. We must see the Life, if we are to seek it. Have we seen it? Has the Life been lived?

Religion had hardened into cold formulas; the dead hand of tradition reached out of the past and held everything under its paralysis; the leaders of religion had ceased to be prophets of the new day and had become priests of the things of yesterday. God was conceived as the Infinite Exactor of meticulous etiquette. The finished product of religion was the Pharisee standing in the temple thanking God that he had fulfilled this religious etiquette and that he was therefore not as other men. Then there quietly appeared, out of the obscurity of a country village, and out of the lowliness of a carpenter's shop, a Man. When he presented himself to be baptized at the river bank, the Baptist, so stern and uncompromising with others, fell back before the quite unassuming dignity of this Man and said, "I have need to be baptized of thee, and comest thou to me?" There was something about the Man that made the best of men feel that they were in deepest need. And yet the worst of men felt drawn to him. Here was goodness attractive, winsome, compelling. As I once read to a highly educated Hindu, "And the publicans and the sinners drew near to hear him," he exclaimed: "Of whom else could that be said? Sinners drawing near to the Holy One! Why weren't they afraid of his goodness—afraid that it would punish and destroy them? They drew near! Here was goodness that was approachable." Yes, the Hindu was right. Here was goodness that was not meticulous, but merciful, not standing on pedestals to be worshiped, but bending in lowly service over the lost. Here was goodness not pharisaical, but friendly, not terrible, but tender. And yet in that very tenderness and friendliness there was a regal something that made men's consciences flutter and tremble like an aspen leaf. Children sat upon his knees, and yet strong, hard Fisherman Peter, stricken in conscience at the moment of greatest fishing prosperity, found his knees giving way under him and crying in spite of himself, "Depart from me; for I am a sinful man, O Lord." Never did majesty and meekness so blend and become so beautiful as here.

And never did word and work so blend in harmony as they did in him. They blended like the words and music of a song. He taught men, and his words had the ring of reality about them. Others quoted authorities; he taught with the authority of his own insight. Others came seeking truth; he came proclaiming it. Truth gushed forth from his soul like a fountain from a hillside. Others worked their way to truth through the logic of syllogism. He used no syllogisms. He announced self-verifying truths. He did not argue them, but left them to argue themselves—as light appeals to the eye, as duty fits the conscience, as beauty speaks to the æsthetic nature, as love goes straight to the heart. And men listened to these words as if they were hearing some long-lost chord, something that belonged to them, that belonged to the very structure and make-up of their being.

[63]

They felt that this was the soul's homeland. His words made sin seem so unnatural, so extraneous, so incapable of fitting into living.

He taught them! But not by words alone. His words held the content of a contact. He lived with them and before them, and in his words they heard the Word—the Word that he was. When he spoke of love they knew what it meant, for they had seen it—had seen it in his face, his deeds, in him. When he spoke of God they felt his presence, for he came not proclaiming God; he brought him. For once the gap between the word and the work was completely bridged. In him they were one.

He taught high things—he lived higher. He taught men to turn the other cheek—the servants struck him on one cheek and he turned the other and let the soldiers smite that. He asked men to go the second mile when compelled to go one. They compelled him to go one mile from Gethsemane to the Judgment Hall; he went with them twain, clear to the cross. He asked them to give the cloak also; they took his coat at the Judgment Hall and he gave his seamless robe at Calvary. He asked them to love their enemies, and when they had nailed his hands to a cross so that he could no longer heal them, he could do one last thing: he could die for them. And he did. But before he died his prayer was, "Father, forgive them; for they know not what they do." His love was complete and so was his life. Even in torture's grasp there was no confession of moral lapse, only of moral completion : "It is finished."

Here was Goodness not only approachable and irreproachable—it was serving. We have said this so much that it has become commonplace. But when I look on Religion and Goodness girding itself with a towel and stooping to wash the feet of humanity I am looking on the utterly new. I search in vain through the non-Christian systems for one authentic note of the self-giving, serving God. True, there is service as a royal dispenser of favors and benefits; but this is deeper, for here is service by a Servant. He did not merely bend over to hand out, he bent over to get under. He stooped under the poverty and the toil, the sin and the shame, the troubles and the trials—under the very lives of fallen men, and when there was nothing left to get under, he got under the cross and bore that for them.

Here was One who showed by word and by work, by trial and by triumph, by smiting and by smile, by goodness and by service what the Heart of the universe is like. And when nothing else seemed to be left to be shown he let them tear his heart asunder on a cross, and when men looked into that wound they read one word, "Love." Looking up through that wound to the universe they knew that at last they had found its meaning: "Love."

By the trailing smoke men in aeroplanes write out some message upon the sky, which the wind soon blows away. Jesus, by his life, wrote out against the eternities the imperishable message, "God is love," and nothing can erase it. Nor can anything transcend it. "If we are to come to God by love, then Jesus is inescapable," said Sir ———, a Hindu, to me one day. He was right. "You can find parallel principles in the Gita and the Upanishads," said the Hindu vice-principal of a college, a very great poet, "but you cannot find the nectar of the life of Christ in either of them." Nor anywhere else. Some Freethinkers in Canada met in conference to try to find a way to live other than Christ's way. They thought freely about everything, including the Ten Commandments, but after two days of discussion one of them, a young woman, naïvely asked: "Well, where are we coming out? Is there any constructive suggestion as to the way to live? The only thing I see is that we should think of the other person when we act."

"Umph," sneered someone, "that's only the Golden Rule."

After two days of freethinking life had led them to a word of His lips. After two thousand years of freethinking and free testing of the way to live, life finally brings us out at this Life.

"The thing that strikes me about Jesus Christ is that you cannot escape him," said a Japanese student, thoughtfully. You cannot escape him —not if you want life.

We know now that God is like this that we have seen in Jesus. He is Christlike. And if he is, he is a good God and trustable. If the Heart that is back of the universe is like this Gentle Heart that broke upon the cross, he can have my heart without qualification and without reservation. I know nothing higher to say of God than that he should live like Christ. "The question to my mind," said a Yale professor, "is not as to the divinity of Jesus but as to whether God will act like Jesus." Strange, a Man lived among us, and when we think of God we must think of him in terms of this Man, or he is not good. We may transfer every single moral quality in Jesus to God without loss or degradation to our thought of God. On the contrary, by thinking of him in terms of Jesus we heighten our view of God. All those who have tried to think of him in other terms have lowered and impoverished our idea of him. The highest adjective descriptive of character in any language is the adjective "Christlike." The highest compliment we can pay to God or man is to say he is a Christlike God, or he is a Christlike man. Says Professor Lewis, "If God is not such as meets us in him, then God cannot greatly concern us at all. If he is not this, then he is less than this, for he cannot be more. But more we do not need, and with less we cannot be content." The issue has gradually brought itself to this: If we cannot be religious after the mind of Jesus, we cannot be religious at all. It is Christ or nothing.

The Norm has been fixed, we now know what goodness is: it is Christlikeness. If so, then sin is un-Christlikeness. That fixes a standard by which evil may be judged. Anything that departs from his mind and purpose is sin. Hinduism has no such standard, so we find the Mahabharata saying: "A man should expiate the sin of the student who rises before the sun; the man with a rotten nail or with black teeth; the man who marries before his brother; the man who kills a Brahman; the man who speaks evil of others." Here is a mingling of the sublime and the ridiculous. There is no Norm.

In some of the universities of the West it is taught that everything is fluid, including morals, that there are no fixed points. But in Jesus Christ we believe we have discovered a fixed point; we have a foothold in our moral and spiritual universe. We know now what God's life is and what man's life ought to be—Christlike.

Let me hasten to say that if Christ is a fixed point, the point is most unfixed. He is behind us in history. He is beyond us in fact. If Christ is God's final Word, he is also God's unfolding Word. The Goal is a flying Goal, hence never surpassed, never outgrown. New light constantly breaks out from his person. Christlikeness holds as the standard for God and man.

Now for the application of all this to the matter we are considering: If God is a Christlike God, then it follows that the Spirit is a Christlike Spirit. The same content of character will be in both. Then if the Spirit lives within us, he will not make us other than Christlike. "The fruits of the Spirit are the virtues of Christ," said the great Schleiermacher. If we are made other than Christlike, it is some other spirit that possesses us—the spirit of weakness, of folly, of clannishness, not the Holy Spirit. For the Spirit will not make us other than Christlike.

Did Jesus ever speak in tongues? Did he ever go off into any visions or dreams? Did he ever traffic in the merely mysterious or occult? Was there anything psychopathic about him? Was he not always poised, always balanced, always sane? Was he not always upon the essential, the worth-while? Was he ever misled by a subordinate issue or did he ever take a by-path? Was there about him any rampant emotionalism? He was indeed tremendously emotional, but was it not restrained and directed emotion—directed toward human need?

[69]

To ask these questions is to answer them.
Then why is it that, with Christ as the essence
of poise and balance and with the Spirit as a
Christlike Spirit, we have the fear that to be
filled with the Spirit is to border on the queer?

The reason is that again and again the teaching concerning the Holy Spirit slips away from
Christ and becomes filled with other and marginal meanings, and that again and again it has
to be brought back and filled anew with the content that Christ put into it. The Spirit was to
be "another Comforter." Note the "another."
He was to be just like Christ. And Christ, the
Man of the Burning Heart, was also the Man of
the Balanced Heart. So the Spirit brings poise,
balance, integration, symmetry, and consequent
power into human life.

We can now see why God could not give the
Spirit "without measure," why Pentecost could
not happen until the Norm had been fixed. God
could not trust us with power until he was sure
that it would make us Christlike. "Be not
drunk with wine, wherein is excess; but be filled
with the Spirit," wherein there can be no excess,
for we can never be too Christlike. Here God
can stand back of us with power to the utmost.
But without this content of Christlikeness he
can do nothing. He is morally bound to do
nothing. It would be disastrous if he did trust
us with power. The reason why we sometimes

cry to a silent Heaven is that it would ruin us if heaven opened and backed our wrong attitudes with power.

The fact is that I have never seen anyone find spiritual power who did not seek something deeper. Spiritual power is a by-product of the Spirit in the life, making that life Christlike. To seek for spiritual power is very liable to send one off on those tangents of self-glorification and self-assertion that lead straight away from the Christian ideal. To seek for the spirit to be made Christlike sends one to a self-surrender that leads straight to the heart of the gospel—a cross. Christ's power lies in a cross: "If I be lifted up [on the cross] from the earth, I will draw." Our power lies in that same cross. Only those who know how to take up the cross for the world know how to move that world.

God waits, then, until we move to a cross-centric which is a Christ-centric attitude. He waits till Christ becomes centric in our thought, in our purposes, in us—then the sluice-gates are opened. Then we know the exquisite sense of being filled with the Spirit and of being made adequate to live and to live abundantly.

To gather up the thought of this chapter: the foundation has been laid for Pentecost, a Pattern of Christlikeness has been fixed. The Spirit will make us Christlike.

[71]

CHAPTER VI

IN WHICH LIFE MEETS LIFE'S ENEMIES

THERE are four pillars upon which Christ's gospel rests: his Life, his Cross, his Resurrection, and his Coming into the lives of men—Pentecost. The gospel rests upon *all four*. Take any one away and you have a crippled gospel—a gospel insufficient to meet human need. The theme of this book is Pentecost, but I dare not discuss Pentecost except in the light of the other three, for Pentecost isolated is Pentecost emasculated. And it is equally true of any of the others.

Some lay the chief emphasis upon his life, others upon his death, others upon his resurrection, and still others upon his coming into the souls of men—Pentecost. But when one pillar is heightened by emphasis and the others lowered by lack of emphasis the temple of Christianity built upon them leans threateningly, or, worse still, topples into ruin. Our gospel rests squarely upon all four.

We have looked at the first: his life. We have seen that the Norm of human and divine life has been fixed, and we have said that the way was clear for an utter coming of the Spirit into the souls of men. Clear? Not quite. Two things more were necessary before that fact could dawn.

We saw that it was necessary that Jesus should step out before us to show us how to live. There has been a renewed emphasis upon this in modern days and we are called to "the Jesus way of life." There has been a throwing of emphasis from Jesus as the way of salvation to Jesus as the way to live. "Are you a Jesus-thinker?" asked a bereaved Hindu lady of a missionary lady. There is a deep insistence that we be Jesus-thinkers, that we look at life through his eyes, that we think his thoughts, take his attitudes and launch out upon "the Jesus way of life." The insistence is that we view people, human relationships, social problems, economic policies, and such a matter as war from his standpoint. The plea is that we take "the religion of Jesus" and not "the religion about Jesus." This insistence is a reaction against the attitude that would appropriate something from Christ called salvation, but would leave the essential attitudes of life untouched. It insists that we take from Christ our cue as well as our cure.

One cannot but sympathize with this insistence. An emphasis on it was long overdue. But at the same time one cannot but see that to stop here with Christ as the supreme Example is to miss the heart of the gospel. The type produced under this teaching, while it is earnest, is strained. It has its fists clinched, its jaw set, and its motto is, "We are going to fight it out along this line if it takes till death." It lacks that inner sense of poise, of inner drawing from the Divine, of inexhaustible spiritual resources. It seems outward and shallow. And it is. It lacks depth.

Moreover, this call to follow Christ as example can appeal only to the comparatively strong, to the morally élite, for to preach Christ as Example to ordinary humanity is to lay a further paralysis upon an already paralyzed will. Sinful men need not merely the Gospel of Example, but the Gospel of Expiation. As Jowett says, "Peace must precede moral growth." Unless a nail-pierced Hand is laid upon our troubled conscience to restore us to fellowship with him we cannot move out to a following of him. There must be a cross in our gospel.

That leads us to the second pillar upon which our gospel rests: the cross.

How we have covered up the cross with theories and overlaid it with argument and have missed the simplicities that lie there!

Once I went to meditate in the moonlight on the top of Gordon's Calvary. I climbed over a surrounding stone wall, up a steep way through two barbed-wire entanglements and up

another steep path before I reached the top.
And when I arrived there I found myself sitting
on a tomb. How we have surrounded Calvary
with stone walls of adamantine theory, placed
barbed-wire entanglements of exclusively correct doctrine, made men climb narrow paths of
impossibly steep propositions, and when we have
arrived at the top we have only a tomb—a dead
doctrine about a dead Christ!

All the time a deep simplicity beats here. In
a home where love meets sin, if that love be a
pure love, at the junction of that love and that
sin suffering ensues, a cross is set up. And the
purer the love the more poignant the cross. This
is not something extraneous and imposed on
life; it is written in the make-up of our being
and in the constitution of our relationships. It
is the very nature of love to insinuate itself into
the sins and sorrows of others. All loving goodness in moral natures has "the doom of bleeding
upon it." It cannot be love and stay out; and
if it gets in, it suffers.

This world is a human family; God is our
Father. He is Love, and when that Love meets
our sin—as it did in the incarnation—at the
junction of the two a cross is set up. That
White Love crimsons into a cross. God being
what he is and we being what we are, the cross
is inevitable. This is not something read into
the account by loving hearts. It is written in

the constitution of the nature of God and in the inner inevitabilities of our relationship with him.

Now, in the home where that love meets sin and a cross is set up, that suffering is vicarious. What should have fallen upon the guilty one falls upon the innocent one. This takes place not by a mechanical transference, but by a vital acceptance. Love accepts it and takes it upon itself because love is love.

And when the Divine Love meets our sin and the cross is set up, that suffering too is vicarious. What should have fallen on us falls on him. I cannot explain it, but I see it and share it.

That mother was right when she said to her sisters who went to the churches in the early morning to worship before crucifixes: "Why do you worship before these dead crosses? See, here is the true living cross," and she stretched wide her arms till they made a cross. She was right, for here was motherhood, suffering, saving, giving herself even to a cross for the sake of the children. The Father-Mother God is not essentially different, except that when we see his arms stretched out upon a cruel cross we know that the suffering is infinite because the love is infinite.

Goethe once said, "If I were God, sin would break my heart." Sin did break God's heart.

The pure-souled Christ, dying on a cross of a broken heart, tells us that. For here was

"The world's sin and sorrow forced through
The channel of a single Heart."

It broke it.
Here was

"A Nerve o'er which did creep the
Else unfelt oppressions of the earth."

And that Nerve felt so deeply the three oppressions of the earth—sin, suffering, death—that his contact with them turned to a torturing cross.

He came that men might have life and that they might have it more abundantly. But three things kept men from knowing life; three things shadowed and shattered life—sin, suffering, death. All his teaching, all his living, all his miracles, all his tragedy at Calvary were to get rid of those three things. He hated sin. He hated suffering. He hated death. When he performed miracles of healing upon suffering men it was not, as some have thought, to attest his claims to divinity. He healed them because he hated suffering. He simply could not bear to see men suffer. But he knew that he could not rid the world of suffering by individual healing, so he went deeper, went to the utmost limit and at the cross became suffering that men

[77]

might be saved from suffering; became sin that
sin might be ended; became death that death
might be banished. He took it upon himself.

These lines touch me deeply:

"They borrowed a bed to lay his head
    When Christ the Lord came down;
They borrowed the ass in the mountain pass
    For him to ride to town;
But the crown that he wore and the cross that he
        bore
Were his own—
The cross was his own.

"He borrowed the bread when the crowd he fed
    On the grassy mountainside;
He borrowed the dish of broken fish
    With which he satisfied;
But the crown that he wore and the cross that he
        bore
Were his own—
The cross was his own.

"He borrowed the ship in which to sit
    To teach the multitude;
He borrowed a nest in which to rest—
    He had never a home so rude;
But the crown that he wore and the cross that he
        bore
Were his own—
The cross was his own.

"He borrowed a room on his way to the tomb
    The Passover Lamb to eat;
They borrowed a cave for him a grave,
    They borrowed a winding sheet;

But the crown that he wore and the cross that he
    bore
Were his own—
The cross was his own.

                        "L. M. N."

It is beautiful poetry and I love it as such, but
I wonder, I wonder if there were anything more
completely not his own than that cross. The
bed, the ass, the bread, the dish of broken fish,
the ship, the nest, the room, the cave—they were
all his. Was he not the giver of all life? But
this cross—this cross, it was not his. He had
done nothing to deserve it. It was not his. *It
was yours and mine.*

The old African chief was right when, for the
first time, he heard the story of the redeeming
God, he jumped to his feet with tears streaming
down his cheeks and cried: "O Jesus, away from
there, that is not your place! You have done
no sin. It is not your place. It is mine." We
may not say it so dramatically, but we do feel
it none the less truly: it is our place, not his.
The sin was ours, the suffering was ours, the
death was ours, but he made it all his—to end it.

I sat on the floor in the Ashram of Gandhiji
and listened to an address given to a small
group of the International Fellowship. I listened with appreciation to the advice he gave,
for it came from a great soul. But all the time
he was speaking I could not keep my eyes from a

little picture on the wall just above his head. I could scarcely make out its outlines, for it was turned toward the shadows, but I soon saw it was a picture of Christ upon the cross. Strange that the picture of the Crucified should be here in the Hindu Ashram. But why strange? The cross is written in the constitution of our universe—why shouldn't it be there in the Hindu Ashram? As Gandhiji went on speaking, a gentle breeze came through the window and turned the little picture from the shadows toward the light, and before he had finished a sunbeam from the window was falling upon the Crucified and he was luminous. As Gandhiji finished his address he turned toward us and said, "Will you sing that hymn?" and when we asked, "What hymn—'Lead, kindly Light'?" he replied, "No. 'When I survey the wondrous cross.'" There we sat—Hindu, Moslem, Christian—and those of us who knew it sang it, some of us with deeper meaning than ever before.

Above the head of the finest giver of the finest advice is this cross. It stands for something more than good advice, it stands for Good News. The philosophers may enlighten me, the moralists may instruct me, the prophets may inspire me, but my need is deeper. I need a Saviour. For I am deeply hurt—sin-hurt. So after the best of men have spoken their advice, and even after the Best Man had taught and shown me

by his example how to live, I know that my need
is not yet met, its depth has not yet been
reached; I find myself gazing on a cross and my
lips are framing the healing words:

> "When I survey the wondrous cross
>   On which the Prince of glory died,
> My richest gain I count but loss,
>   And pour contempt on all my pride."

This cross has been turned toward the shadows.
The shadows of controversy, of legalism, of narrow partisanship, of greed and unbrotherliness
have been obscuring it. But a gentle breeze of
the Spirit is going through our hearts and is
turning that cross from the shadows toward the
light, and that cross is becoming the one luminous spot in our universe—a place where
through his becoming suffering for us we find
our happy souls singing down the years, through
his becoming sin for us we find ourselves sin-
healed, through his becoming death for us we
find ourselves with life—abundant life.

We are now another step nearer Pentecost.
His life showed the way, his death cleared the
way—to life.

CHAPTER VII

IN WHICH LIFE TRIUMPHS

WHEN Jesus hung upon the cross there trembled upon his lips a tragic question, "My God, why?" It seems as though all the questions that haunt the mind of man were gathered up in that question, "My God, why?"

The cross raises and meets—and meets adequately—the supreme question before the mind of man—his moral need, his sin. This question is central and decisive, but it is not the only question concerning life, and had the gospel stopped there and not raised those other questions about life that afflict and often paralyze the very souls of men, it would have been an inadequate answer to life. Fortunately for the race, the cross does raise all those other questions and raises them in an acute form. At the cross these questions were asked not by a philosopher in the quietness of scholarly seclusion, as is often the case, but they were gathered up in a suffering soul and a suffering body so that out of the heart of pain came the question, "Why?"

The question as to whether goodness can live in a world like this was raised that day. Will the universe back goodness? Or is it supremely indifferent, or, worse still, hostile? Does the

universe care whether Caiaphas is on a judgment seat and Christ is on a cross? Barabbas
means "son of the father," and according to a
well-authenticated reading his surname was
"Jesus," so that he was Jesus, son of the father.
Our Saviour Jesus was also Barabbas, "Son of
the Father," but one son goes free though his
hands were stained with blood; the other Son
goes to a cross though his hands had blessed
little children and had touched sightless eyes
and had healed them. Does the Father care anything about his sons? The most searching question we can ask about the universe is whether a
moral purpose runs through it or whether it is
supremely indifferent to moral ends. Never
did a conjunction of events raise this question
more acutely than when the gentlest Heart that
ever beat was breaking on a cross.

How far can slander go? They had lied about
him, and now their lies prevail. We have been
taught that the universe is built for the success
of truth; but here it seems to be supporting lies.

Again, how far can faith in people go? Can
men be depended upon at all? The Man who
was most tender and faithful to men finds himself forsaken by men. "They all forsook him,
and fled," says the bitter account.

How dark and discouraging can things become without any word from God whatever?
"Let be," said the crowd, "let us see whether

God will come and save him." And he did not. Have we not cried to mute heavens and have not cavernous depths thrown back our voices upon us, unanswered?

"My son, the world is dark with griefs and graves,
 So dark that men cry out against the heavens."

How worth while is human life? Is this whole world in which we live a scene of maya, illusion? Was not Buddha right when he pronounced existence and evil as one? Is not pessimism the only attitude we can take toward life? Do we not want release from life rather than its continuance? Is not the death-day happier than the birth-day Was the actor right who when dying said to those about him, "Let down the curtain, the farce is done"? The Jews wanted Jesus to be taken down from the cross lest he spoil their feast day. Does not Jesus, hanging on a cross, spoil our feasts of shallow optimisms about life?

A home life is built up out of tender relationships, out of weeks and months of prayer and pain, out of self-givings too gracious for words, out of loves that seem to make life worth while and beautiful—and the end? The mother is turned over to the care of a penniless stranger and the Son gasps in torture upon his cross.

My God, why?

Have we never seen our life-work, built up

through the patient years, fall to pieces around us and leave us nothing—nothing except our cross? That is what happened that day to him.

And just when we needed God most, needed the balm of his presence to make bearable our wounds, needed one little ray of light to reassure us amid the gathering darkness, one word to tell us he was there, even that was denied.

My God, why?

From the parched lips of Jesus came that day the question that gathers up all the questions that are wrung from our pain-parched souls to-day.

Is there any answer? Certainly, none that is written out—none that comes to us from God in the logical style of the philosopher. And if there were, I'm not sure it would be an answer. It would be academic, and our questions are not academic. Our questions are life-questions and demand a life-answer. Has Life answered?

Yes!

If Calvary raises these questions, Easter morning answers them. The cross raised the questions, Easter morning raised the Man who gathered up the questions in himself. If life has spoken its hardest, cruelest, bitterest, most pessimistic and despairing word, Life meets it fairly and squarely and answers it. The answer to the raised questions is the raised Christ. Life's last word is not a cross but an Easter morning. What are scars, if at last they become radiant? What is a cross, if at the end it lifts me? What is pain, if my pain becomes a pæan? What are separations if I come back more completely and fully than before? What is man's slander, if God affirms? What can winter do, if spring beats in my veins? What of Calvary, if just beyond it lies an Easter morning?

I know now that life can speak no harder word than it spoke at the cross, and I know now that Life can speak no more adequate word than it spoke at the resurrection. He is risen! Let that word suffice.

Here is a complete affirmation to life—to the whole of life, including the physical. Do not tell me that he arose spiritually and that this is the meaning of the resurrection. This leaves more than half my questions unanswered. For if the only victory here is victorious spiritual survival after death, it leaves behind the whole question of the worth-whileness of life in the body, the worth-whileness of the whole fabric of the earth-side of existence. Unless we can be firmly convinced that human life here and now is a good thing, we will never be able to give ourselves whole-heartedly to life, to its reforms, and to the establishment of the kingdom of God on earth. If Jesus' resurrection were only spiritual, it would lead us to feel that the victory lies on the other side of the grave, and this would drain off the best thinking from palpitating human problems to a looking and longing for release from them. Religion would thus throw open the gates to escape, not the gates to life. But in the physical resurrection of Jesus we find a mighty affirmation to the whole physical side of life; the spiritual victory is to be an embodied victory; the whole force of religion is thrown not to the other side of the grave, but to this side; religion is to be back of the belief in life and is therefore behind life and its uplift. Its aim is the kingdom of God on earth. It is a *Yes* to human life, and not a *No*. The resurrection, therefore, affirms in one supreme act the whole of life—the physical and the spiritual, the present life and the future life—and affirms it in the face of its supreme denial—the cross.

"Religion, an opiate to the people," so the Soviets say. Not if Christ is religion. On the cross he refused the deadening drug offered to him. Had he taken it, he would not have needed to cry this cry. But he met the whole issue with brain unclouded and nerves unsoothed, and he raised these questions to high heaven. And he answered them! Religion is not to be an opiate —it is to be open-eyed, even if those eyes are blurred with the tears of pain.

The hoary East smiles at the optimisms of the Christian and says: "It comes out of your contact with the young and inexperienced West.

Wait till you have seen more deeply and have felt how cruel and bitter life can be, then pessimisms will take possession of your spirit too. Then Buddha's litany will become yours and you will be glad to have him throw open the gates of Nirvana to you." This would be true had there been no Easter morning in our history. Easter morning stands for an optimism won out of the heart of pain. Our gospel is the most pessimistic of faiths in that it dared to look at life through a cross, but it is the most optimistic of faiths in that it now looks at life through an Easter morning. It puts an unconquerable courage at the heart of life, so that whenever the real gospel is accepted, there life lifts up its head, there it refuses to be beaten; it finds its moral courage to live.

The non-Christian faiths have no Easter morning in them. Hence pessimisms lie like a paralyzing pall upon the souls of these great peoples; they have lost their moral nerve to live, reforms languish or are sporadic, religion does not stand behind life. It offers to make one indifferent to life and finally to escape from it. A modern philosopher says that Neo-Platonism was a deification of the word "Not." It therefore died. That word "Not" has been deeply deified in the East: "Neti," "Neti"—"Not that," "Not that"— is the highest that can be said of Brahma. And the highest that can be affirmed of life is its virtual negation. If religion approves a negation of life, it will die, for we want and need nothing so desperately as life.

"We have a proof in our religion that you haven't in yours," interrupted a Moslem one day while the Christian preacher was speaking, "for when we go to Arabia we can find the tomb of the Prophet, so that we have proof that he lived. But when you go to Jerusalem you cannot be sure you have the burial place of Jesus. You have no tomb as we have."

"True," replied the preacher, "we have no tomb in our religion because we have no corpse."

Our gospel ends not in a corpse, but in a Conqueror; not in a tomb, but in a triumph. And because of this very fact a radiant optimism lives at its heart. It is a gospel of *in spite of*. It does not depend on *the-account-of's*, for it can live on the *in-spite-of's*. And live radiantly.

We move sadly along the road to Emmaus. The cross has shattered our hopes and our universe. "We had hoped" are the only words left out of the shattered yesterdays, and these are upon our lips. A Stranger joins us. And while he talks with us and walks with us something happens to us—our hearts begin to burn within us as he talks with us by the way. Life seems to be different—anything, everything seems possible. We who walked the Way of the Drooping Heart now walk the way of the Burning Heart, because we walk with the Christ of the Emmaus Road.

And as we walk with this Christ of the Emmaus Road we are on the now open road to Pentecost.

CHAPTER VIII

IN WHICH LIFE BECOMES AVAILABLE

THE three things necessary before this Gift of Gifts could be given had now been accomplished; Life had been shown in his life; Life had suffered that the three things that cripple life—sin, suffering, death—might be cleared away; Life had utterly overcome in the resurrection, and now Life was ready to be given. Pentecost could now bring the climactic facts to men. He lived, he died, he arose, he gives himself in experience—these four facts stand together and constitute our gospel. To lose any one of the four is to lose the gospel. This is a self-evident fact.

To take the first three, but to stop short of the fourth, is the supreme tragedy of present-day Christian living. We emphasize his life, his death, and his resurrection. The consequence is we have an objective gospel. It lies in history —not in us. And because it lies in history and is objective the characteristic of Christian living is dimness, a sense of far-away-ness, unreality. Ask the average Christian to-day wherein lies his greatest problem in Christian living and the reply will probably be: "I believe it, but do not know it; I remember Christ, but do not realize him; to me it is all dim and unreal." His prayer is,

> "I ask no prophet ecstasy,
>   No sudden rending of the flesh,
>   But take the dimness of my sight away."

It is true that we may find the Christ of the Emmaus Road joining us now and again, and while he is with us our hearts do burn within us and we do recognize him in the breaking of the bread. But he is soon gone. He leaves us with a beautiful memory, but that beautiful memory turns to an inner ache, for he seems so fleeting, so furtive, so unsubstantial, so unavailable. This is true of all pre-Pentecost experience.

Even the Christ of the Emmaus Road is not sufficient, for while he is triumphant, he is still in history. He must become THE CHRIST OF EVERY ROAD, especially the Christ of those Inner Roads of Personal Life and Experience.

The sixth chapter of Romans vividly describes the potentialities of the Christian life in view of what Christ has done for us by his life, his death, and his resurrection. Our hearts beat faster as we hear it. But they turn cold within us when we see that on the very heels of this description of the sixth, the seventh chapter ensues with its litany of defeat and despondency and death. Why this appalling contradiction? The reason is not hard to find—the Spirit is not mentioned in the seventh chapter. He is not a working factor there. It is pre-Pentecost. But the eighth ensues, and there the Spirit becomes a living factor—he is mentioned nineteen times —the whole spiritual climate changes. The litany of defeat turns to a litany of victory, and the happy soul wings its way through those abounding verses. The eighth chapter is normal Christianity. So naturalized have we become in a pre-Pentecost state that we take it for granted that the seventh is the best that the gospel can offer and that nothing more is expected of us than to moan and drone: "We have done those things which we ought not to have done, and we have left undone those things which we ought to have done, and there is no health in us." No health in us? There is health in us if the Spirit lives within us. We have no business to be living subnormal, unhealthy, anæmic spiritual lives and call them Christian. They are sub-Christian. Our greatest difficulty is not antichristianity, but this sub-Christianity. It takes the facts of Christ's life—his life, his death, his resurrection —but not the living fact of Christ. To take the first three and miss this is, I repeat, the supreme tragedy in present-day Christian living.

Paul says, "I do not frustrate the grace of God." He took everything that grace offered him, he did not annul or frustrate the grace of God by stopping short. We do. All stopping short of Pentecost is frustrating the grace of God at the vital point. We stop at the very point where all the rays of Divine Love passing through the prism of his life, his cross, his resurrection, center and fuse into experience, an experience in which the soul is kindled into flame.

Since we have seen that the four stand together, and that failure to pass on from the first three to the fourth results in spiritual tragedy, we are now in a position to inquire what really did happen at Pentecost.

Certainly, something did happen, something very decisive. Draw a line through the New Testament and on one side is spiritual fumbling, hesitancy, inadequacy, defeat, and on the other side is certainty, courage, adequacy, victory. That line runs straight through Pentecost. When we read the Acts of the Apostles, which is taken up with the doings of the apostles after Pentecost, we are struck with the incongruity between the apostles and their acts. Here were very ordinary men doing extraordinary things, thinking in an extraordinary way, leaving an extraordinary effect in the changed lives of men and society. The very temper and spirit of their lives was extraordinary. They seemed to have found power by which to live. And far from being rampant emotionalism the striking thing is their amazing balance and sanity. They burned with zeal, but they met issues and crises of the most far-reaching consequences and met them with poise and insight. They picked their way through intellectual and moral bogs and quagmires and marked out paths which we to-day tread with safety and salvation. And, more than that, they brought to bear upon life a power that redeemed men and made them immediately God-conscious; that changed the moral and spiritual climate; that turned dull, drab life into the spiritually gay and taught a sad world to sing—and to sing *in spite of*. Dean Church tells us that the joy that throbs through early Christian literature is one of the most solemn things in history. Life in the Spirit, he says, had convinced men that at last the routine of sin and vice had met its match, that a new and astonishing possibility had come into view. He declares further that men not merely here and there, but on a widespread scale, could attain to that hitherto hopeless thing for the multitudes, goodness.

Something extraordinary did happen at Pentecost. What was it?

I am persuaded that two outstanding things happened. First, God, the Living Spirit, became to them immediate, experimental, vital—overwhelmingly so. In the fires of that Living Presence the old self-life was burned up, their interests became merged with his and henceforth they had one passion—Christ. One desire, thereafter, consumed them—to share him with men.

Second, religion here broke its fetters and became universal. I used to think that with Paul our gospel broke its cramping Jewish fetters and became universalized. I am persuaded this came before Paul. It is true that Paul worked out the implications of the universalities at Pentecost, for his chief emphasis was upon the Spirit —upon the Spirit and not upon "justification," as has been so largely held. His emphasis upon the Spirit made it easy for him to think in terms universal, for where "the Spirit of the Lord is, there is liberty"—liberty from the inner fetters of self and liberty from the less-than-universal ideas and customs.

At Pentecost religion penetrated to the inmost depth of personal need and then rebounded to universality. Never was religion more personal, never was it more universal and social. It met and solved the needs of a Man and showed itself capable of meeting and solving the needs of man. It gave inner freedom and a world-view. The personal experience at Pentecost has a cosmic setting. This is important, for no religious experience can continue to be valid unless it fits in with the sum total of things. It must have a cosmic setting if it is to be personally satisfying.

We have looked on the experience of Pentecost as having depth; can we also look on it as having breadth? The conservatives in Christendom have been insisting on depth and the progressives on breadth. Will they both find in Pentecost their insistence—and more? They must if Pentecost is to meet life, for life demands that we have both depth and breadth. Depth without breadth is narrow, breadth without depth is shallow. Pentecost is both deep and broad, for it meets the whole of the life facts. It gave men an inner freedom and a world-view. They found God and a philosophy of life. But this world-view came not through philosophy, but through fact, and because of this we have missed its significance. We have been too dull to see and too unchristian to follow out the implications of Pentecost. Had the Christian Church followed out the intimations and implications of what took place at Pentecost, we would have been saved from the narrow, contentious centuries and from the graveclothes that still bind religion to-day.

Doctor Eucken once wrote to a friend these penetrating words: "If Christianity is to conquer the world, it must on the one hand return to its living roots, and on the other apply itself in ever-widening circles to the problems of the present time." When we return to those living roots do we find the facts there so universal that we can without strain apply them in ever-widening circles to the problems of the present time? Can those living roots bring forth fruit to-day without a graft of more universal ideas from the outside? Or do we find that the very life of those roots is universal life?

The more I look at Pentecost and the more I feel the life that throbs there, the more I am persuaded that with the coming of the Spirit life has been met at its depths and life has been met in its breadths—the whole of life has been met. At Pentecost we see the effects of the coming of the Spirit in their pristine purity, before these wonderful facts have been overlaid by the narrow, cramping centuries. And the immediate effects are that religion here broke into universal forms.

There was deep emotion at Pentecost, but it was a by-product of this inner and outer freedom which they suddenly found was theirs. How could their hearts keep from emotion when they experienced the immediate sense of the Divine, looked out and saw opening vistas, heard the cracking of fetters and felt themselves and their whole outlook universalized?

CHAPTER IX

PENTECOST AND THE ORDINARY

LET us look at some of the universal forms into which religion broke on that momentous occasion—the spiritual birthday of a New Race.

The account says that the Spirit came upon the group while they were in an Upper Room— a home. The home, according to tradition, was that of Mary, the mother of John Mark. The significance lies in the fact that the Spirit came upon them, not when they were in the Temple or in any other specially sacred place, but in a home, the most common and ordinary and universal place in human life.

Here was religion loosed from specially sacred places, and centered in that universal place of living, a home.

In all ages, among all people, religion has been associated with sacred places. Thousands drag their weary bodies to the banks of the Ganges, that they may die in sight of this sacred stream. I watched a woman who had measured her length on the ground for fifty miles while the thermometer was 120 degrees in the shade, that she might ring the bell in the temple in order to awaken the Divine in her behalf. I saw a Mohammedan saying his prayers in the train. He knelt upon his prayer-mat on the floor and tried to face toward Mecca. It was difficult, for the train was winding through mountainous hills. But he was equal to the occasion, for I noticed a compass on the floor beside him, and as the train twisted he moved with it and kept facing toward the holy place of Mecca. I have watched the Jews kiss the foundation stones of the ancient Temple and groove them with their tears. The Indians of Latin America, taking long pilgrimages to a sacred shrine, can be heard crying, "Adios! Adios! Christos"—"Farewell! Farewell! O Christ"— as they leave with tears and return to their homes. They had left him behind in the sacred place.

How often we put religion into a sacred day, Sunday, and a sacred place, the church, and leave it there—embalmed! The serious thing about all this is that in making one place sacred all other places are consciously or unconsciously desecrated. The Hindu has his sacred places and then considers all the rest of life maya, or illusion. The Moslem turns toward Mecca and thereby turns away from where he lives. In India he is more devoted to Arabia than to India, more to Mecca than to man. In a Jewish synagogue on the Sabbath a man arose in front of me and motioned to me to push out of sight the pencils in my outer coat pocket. It defiled the holy place and the holy day to have those pencils (signs of trade) in sight. A Hindu said to me when I asked him if he had found God: "Here are people who have searched for God for a lifetime and have not found—what can I expect to find in so short a time? I get up at four and go through my religious exercises and ceremonies until nine, and then I go to my business till five, and between those hours God knows what I do! But I become religious again after returning from my business until time to go to bed." That gap! Not in India alone is this done, for in putting Christ into specially sacred times and places we often leave him there and say with the Latin Indians: "Adios! Adios! Christos," and plunge into the secular with a secular spirit. That gap!

In view of this universal tendency to put God into sacred places and leave him there, it is important to remember that when God gave his highest Gift, himself, he gave it not in an especially sacred place. He gave it in a home. He made thereby the commonplace the uncommonplace.

Religion, then, is to center not in the temple, but in the home. The whole of life is to be raised to the sacred. And the gift of the Spirit is not to be associated particularly with sermons and services, but with power to live radiantly every day in every way, to lift the sordid into the sacred, to make our bodies the temples of the Spirit and our homes the home of God. This is in line with the teachings of Jesus, for the home, not the temple, was the one institution he defended—the temple would be destroyed, but the home, joined together by God, must not be put asunder. The home is the hope of our race. Unless religion can be at home in the home, no amount of religion in the temple can save us.

The home was to be the highest unit of human life. The Hindu system says that the stage of the girishta, or householder, is not the highest; he passes on through this to the Sanyasi, the homeless, in which state he hopes to attain salvation. But here was salvation centering in a home and glorifying it. Unless religion can be brought in from the marginal, from Sanyasi-ism, from monkism, from the exceptional type— no matter how fine it may be—to the very center of life, to a home, and there made valid and vital, it will touch but faintly the future of our race. Pentecost does bring it in from the marginal and does set it at the very center of life.

I have almost run away from physical healing through prayer, and yet again and again I have been all but forced into it. In the home of an American Y. M. C. A. secretary in China I once told a story of a remarkable healing. The little daughter of eight years listened with wide-open-eyes. At the close she calmly remarked, "Why, that sounds like a miracle, but of course it might have been only a coincidence." The dear little skeptic of eight discussing whether it was miracle or coincidence! I will give the story, for some older skeptics might like to work on it. It was this: We were having a vacation in the mountains and one of the missionary ladies, in stepping out of a boat, sprained her ankle very badly. It swelled immediately to about twice its normal size. The doctor said she would have to be in bed for ten days or two weeks. She was a very devoted worker and to spend her vacation in bed was hard. She asked her husband and me to come in and pray with her. We did so, and a few minutes after we had left the room she walked out on the veranda radiant. "I'm healed," she said, and she walked up and down without a limp. We had planned to walk the next day to another lake nine miles away, on a fishing trip. She announced that she would go as planned. She presented herself to the doctor the next day, told the story, and asked the doctor about going on this walking trip. The doctor, being wise and being Christian, said that he could say nothing against it. She walked the nine miles without a limp, and walked back the next day with no reaction.

Now, the point about the story is this: I have heard of God healing people for special Christian service, but this was for a fishing trip! Is God interested in fishing trips? Is God interested in our pleasures and recreations as well as in our duties? Is all life sacred? I know what that little incident did for that vacation: it lifted that summer into a sacrament. It hallowed our happiness. On that same fishing trip the next day we were at the lake by daybreak, and after our lines were set we were reminded that we hadn't had our morning devotions and concluded to have them sitting there. In the midst of my prayer my reel suddenly spun with a big one! The prayer was as suddenly broken off, the big one reeled in, the lines reset and the prayer resumed! There seemed to be no real interruption. Why should there be? Can't we take God into everything? We must be able to take him into everything or into nothing. To take God into everything does not mean that we lower religion, but it does mean that we lift life. To take God into our pleasures does not mean that we make God common, but it does mean that we make our pleasures uncommon. For when we apply this principle of taking God into our pleasures we will find a good many of our pleasures dropping off as incapable of fitting in. A Christian has no right to take any pleasure into which he cannot take God.

On my first trip to India I was having my evening prayer hour in my cabin as we pulled into Plymouth. An urgent Inner Voice said, "Get up, hurry upstairs on deck." I put it aside as a temptation, for I had made it a habit not to let anything interfere with that prayer hour. But after awhile I thought I detected the Voice of the Divine and hurried upstairs just in time to see my trunk—the only possession I had in the world—go over the side into a tender. It was being put off at Plymouth by mistake. I rescued it and resumed my prayers. I had always been sure that God was interested in my going to India as a missionary. Had he not called me? But was he also interested in the baggage? Could I depend on him to see that I had baggage as well as blessing? The years have said "Yes" to these questions, for I've never wanted for a single thing that I've needed. He has never let me down. He makes every common bush flame with God, and hallows every happening.

I am glad the Spirit's coming is not associated with dark cloisters, musty corners, and dim lights, but, rather, with the laughter of little children, with the pains and problems of human relationships, with life as it is in the home. Strengthen me in my heart and in my home and let the world come on. The Spirit comes to save and strengthen both heart and hearth—an everyday Power, for everyday living.

Christ was born in a manger, the church was born in a home and finds its center there.

CHAPTER X

PENTECOST AND PERSONALITY

THERE is another phase where Pentecost lifts religion out of the limited and local and makes it universal.

We note that the Spirit came, not upon the twelve alone, but upon the whole body of the followers of Christ. Of "the five hundred brethren" who saw Jesus after his resurrection only one hundred and twenty were at Pentecost, so that three hundred and eighty believers did not elect to receive God's highest gift. These three hundred and eighty drop out of the account; we hear of them no more. The only record they leave is the record of their number. Without Pentecost we add to statistics, but to nothing else. While not all of the five hundred were at Pentecost, the principle holds good: the coming of the Spirit was not for the purposes of the twelve alone. Had the Spirit been given to the twelve alone, there would have been built up in Christianity a spiritual hierarchy that would have killed its essential spirit. A specially sacred class with the highest sanction would have been created.

But here was religion loosed from specially sacred classes and centered in a man as a man.

As the Spirit loosed religion from specially sacred places and put it in that very universal place, the home, so it was further loosed from specially sacred classes and centered in that most universal place, human personality, apart from position and calling. The Holy Spirit was given to a man and not a minister, to a person and not a priest.

This is important, for in every clime and nation religion has tended to run more and more into the hands of specially sacred classes. The Brahman in India, the mulah in Islam, the monk in Buddhism, the priest and clergyman in the West have been considered specially sacred. In making special classes sacred other men as men have been rendered non-sacred, or desecrated. This cuts straight across the genius of our gospel, for the gospel believes in the worth of human personality apart from race and birth and color and position and calling.

Someone has said that the highest test of the civilization of any country is the test of the sacredness of a person. This is not only true of a civilization, but is pre-eminently true of a religion. What does it think of a person? That is the supreme test.

Our gospel centers in a Person and it creates personality. As H. Wheeler Robinson says, "In sharpest contrast with the original Buddhist solution of the mystery of life by the elimination of personality as an illusion, the Christian of all types finds an intensification and justification of his personality as the first result of his faith."[1]

Trace this through the teachings and life of Jesus and everywhere there is a new sense of human value. A man sat by the roadside begging, and when he heard that Jesus was going by he cried out to him to have mercy on him. The crowd, including the disciples, told him to keep quiet. They were not interested in him. He was only a blind beggar. But Jesus stopped and asked them to call him. Then they ran eagerly to him and said, "Arise, he calleth thee." They began to be interested in him when they found Jesus was. Their interest followed his interest.

As a race we had little interest in certain classes of people until we found he had an interest in them. Take the child. When a child was born to the Roman father it was often presented to him to decide whether it should be kept. He moved its arms and its legs to see whether they were normal; and if they were not, or if he did not particularly like the child, he broke its back over his knee and threw it out. It was only a baby. I saw in a Hindu temple a

[1] *The Christian Experience of the Holy Spirit,* page 27. Reprinted by permission of the author and James Nisbet & Co., Ltd., publishers, London.

figure of Shiva with his trident piercing the prostrate form of a child. "A child has been born to me, a fetter has been forged for me," said Buddha. Over against this we hear the tender, worth-giving words of Christ, "Suffer the little children to come unto me, and forbid them not, for of such is the kingdom of God." To-day we are beginning to follow his interest in the child. It is not too much to say that practically all the emphasis upon the child in modern life can be traced back to this Gentle Heart. Even outside of Christianity this is so. "I am so glad to see you taking care of these little illegitimate children," were my words to the Hindu superintendent of a Hindu Foundling Home.

"Yes," he replied, "and we learned to care for them at the feet of Him who said, 'Suffer the little children to come unto me.'"

In the Bezan text we read in Acts 1. 14 "with the women and children." It seems befitting that the children too should be at Pentecost. If they were of the kingdom of God, then the powers of that kingdom belonged to them too.

We are following Jesus' interest in the un-privileged, the low-caste. "Low-castes and dogs not allowed," is a sign on a Jain temple in Gujerat. A priest with a hard face and a police-man with a drawn sword stood before the gate of a Hindu temple in South India and let me

photograph them. The low-caste people had
been forbidden to go along the road leading to
this temple, lest they defile it. But they had
sat for weeks and months before the barrier of
that forbidden road and by passive resistance
had finally won. It was the silent protest of the
human against inhuman religion. But the priest
and the policeman—religion and the law—stood
at the temple gate blocking any further progress. The low-caste could go on the road, but
they could not enter the temple. The blockade
of the priest and the policeman was futile. The
face of religion might be hard and the sword
of the law might be sharp, but to try to stop
the rise of man is impossible. And what was back
of all this, in this seemingly pure Hindu situation? A Hindu protester in behalf of the low-
castes writes from the scene and says, "Christ
is being crucified again on the four posts of this
temple." The Hindu felt that the Son of man
was being crucified in the sons of man. And
he was! The Hindus were consciously or unconsciously following his interest in people.

We are following his interest further. We
are seeing that Jesus did not merely love people's souls, he loved people. "If those people
had loved me a little more and my soul a little
less, I might have been a Christian," said a
Hindu student on his return from England. He
knew that Christ did not go around fussily lov-

ing people's souls; he loved people and was interested in everything that concerned them. The Hindu student demanded that the Christian do the same. And he was right.

Our gospel stands for this and for nothing less than this. A man is now no longer a man, he is "a man for whom Christ died." But, more, he is a man in whom the Spirit dwells. "Ye are the temples of God." "Your bodies are the temples of the Holy Ghost," said Paul to a crowd of redeemed slaves and libertines. They had found this highest of gifts, the Spirit, apart from the question of position and place. If the highest Gift is open to a man as a man, who shall deny to him the lesser gifts of life?

This emphasis upon the worth of human personality is done so quietly, so without strain, at Pentecost, that we scarcely catch its significance. Pentecost showed us the way to a spiritual democracy that would have saved us from contentious centuries during which Christendom struggled over orders and validities and supremacies. When the question of validity of orders and successions is being discussed I find myself falling asleep. I am simply not interested. It is all so irrelevant. For here at Pentecost the highest was open to a person as a person, and Peter and James and John stood in a position not one whit different from the humblest of seekers and believers. The Holy Spirit was given alike to all,

[111]

and this directly and immediately without the intervention of anyone.

For it must be noted that when the Spirit came *no one was leading the meeting.* Peter was leading at the time of the choice of one to take the place of Judas—a choice which was made by lot, a method which they abandoned when Pentecost gave them dependence on spiritual insight. But when the supreme moment came, Peter and the rest of the apostles were pleading, not leading; they were recipients, not channels. The same thing happened at the Gentiles' Pentecost, for the Holy Ghost fell on them that heard the Word right in the midst of Peter's speaking. Both at the Jews' Pentecost and the Gentiles' Pentecost the Gift was immediate and first hand without anyone's intervention. It is true that in Samaria the people received the Holy Spirit when Peter and John laid their hands on them, and the same thing happened at Ephesus when Paul did the same. But all this simply proves that the Supreme Gift may be given with or without the intervention of leaders. If the Spirit is given without their intervention, it would imply that no human leadership or priesthood is absolutely essential. On the other hand, if the Spirit is given simultaneously with the laying on of hands, this may mean no more than that the crisis thus precipitated in the life of the believer brought about inner conditions of receptivity and self-surrender and faith and thus brought about the obtaining of the Gift. The coming of the Spirit may have been with, but it certainly was not on account of, the laying on of hands, for the Spirit came without it.

We ministers take ourselves too seriously. We are sacred only if we are sacred. Our calling is sacred only if it is sacred. By taking thought about orders and position we can add not one cubit to our stature. We are what we are. And our position as ministers gives us no spiritual privilege not open to the lowliest believer. I would not have it otherwise. I should refuse a gift not open to every other man on the same terms.

Pentecost was the sentence of death to all Brahmanism, all priestly pretension, all spiritual snobbery. If we still have pretensions, it is because we have no Pentecost.

In the New Testament a minister is a *diakonos,* literally, "one who goes through the dust"— the figure of the camel driver who walks through the dust leading the camel while another is seated on top. But we will never be New Testament ministers and be willing to go through the dust unless and until we are inwardly humbled to the dust. Pentecost does that. It strips us of all pretension, all pride, all place and makes us persons. The apostles had apostolic

[113]

power because they had no apostolic pretensions. We have taken the pretensions and have lost the power.

Pentecost laid the foundations of a spiritual democracy. And if we have ears to hear what the Spirit saith, we will find that at Pentecost were laid, not merely the foundations of a spiritual democracy, but democracy in every other realm. Here religion is behind the idea that a man is a man. God treats him as such. So must we.

CHAPTER XI

PENTECOST AND SEX

‚AKIN to what we found in the previous chapter and leading us along the same lines, but going deeper, is the fact that at Pentecost the "one hundred and twenty were there *with the women*." Women received the highest Gift of God, himself, on the same basis as men. This sounds so commonplace that we lose its astounding significance. In every land religion has been identified with a specially sacred sex. That sex has always been one sex—the man! "Every male that openeth the womb shall be called holy to the Lord," was said in Judaism, and in every other religion, except the religion of Jesus. Man came first to power and the physically weaker portions of humanity, the woman and the child, have been kept out on the edges. Only now are they slowly coming into their own.

But here at Pentecost the highest was thrown open at once to woman and religion was loosed from specially sacred sexes.

This is startling when we view this fact with the background of contemporaneous views concerning women. Every day the pious Pharisee thanked God that he was not born "a woman, a leper, or a Gentile." Note her company! The holiest among the Pharisees were called "the bleeding Pharisees." They went around with their eyes on the ground lest they look on a woman; hence they were constantly striking their foreheads against posts and trees and walls, and so were called "the bleeding Pharisees." When the disciples returned from the Samaritan village they "marveled that he talked with a woman." Manu, the lawgiver to the Hindus, says: "One man alone may be a witness, . . . but not even several women, although they may be pure, on account of the lack of reliableness of woman's mind." Again he says, "One should not be seated in a secluded place with a mother, sister, or daughter. The powerful host of the senses compels even a wise man."

When Buddha allowed woman to be taken into the Sangha he did it with sadness, saying that now the Sangha would only last a thousand years. I listened to a debate in the Burma Legislative Council regarding the admission of women as members. A stately Buddhist arose and said: "Of course not. They cannot attain Nirvana as women; how, then, can they attain a place in these legislative halls?" Both within Hinduism and Buddhism a woman as a woman cannot be saved, she must be reborn as a man if she is to attain salvation.

A friend of mine taught a Maharani for many years before she was married. She gave her the best that modern education and Christian principles could give, though the Maharani still remained a Hindu. After her marriage she told my friend that the other women relatives made it so difficult for her that each day she would take her little silver cup and drink some of the bath-water in which her husband had bathed as a sign of her submission to and worship of her lord. In Hinduism a woman is called "Samsara," the weary round of rebirth—something to be got rid of before salvation can be obtained.

I saw a Mohammedan herding his "females" into a compartment next to mine in the train. There was a great hubbub as palanquins came and went, but the women were finally herded in and the train started off. He must have called the roll and found one missing, for he waved his hand very wildly to the guard on the platform, saying, "Stop, stop, one has been left behind." The train was flagged and from the other end of the platform a palanquin ran up and a little woman ducked into the compartment. The train started off, and again he must have called the roll, for more wildly than before he waved his hands to the guard saying, "Stop, stop, one more has been left behind." Again the train was flagged, and another palanquin was hurriedly brought up from the other end of the platform, and when they opened it up *two* slipped out into the compartment! This must have been the required number, for this time the train went off. The tragic thing was that no one on the platform smiled. It all seemed so taken for granted. I am not sure whether I smiled or wept—perhaps a little of each, for it was comic, but it was more deeply tragic.

Mrs. Jones once asked a zenana lady if she knew much about the world. In reply she pointed to a tree growing up over the zenana wall and said, "That treetop is the only thing I have ever seen of the outside world."

These incidents and statements about women have been out of the East. Take one out of the background of the West—the cry of a modern university woman written to me recently:

"I was, being human, born alone;
I am, being woman, hard beset;
I live by squeezing from a stone
The little nourishment I get."

Man has usually taken the bread and has given woman the stone from which to squeeze her nourishment. In the West man has fought step by step the upward rise of woman. Nearly everything he has given he has given grudgingly and under compulsion.

When we turn from all this to the gospel of Pentecost, we find woman not squeezing her spiritual nourishment from a stone, but facing

God and life on exactly the same terms as man and being offered and given the highest gift that can be given in heaven and earth—the Spirit, God himself.

The amazing thing is that it is all so taken for granted; no questions were raised, no discussions took place, women took their place at Pentecost naturally and unhesitatingly. Why? Here too the Norm had been fixed: they had seen Jesus accept women as disciples naturally and without strain; single and married women accompanied him and the disciples on their tours through Galilee, and *the breath of scandal never touched it!* He raised the whole moral tone so high, treated women so naturally and purely that thoughts of evil withered in this white purity. So lofty was the whole that the account can say, "Now Jesus loved Martha and her sister and Lazarus," and we can see nothing but beauty in it. That statement would have damned any other religious leader. It makes Jesus' purity stand out the more. Pentecost is all of a piece with this, hence woman comes to it as she would come to her very own. There were no patronizing attitudes, no loud talk about giving woman's rights; it was done simply and naturally.

The implication is that if this highest were open to woman, then everything else down the line is open. India to-day is seething with de-

bates and resolutions and conflicts and conten-
tions over how many human privileges can be
given to women. And here at Pentecost it was
all done so quietly and unobtrusively and naturally that we scarcely hear the doors opening.
But they are all open!

Paul, once a narrow, hating Pharisee, but now
under the sway of the liberating Spirit, could
say: "In Jesus Christ there is no room for Greek
and Jew [racial distinction], Barbarian and
Scythian [cultural distinction], bond and free
[social distinction], male and female [sex dis-
tinction], but Christ is all and in all." Amazing
liberation from bondages the Spirit brings! No
wonder Paul cries again: "Where the Spirit of
the Lord is there is liberty."

With this fact within our gospel we do not
wonder at the following incident: I was speaking through an interpreter to a large crowd
of men in a native state when, to my surprise,
I saw a woman making her way through the
crowd. I wondered what she was doing out in
that crowd at night, for no women were supposed to be there, and why was she making her
way forward toward us? Before I knew what
was happening she was showering flowers on my
interpreter and on me. It suddenly dawned on
me what it meant. As a woman she had heard
notes in our message that meant hope of liberty
and opening doors to her, so she expressed her

gratitude to that gospel in this way. I caught one of the falling flowers in my hand and held it there all the rest of the time I was speaking. I have it still. I hold it as the acceptance of a challenge to give this gospel till all shall know this equality and freedom.

And no wonder that this could happen: One of the most prominent Hindu women in India came with a devidasi, a temple girl, to a Y. W. C. A. secretary, and said: "I bring this girl to you to rescue. I once heard my husband read a story from your sacred book, of a woman taken in adultery and what Jesus said to her and how he saved her. We have no such story in our books, so I bring the girl to you."

It is quite true that there is no other such story in either East or West of how gracious redemption is offered even to fallen women, but greater still is the fact that to women access is offered to the very highest moral and spiritual attainment—spiritual power is available, God himself is available. All doors are open.

Yet with this fact within our gospel we still debate in Church Councils the right of women to preach and grudgingly give crumbs of privilege. If the fact of the Spirit has been given to them, who shall deny them the right to share it in every way and in every place?

At Pentecost woman was given her chart and charter of equality and freedom. The subsequent centuries lost both Pentecost and the equality and freedom of women. We shall regain the latter as we rediscover the former.

Another thing connected with equality at Pentecost is the fact that along with the one hundred and twenty were "the mother of Jesus and his brethren." They seemed to be there on exactly the same basis as the rest and received the Holy Spirit on exactly the same terms as the others. Even being the mother of the Son of God made absolutely no difference.

Here was religion loosed from specially sacred families.

It would have been easy to build up within Christianity a spiritual aristocracy based upon blood, as has been done in Brahmanism and Mohammedanism and as is now being attempted through Nordicism. Had Mary and his brethren been separated in the slightest here, had they been put in a class by themselves, had they received the Spirit on other terms and under other conditions, the foundations would have been laid for spiritual and blood snobbery. But quietly and unobtrusively they took their place alongside of the rest, and in that decisive moment all superiorities were canceled or lost sight of.

Years later in John's Gospel we hear this same note sounded: Who "were born, not of blood, nor of the will of the flesh, nor of the will of man, but of God." Pentecost had proved to them that spiritual birth was not of blood. Think what a blow this was to all assumptions of superiority based on blood. See how the Duchess of Buckingham writhes under it as she writes to Lady Huntingdon in reference to the Wesleyan Movement, a movement centering in Pentecost: "Their doctrines are most repulsive and strongly tinctured with impertinence and disrespect to their superiors. It is monstrous to be told that you have a heart as sinful as the common wretches that crawl the earth. This is highly insulting, and I wonder that your ladyship should relish any sentiment so much at variance with high rank and good breeding."

As Brahmanism in the West was writhing under the impact of this simple principle, so to-day Brahmanism in the East is in a state of tension over it. The fact is that the tensions of East and West in regard to human equality are largely, if not entirely, due to the quiet challenge of this principle of the spiritual equality of men in the sight of God. The Duke of Argyle was right when he said that "no method of reform is so powerful as this: if alongside of a corrupt custom or system is laid one incompatible principle, then that principle without any noise works against it and finally overthrows it. It was thus that Christianity, without any direct blow at slavery, laid alongside of it the incompatible principle of brotherhood and finally over-

[123]

threw it." Slowly but surely this principle is pushing to the wall everything incompatible with it.

"Blood tells," they say, but not at Pentecost. The word there is, "He hath made of one blood," and that word is finally winning its way. Two things you cannot stop: You cannot stop God and you cannot stop man. Here at Pentecost man as man comes into his own.

The lesser family of Mary was lost in the larger family of the Father, and here the Elder Brother stretches forth his hands and says, "Who is my mother, and who are my brethren? Whosoever shall do the will of my Father the same is my brother, and sister, and mother." The emphasis is not upon the extraneous but upon the intrinsic; the thing that tells is not blood, but brotherhood. Pentecost opens up the glory of being ascendants, not descendants.

CHAPTER XII

PENTECOST—CONSERVATIVE OR RADICAL?

Peter at Pentecost, quoting Joel as to what would happen when the Spirit came upon life, said, "It shall come to pass in the last days, saith God, I will pour out of my Spirit upon all flesh; . . . and your young men shall see visions, and your old men shall dream dreams." Peter saw that in the life of the Spirit the young man and the old man would each be quickened, each be the channel of the Divine, and each contribute to the whole.

In every religion old age has usually been the sacred age. The religions of the world have been in the hands of graybeards, hence conservative. But at Pentecost a new and astonishing possibility came into view—all ages, the young and the old, were to bring their contribution to the interpretation and enrichment of this gospel.

Here was religion loosed from specially sacred ages.

As religion has usually tended to run into the hands of the old, it has become the most conservative influence in human life. "Our religion is in danger," has been the cry that has blocked reform in every age and clime. This is so true that the criticism that "religion is an opiate of the people" has some truth in it. But this could not be leveled at the life of the Spirit as it blossomed forth at Pentecost, for here the young and the old, the progressive and the conservative, would correct each other and contribute to each other. The Spirit is the Spirit of comprehension, not narrowness, of inclusion, not exclusion.

Among all peoples we have political parties divided along the lines of progressive and conservative. This has happened everywhere. It would seem to imply that the human mind is built that way, hence it is inevitable that we have the radical and the conservative in religion also. It would be a tragedy if we did not have them both. If we were all radicals, we would blow up! If we were all conservatives, we would dry up! But between the pull of the two we make very definite progress in a middle direction.

Conservative old age shakes its head about the youth of every age. But it has always been so. Over against these ancient and modern wails we find the gospel proposing to take the ardency of youth, its restlessness with things as they are, its revolts and visions, and use them for purposes of the Kingdom. At the same time, by its emphasis on the place of old age, dreaming dreams, it calls on youth to remember that just because a thing is new it is not necessarily true, that truth won through struggle and pain must be conserved, and that the safest way to go forward is to do as the motorist does, who, as he drives forward, looks into the mirror reflecting the road behind him. It tells him to study the past as a starting point for the future. Old age needs the visions of youth; youth needs the dreams of old age.

In spite of this comprehension at Pentecost we still condemn each other if we differ the slightest in viewpoint or view. In North India a huge Afghan became a Christian. He was a giant in body and simple as a child in soul. He was known throughout the country as "The Christian"——and he was! But one day a little Mohammedan blasphemed Christ in his presence. The giant was so aroused that he took him by the scruff of the neck, hung him over the open mouth of a well, and said, "If you don't take that back, I'll drop you in." The Mohammedan, dangling over the open well, decided to take it back!

We can excuse the simple-hearted giant, but what can we say of Christians, two thousand years after Pentecost, who still drop their brethren into open wells of perdition because they do not happen to possess the same mentality or belong to the same group? At Pentecost, "Peter stood up with the eleven." They were one——and yet how divergent in outlook! The Zealot and

[127]

the Publican one! The miracle of inclusion had happened.

At the recent Jerusalem Conference we found certain questions becoming acute. We could feel the tingle of the Fundamentalist-Modernist controversy in the air as we neared Jerusalem. We could also feel the coming clash between the German and the American outlooks on the kingdom of God—one said that it was a supernatural gift from above, the other that it was a task. When the Conference was nearing its close we found that we hadn't settled the Fundamentalist-Modernist controversy—we had simply transcended it. We saw that there was something bigger than each—the gospel. In our quest to live and give that gospel, our questions seemed to solve themselves. Christ held us both! And as for the two views of the Kingdom, we saw, before the close, that the Kingdom was both a gift and a task, that each needed the other to complete it and that there was far more in Christ than either had caught.

Everywhere we find both the conservative and the radical appealing to Jesus as approving their standpoint. Which was he—conservative or radical? As I hear him challenging almost every single religious conception and institution of that day—the current views concerning God and man, the meaning of religion, the Sabbath, the Temple, the Law, the authority of the Sanhedrin—I am convinced that he is a radical. But when I see him gather up every truth out of the past, conserving and completing it and saying, "I came not to destroy but to fulfill," I know that he is a conservative. He is both. He says, "The kingdom of heaven is like unto a man that is an householder, which bringeth forth out of his treasures things new and old." The wise scribe of the Kingdom is to be both radical and conservative—he brings forth "things new and old." But note the order—the new is first. And at Pentecost the young men seeing visions came before the old men dreaming dreams. The gospel does lean toward the radical, for it involves change. It is "the ought-to-be" standing over against the "is."

At the Lausanne Conference—a Conference largely in the hands of the old and looking to precedent rather than to progress—a youth, aroused to action by the sheer conservatism of things, started down the aisle toward the platform and was declared by the chairman to be out of order. The youth came on with the significant words upon his lips, "It is my business to be out of order." It is the business of youth to be out of order, just as it is the business of old age to be in order. Between the clash of the two there may be seeming disorder, but in reality it is the birth-pangs of a higher order.

As the mind of man seems naturally to break

up into conservatism and radicalism, we will always have both with us, and since we cannot get rid of each other, we might as well make up our minds to live together as brothers. The Chinese Christians, in their matter-of-fact way, came to this conclusion and issued this significant statement, "Agreed to differ, but resolved to love and unite to serve."

Do not misunderstand; Pentecost does not point the way to a false tolerance which is essentially indifferentism. It does allow each the right to hold convictions and to differ, but it also undertakes to gather up youth's power to see visions and old age's proneness to dream dreams and out of the two create something entirely new—the kingdom of God.

One observation must be made before we close this chapter. The gospel provides, among other things, two utter necessities for human living: a static norm and a progressive ideal. In presenting the character of Christ, fixed in history, it provides an anchoring place for our minds and keeps them from going adrift in every passing wind of modern speculation and tendency. But it goes further: in its teaching concerning the Holy Spirit it provides a progressive dynamic that is capable of infinite adaptation to a growing life. The Spirit "guides us into all truth." Hence the Spirit is forever unfolding what was infolded in the person of Christ and is forever applying it to changing conditions. The gospel has, therefore, about it a sense of newness, of surprise, of eternal freshness. He who lives under the sway of the Spirit lives under a perpetual dawn. A surprise awaits him around every corner. Vistas open everywhere. He knows in the inmost depths of his being that what he has cannot be outgrown, for he knows that he possesses, not a set of dead truths, but the very Spirit of Truth.

The gospel will, therefore, never be out-known nor out-grown. The Spirit is its principle and power of rejuvenation.

CHAPTER XIII

PENTECOST AND RELIGIOUS IMPERIALISM

PENTECOST goes further in its amazing sweep toward universality. The account says that when the Holy Spirit came, "the multitudes were astonished to hear, every one in his own language, the wonderful works of God."

Here we come to one of the most puzzling portions of the account. What does this speaking in other tongues mean? Certainly, there seems a difference between what happened among the Corinthians and what happened at Pentecost. At Corinth the tongues were unknown and needed an interpreter, here they spoke directly, without an interpreter, in the languages of the people who heard. At Corinth the tongues were for the purpose of communion; at Pentecost for the purpose of communication. But that is only a part of the purpose. The happening at Pentecost seems to have a far greater significance than that a group of people should hear the gospel message. To catch its significance we must remember how racially exclusive all nations have been, how they have considered other tongues and cultures barbarian and their own tongue and culture sacred. This was especially true of the Hebrews. The whole tendency would be to identify the gospel with their own tongue and culture and nationalism. And when they preached that gospel they would, along with it, seek, consciously or unconsciously, to impose on other people their own language, culture, and nationality. But what would be the effect if, at the very beginning, they should find the gospel overleaping the barriers of tongues and breaking forth into the languages of all nations? The effect would be that it would deeply impress everyone concerned that the gospel could not and would not be confined to or identified with any particular language or culture or race. It would do more—it would thereby make sacred all languages, all cultures, all nations, for they were all to be the vehicle and instrument of the Divine.

Here was religion loosed from specially sacred languages, cultures, and races, and all languages, cultures, and races made the medium of the Divine.

In all climes there have been specially sacred languages. The Hindus believe that Sanskrit is eternal and that the Vedas have come down from the eternities and cannot be translated without loss. The Moslem believes that the Koran is from heaven, and that the Arabic language is unsurpassed in eloquence and that to translate it is to lose its significance. The Roman Catholics cling to the Roman tongue

[133]

throughout the world and the Eastern Church holds to the Syriac. We know with what pious regard the Jew held and still holds his language.

And cultures and nationality? The ancient Aryans coming into India said in reference to the indigenous peoples, "They should be destroyed because their customs are different." The ancient Jew prayed the prayer, "O God, thou hast made us for thyself; as for the rest of the nations they are but spittle."

Now see the significance of what happened at Pentecost when all of this was canceled at once: the gospel was not to be identified with any particular race or culture or language. What a struggle took place before the gospel was loosed from its Jewish fetters! Without this which emerged at Pentecost it could never have been done. The Jerusalem Christian leaders nearly killed it by cramping the emerging chrysalis too tightly in Jewish forms. They tried to impose Judaism along with the gospel. Paul was always suspect with the Jerusalem leaders because he refused to allow this imposition on the Gentiles. "He was not asked," says Bullock, "to preach publicly at Jerusalem, for his semiforeign Christianity would not have been acceptable. . . . But had he yielded, Christianity might have become a legalism, a temporarily reformed Judaism, a limited Jewish sect, sooner or later dying out in its own soil, pot-bound."

Nor are we free from this danger to-day. There is exaggeration in Bertrand Russell's statement, but it contains some truth: "What the missionaries bring to China they think to be the gospel. In reality, it is Americanism." I found the cultured Latin Americans thinking that in bringing an evangelical gospel to Latin America we were really trying to impose North American culture on them. The Christian movement must free itself from all suspicion of imposing national cultures and languages on other people or it will not get very far.

In taking the attitude of not imposing one's own language and culture upon another people a very important change of attitude toward other peoples takes place. It gives a turn to the mind that makes for sympathy, understanding, and good will. It causes us to look for the good in other national characters. We begin to rejoice in any good found anywhere, for that basic good will be used to enrich the whole.

The fact is that each nation needs every other nation. A cross-fertilization of each national life with the genius of other peoples will enrich the receiver as well as the giver. To impose one culture upon the world would be to impoverish the world. I sat in a train in America while the Great War was on and asked a traveling companion, evidently a foreigner, what he thought of things in Europe. He ended up with this expressive sentence: "To ——— mid 'em over there: I'm an American." Carlyle said that the true mark of an Englishman of his day was "to hate the Frenchman like the devil." My friend thought the true mark of an American was to consign others to hell. Little did he realize that in taking this attitude he was consigning himself to the hell of littleness, of soul-shriveling.

There are two ways to look on other peoples. One is to look on them as subjects for exploitation, the other as subjects for expression—one is predatory, the other is Pentecostal. Among the ancient Hindus was what was called "the horse sacrifice." A charger of a gray color, with certain propitious markings, was turned loose to graze, followed by an army ready for battle. The lands through which the charger went had to give him grazing or fight the army that followed. At the end of the year all the lands conquered belonged to the king who performed the horse sacrifice. That custom is very ancient and very modern. To-day we send out trade and investments and the army follows. Give grazing place to our trade or fight our army! Thus the world has been exploited in the name of empire. This creates frictions, hate, and finally war. It impoverishes everybody concerned. This is the way to seeming wealth through the exploitation of peoples. Pentecost was the way to real wealth through the expression of peoples. Each

that they would fall upon the people's souls like dew! I didn't like that, but the people did—and that is the point! The Latin American needs our straightforwardness and love of truth and we need his graciousness and love of beauty.

Was Jesus, in his temper of mind, Latin or Anglo-Saxon? Certainly he was blunt and Anglo-Saxon when he talked to the Pharisees! They never forgot it. How he loved truth! But how gracious he was! With what rare graciousness he saved that woman taken in adultery! And when he pointed out the sin of the woman by the well, instead of saying, as we Anglo-Saxons would probably have said, "Woman, you are an adulteress," he graciously said, "Go, call your husband and come hither." How delicately gracious that was! And the graciousness won her. It was said of him that "he was full of grace" (Latin) "and truth" (Anglo-Saxon). He was both. The gospel interpreted through the graciousness of the Latin and through the straightforwardness of the Anglo-Saxon will, in combination, enrich us both and create out of the twain not only a new man but a richer man, in Christ Jesus.

Was he Eastern or Western? He was so masterful that the West is drawn to his sheer strength of character; he was so mystical that the East is drawn to his sheer depth of being. He was both—and more. The masterful West needs the mystical East, the men of induction need the men of intuition—each is incomplete without the other. Each can bring the riches of its genius to the expression and interpretation of this gospel. It will take the sons of men to interpret the Son of man.

When the Spirit takes hold of each national genius what a wonderful symphony it will be!— the love of truth of the Anglo-Saxon, the deep thoroughness of the Teuton, the passion for sharing of the Slav, the love of beauty and art of the Latin, the oak-strength of the Scandinavian, the music-loving gay spirit of the African, the matter-of-fact reasonable outlook of the Chinese, the gracious spirit of the Japanese, the profound mysticism of the Hindu—each giving its peculiar manifestation of the Spirit for the common good.

"Isn't he the Eastern Christ?" I asked of a Hindu. "No, he is the Universal Christ," he replied. The Hindu was right.

And to express this Universal Christ we will need not only the language and culture of every nation, but the language of art and philosophy and science as well. All life must express the Supreme Life.

I once heard a professor, one of the leading philosophers of the world, give an address in which he brought man up through the different stages of development. He said that man came to a place where he was incomplete, that through his own resources he could not complete himself, that something from without, from above, must complete him. I held my breath, for I expected him to say the word. But he passed on without saying it. At the close I said to him, "Professor, why didn't you say the word? It trembled on your lips, but you did not get it out?"

"What word?" he eagerly asked.

"The word from above that would complete us—Christ," I replied. "If you had said that word, it would not have jarred the slightest, philosophically, would it?"

"No," he thoughtfully replied, "for that is what I meant."

"Then, why didn't you say it?" I urged.

"Well, I leave that to you, a religious man, I'm a philosopher," he replied.

"But I am not content for you to leave it to me," I said, "for I want all life—philosophy, art, science—to interpret Christ."

When that comes to pass then the philosopher, the artist, the scientist, the statesman will hear, every one in his own language, the wonderful works of God.

The words of Dean Inge are worthy of being pondered: "Remember that the new knowledge has as good a right to hear and speak in its own tongue the wonderful works of God as the educated Christian in the fourth and fifth centuries had to formulate the Christian faith in terms of the new-Platonic philosophy. What philosophy was then science is now."

I inwardly revolt when I hear an attempted reconciliation of science and religion by assigning to each a separate province—science to take the province of physical fact, and religion the province of value. Ultimately they must speak the same things or both be false. Rather I want to hear each tell in its own language a common message, the wonderful works of God.

A brilliant artist, finding this new life in Christ, in the joy of that discovery goes back to her art and discovers, to her surprise, that she is more attuned to life, hence more creative. She writes, "I have a passion to express this new Life through my art." That is the passion that all life must feel.

Is there a place where all languages, all cultures, all life may meet and find their meaning? The editor of the Indian Social Reformer says that the lines are now being drawn between Westernism and Hinduism, that these two are at death grips and the end must be a compromise. I suggested that a compromise would be weak, that we needed someone in whom the truths in Westernism and Hinduism could be gathered up, reconciled, and fulfilled. The only one who could do that is Christ. Is he not the reconciling place between God and man, between languages and cultures, between science, art, and philosophy? Is he not the place where all things "consist," or hold together? Will there not be a brotherhood of man and a brotherhood of facts —all centering in him? Is he not more than the reconciling place? Is he not the place where all life finds meaning?

All life experiencing this Life answers "Yes!"

At Pentecost all life, language, culture, national genius, art, science, philosophy—all life is gathered into a common center, Christ, and then it goes out from that common center to tell, each in its own language, the wonderful works of God.

CHAPTER XIV

PENTECOST AND RITUALISM

THERE is one simple fact which, if noted and its implications worked out, would have determined much during the history of Christianity. When the Holy Spirit came upon the group we would expect them to be assuming some specially sacred posture of body. Religion has always been identified with special postures. The Hindus in their yoga system have worked it out to a science. The breath must be controlled, the attention concentrated between the eyebrows, the feet and the hands and the whole of the body must be according to prescribed posture. The Moslem too has marked out his prayer postures, and it is done with mathematical precision. You cannot think of Buddhism apart from the characteristic posture of Buddha, legs crossed under him, hands folded in his lap, and face impassive.

But here at Pentecost the group was in the attitude that is most universal—"they were sitting." They were not even kneeling!

Here was religion loosed from specially sacred postures and all postures made sacred.

Had there been a special posture at Pentecost, we would have been in bondage to that posture.

But the gospel was to make sacred all postures. None was to be less or more holy than the others.

Jesus prayed with his eyes wide open: "Jesus lifted up his eyes to heaven and said, Father, I thank thee." A friend and I were threading our way through the crowds of a Berlin street and seemingly talking to one another, but we were really talking with God. Why not? "Do you think you could pray in this restaurant while the crowds are coming and going? I wish you could, for I need it," said a friend. And we did with our eyes wide open! Never did God seem nearer. One of India's saints, old Doctor Hume, stopped me on the road, put his hand on my shoulder and said, "Shall we talk to the Father?" The Father was there! A wealthy American business man was taking me in his car to an appointment. "I have not offered to take you on this trip for nothing," he said. "I need God and I want you to help me." We talked about it, and when the moment for surrender came, I said, "You drive the car and I'll pray." He threaded his way through the traffic, but the real road we were on was the Highway of God. And we met him there!

At Pentecost the common posture was religious. On the other hand, how deeply irreligious some religious postures can be! There is a picture of a monk with folded hands seemingly in

[145]

the attitude of prayer. When you get nearer the picture you find he is squeezing a lemon over a punch bowl! But who has not seen God in the sparkle of the eye, in the warm handclasp, in the quiet touch of conversation? Who was it that cried from the trenches, "God, God, I see him everywhere"?

At Pentecost God became naturalized in human life. All the natural became the religious and all the religious became the natural. The account says, "Day after day they resorted with one accord to the Temple and broke bread together in their own homes; they ate with a glad and simple heart, praising God and looked on with favor by all the people." The "simple heart" meant the undivided heart; the distinction between the religious and secular portions of life had broken down. They were one. They could eat the communion bread and the common bread with an equal sense of the Divine.

Akin to this and pushing it further is the fact that when the supreme moment at Pentecost came and the Spirit was received, they were undergoing no rite or ceremony of any type or kind. It seemed that God was determined that his highest gift should be bound up with nothing extraneous. It should be given in simplicity and received in simplicity with no interventions.

Here was religion loosed from all specially sacred rites or ceremonies.

[146]

Our gospel uses rites and ceremonies, but it is not bound up with any of them in the sense that any rite or ceremony is essential to receiving God's highest gift, himself. If rites and ceremonies are not essential at this highest place, they are not essential anywhere down the line.

And yet how we have fought over them through the centuries! I stood within the Inquisition Room at Lima, Peru, where men were tried for heresies. There were glass panels where those standing outside could see whether the wooden statue of Christ alongside of the ecclesiastical judge would nod or shake its head in approval or disapproval. The judge pulled strings underneath the table. The nod of the head of the wooden Christ meant that the victim would be tortured on the rack and the shaking of the head meant liberty. We talked about this in the Inquisition Chamber and a brilliant Roman Catholic teacher turned to me and said, "Poor Christ, how we have made him approve our follies through the centuries!" We have fought over rites and ceremonies and have tried to make him nod Yes or No. The fact is that he probably said neither Yes nor No. The rites and ceremonies were irrelevant in the light of the bigger thing he was giving.

John in administering the rite of baptism said, "I indeed have baptized you with water: but he shall baptize you with the Holy Ghost."

[147]

The special characteristic of Jesus was that he should baptize with the Holy Ghost; in other words, he should give men God. Here at Pentecost that giving of God to men was bound up with no rite or ceremony. So when men set up their stately sterilities and complicated systems of dogma and ritual and appeal to Christ for a nod of approval, I know that it is the nodding of a wooden Christ fashioned by ecclesiasticism and not the living Christ of the New Testament. One used to be able to drop a good-sized gift into the hands of the caretaker and see the wooden Christ of the Inquisition, but now I am told the authorities, feeling ashamed, have locked it up in jail. It would be well if this wooden Christ of ecclesiasticism, nodding approval of every particular sect and ceremony (and, of course, nodding disapproval to the rest), were locked up in the vaults of oblivion. We might then discover the real Christ.

How wooden and blocked off we've made him! I was once pleading with a great crowd of Hindus and Moslems to see this living Christ, when I was flanked by the Christians. Before the great crowd of non-Christians they insisted on the literalness of the words, "This is my body," and they did it with much vehemence and bad temper. It all seemed so wooden! I could not help feeling that we were haggling over a statement about the literal body of Christ while the

[148]

real Body of Christ was being torn to pieces before the non-Christian!

New Testament Christianity used the rite of baptism, but was not bound up with it, so that Paul, the chief exponent of that Christianity, could exclaim, "I thank God I baptized none of you, save Gaius and Crispus." They used the rite of the communion of the bread and wine, but were free to substitute for it the simple *agape* meal when it expressed to them deeper vitality. And when the question of circumcision became acute, those brave souls insisted that not outward rite, but inner character, should be the essential thing in Christianity. "Neither circumcision availeth anything, nor uncircumcision, but a new creature." They were simply holding to the lines that Pentecost marked out.

It is true of rites and ceremonies and ecclesiasticisms that if they save their lives by being made essential, they lose them—they become mechanical, dead; if they lose their lives in a larger meaning, then they come back vital and vitalizing. Only as we are free from them are we free to use them. Pentecost was free from them, hence the early church could use them.

I believe in Christian baptism because I do not believe it to be absolutely essential. As a method of expressing and declaring one's faith before the world nothing is more beautiful and expressive, but as a *sine qua non* for finding the

[149]

Spirit nothing has been more disastrous. For under this conception the baptized are supposed to keep up the idea, which in many cases amounts to a fiction, that they have necessarily found the Spirit in baptism, and the consequence has been that while the rite has been thereby raised, the fact of the Spirit in the life has been thereby lowered—lowered almost to becoming meaningless.

The increased emphasis in the West on ritual and worship may be beautifully helpful, but it may be a blasting hindrance to the real life in the Spirit. If we hold no illusions about them, we will suffer no illusions through them. The early church used them, the later church abused them, and the wells that Pentecost dug were filled up with ecclesiastical rubbish and doctrinal debris.

The one hope is to get down beneath these later accretions to the pure spring of divine life that bubbles out of Pentecost. Nothing is essential but God, and no rite or ceremony is essential in finding him.

CHAPTER XV

PENTECOST AND MATERIAL POSSESSIONS

OUT of Pentecost comes a message that confronts the thinking of this age and bluntly challenges it. We live in an age that frankly accepts accumulation of material things as the standard of human success. When we ask the question, "What is he worth?" we know the meaning is not what is he worth in character, in contribution to human living, but in material accumulation.

I sat in the train one day and spoke to a traveling companion about God.

"God?" he said. "This is God"—and he tapped the money he had in his pockets till it jingled. "Do you see that stone out there? We have no more soul than that stone. Heaven is when you have a good living and hell is when you haven't."

Here was a frank paganism, bluntly stated. I was no more shocked by it than I am by that same paganism, less frankly stated, but not less actually lived, in Christian lands and even in Christian churches. Here this secular outlook is accepted as a way of life, while all the time there is a ghastly contradiction at the center of things.

The contradiction is this: While we accept

this pagan way of life our gospel produces and presents this: "The believers all kept together: they shared all they had with one another; they would sell their possessions and goods and distribute the proceeds among all, as any might be in need" (Acts 2. 45, Moffatt).

The Spirit in them impelled them to share; the Spirit in us impels us to accumulate. Which Spirit is in us—the Spirit of Pentecost or the spirit of paganism?

At Pentecost was produced the spirit of sharing so that life and religion were loosed from distinctions and disabilities based on material wealth.

We must not explain away or soften what happened at Pentecost. Their sharing of goods with those who had need was no mere interim ethics introduced on account of the belief in the near coming of Christ. It was inherent in their gospel. They had freely received, they would freely give. The limit of giving and retaining was the "need" of each. They could retain to the limit of their own need, they would give to the limit of the needs of others. Need, not want, in the case of each was the determining factor. No man kept what was beyond his own needs. What constituted his needs was determined and decided by the inner Christian Spirit. There was no compulsion—this utter sharing was spontaneous and voluntary, and there was no

[152]

rule against holding of private property. Peter said to Ananias, "When it [the land] remained unsold, did it not remain your own? And even after the sale, was the money not yours to do as you pleased about it?" (Acts 5. 4, Moffatt.) There was no rule against holding of private property, but there was common consent that to hold private property beyond actual need was unchristian.

This, instead of being an extravagant excrescence due to early enthusiasms, is an inherent attitude in our gospel and is workable. This was the working out of the principle that they were to love their neighbors as they loved themselves, and they were to do unto others as they would that others should do unto them. There were no hard-and-fast rules, but they were guided by principle, the principle that the self-interest and the other-interest should balance. They distributed to each man as he had need, including themselves. After their own needs were provided for they distributed the rest as far as it would go to the needs of others. But actual need, and not desire or luxury, was the determining thing.

This must vary from age to age and from place to place, and an enlightened, close-to-the New-Testament Christian conscience must decide where the line between need and luxury is to be drawn. The line seems somewhere here: I have a right to use for myself only that which will make me more efficient and more fit for the purposes of the kingdom of God. Beyond that line lie luxury and unchristian territory.

Fritz Kreisler, perhaps the world's greatest violinist, has struck somewhere near the Christian line in these great words:

"I was born with music in my system. I knew musical scores instinctively before I knew my A. B. C's. It was a gift of Providence. I did not acquire it. So I do not even deserve thanks for the music.

"Music is too sacred to be sold. And the outrageous prices the musical celebrities charge today are truly a crime against society.

"I never look upon the money I earn as my own. It is public money. It is only a fund intrusted to my care for proper disbursement.

"I am constantly endeavoring to reduce my needs to the minimum. I feel morally guilty in ordering a costly meal, for it deprives someone else of a slice of bread—some child, perhaps, of a bottle of milk. My beloved wife feels exactly the same way about these things as I do. You know what I eat; you know what I wear. In all these years of my so-called success in music we have not built a home for ourselves. Between it and us stand all the homeless in the world!"

Here is the Christian spirit at work in his reducing his own needs to a minimum, that he might have more to share. Gandhi has taught us that one can be rich not only in the abundance of one's wealth but in fewness of one's wants. In his Ashram he has the principle of non-thieving, thieving being defined as holding in your possession something that someone needs more than you.

Emerson refused to accept an income of more than twelve hundred dollars per year, for he said he wanted time to think. The early Christians refused to accept or retain beyond their actual needs, for they wanted hearts at rest from themselves to soothe and sympathize.

Someone has said that the trouble with money is that it costs so much. One of its costs is that sense of spiritual dullness seen in so many Christians who are financially secure. The sense of adventure, of living upon a living God, of trust, of surprise, leaves the life and deadly security and dullness set in. Bonds in the bank often become bonds upon the soul, stocks in vaults become stocks upon the feet. Spontaneity is gone and deadly dullness brings soul decay. "I hate luxury," said Goethe, "for it destroys the imagination."

The only way to keep the sparkle in life is to accept the cross of limitation of need to a minimum, and the sharing of everything beyond that minimum.

Another of the costs of money is that it sets

up a barrier between man and man—it creates a new caste, it kills brotherhood. The early Christians let go everything beyond actual need and kept the brotherhood. We keep beyond actual need and let go the brotherhood. John Woolman, the Quaker saint, once said, "People may have no intention to oppress, yet by entering on expensive ways of life their minds may be so entangled therein and so engaged to support the expensive customs as to be estranged from the pure sympathizing spirit."

In the gospel account it is said that after the healing of the demoniac and the destruction of the swine "the keepers fled into the city and told everything—and what had happened to him which had demons." "Everything—and"! To them swine was "everything" and a healed man an after-consideration. That is paganism: possessions everything—persons secondary. In our gospel persons were to be everything and possessions allowable only as they contributed to persons and to human brotherhood.

Among the Hindus the god of prosperity is Kuvera, and at Saranath one can see the figure of Kuvera standing upon the prostrate form of a man. Prosperity standing on a prostrate person! This is the thing that haunts me about the prosperity of the West. I wonder how much of it is standing on the prostrate forms of sweated labor, on the shriveled bodies of little children working in factories, on exploited weaker peoples.

Kuvera in his swollen pride once asked the big-bellied god Ganesh to dine with him. Ganesh ate him out of house and home. If Prosperity invites Greed to dine with him, the end will be the ruin of Prosperity. Selfishness is suicide. There is no prosperity save the prosperity of personality, there is no wealth save the wealth of the worker.

Paganism stands for prosperity based on exploiting people. Pentecost stands for brotherhood, based on sharing possessions with people.

And because our gospel stands for the greatest thing in the universe—persons—the universe is with it. The future belongs to it. But history tells us how hard the universe is on selfish luxury. Soul-decay inevitably sets in. A member of an evangelical church remarked that he was satisfied if, at the end of the year, his personal expenses had not exceeded two hundred thousand dollars. That man need not wait for the hereafter to lose his soul, he has already lost it. It has withered and died within him—smothered by luxury.

Pentecost stands for life, hence its central impulse is sharing. We live only as we give.

"Measure thy life by loss instead of gain,
Not by the wine drunk but the wine poured out:
For love's strength standeth in love's sacrifice,
And he who suffers most hath most to give."

CHAPTER XVI

PENTECOST AND THE NATURAL ORDER

WE have tried to strip off the phenomena of Pentecost and see the inner fact. The inner fact is the palpitating, cleansing, intimate sense of God, the Spirit that came to those who waited there.

Now, after having stripped away the phenomena, I am inclined to put them back, for I am persuaded that they belong there. Do the sound of a rushing mighty wind, the place being shaken, and the appearance of tongues of fire belong there, or are they the result of an overwrought imagination?

I can dismiss at once the idea of overwrought imagination, for whatever Pentecost brought to men it certainly brought amazing poise, balance, clear-sightedness, effective spiritual and moral living.

Then do these physical phenomena connected with Pentecost belong there? If they do not, then one great vital question about spiritual living remains unanswered at Pentecost. That question is this: Is this physical universe for or against or indifferent to the moral and spiritual life? Is the physical environment in which we are compelled to live out our spiritual lives an enemy, an indifferent spectator, or an ally?

John Stuart Mill held that the physical universe is an enemy. The cosmic process (that is, "nature") encourages "ruthless self-assertation," the "thrusting aside of all competitors;" "it teaches the gladiatorial theory of existence;" "it has no sort of relation to moral ends;" "the imitation of it by man is inconsistent with the first principle of ethics." The conclusion is inevitable, "Let us understand, once for all, that the ethical progress of society depends not on imitating the cosmic process, still less in running away from it, but in combating it." Nature, according to Mill, is an enemy of the moral and spiritual life.

Matthew Arnold, on the other hand, takes the view that nature is inhumanly neutral:

"Yet even when man forsakes
    All sin—is just, is pure,
Abandons all which makes
    His welfare insecure,
Other existences there are that clash
        with ours.

"Streams will not curb their pride
    The just man not to entomb,
Nor lightenings go aside
    To give his virtues room:
Nor is that wind less rough
    That blows a good man's barge.

[159]

"Nature with equal mind
　Sees all her sons at play:
Sees man control the wind,
　The wind sweep man away;
Allows the proudly riding and the
　floundering bark."

Here is the view that nature is utterly indifferent to moral ends. This view is probably
the most widely prevalent.

On the other hand, is "the universe a system
of things in which there is a ceaseless and unrelenting reaction against evil," as Doctor
Denney affirms? Does sin bring forth death, as
the Scriptures state? A Chinese proverb says
that "a nation first smites itself and then others
smite it." Does the universe as well as nations
smite those who smite themselves by moral
lapses? Is it true that if we sow to the flesh we
shall of the flesh reap corruption? Is the soil
of the universe the kind of soil that favors righteousness and withers sin?

Kant said that the two things that filled him
with awe were "the moral law within and the
starry heavens above." Is the moral law written within also written in the starry heavens?
Is the universe a universe or a multiverse?
Do the stars in their courses fight against
Sisera?

History gives a plain answer to those questions. Carlyle says that "sin has been, is, and ever shall be the parent of misery." And that means not only moral and spiritual misery, it means physical misery as well. We do not break the moral laws of our universe, we break ourselves upon them. If, as Cairns says, the moral basis of modern society were suddenly withdrawn, if all moral feelings and actions were suddenly wiped out, the physical ruin and chaos that would result would be appalling.

Whatever the hours may seem to say, the years and the centuries say that the universe is with those who are with moral laws and against those who are against them.

Can we believe, then, that the sum total of things is behind the will that is surrendered to God? I am persuaded that this is so. I am not surprised that at Pentecost the physical universe responded with a physical miracle of approval and co-operation to the moral miracle that was taking place in the souls of men. If the spiritual fire of the living Spirit were going through the souls of men, why should not the cloven tongues like as of fire rest upon their heads? If, in that decisive hour, the foundations of their spiritual lives were being shaken and rebuilt, why should not the place where they were sitting be shaken? If they were being infused and filled with the new life and power of the Spirit, is it any wonder that there was a sound from heaven as of a rushing mighty wind and that it filled all the house where they were sitting?

If nature and human nature have the same goal of righteousness, would nature be indifferent when the supreme miracle of the creation of a new humanity was being enacted? Would nature not bend over in eagerness and watch the sight, and, more, would it not break out in corresponding miracle to show its approval and oneness with it? It would if the same God is in nature and human nature. This word at Pentecost is at one with the word of Christ when he said, "But that ye may know that the Son of man hath power on earth to forgive sins (then saith he to the sick of the palsy), arise, take up thy bed and go unto thine house"—the physical and the spiritual miracle dovetailing and attesting the same Divine Master.

The *British Medical Journal,* hitherto representing the attitude that attacked disease from the side of the physical and not from the side of the spiritual, as Jesus did, now says that "there is no tissue of the human body wholly removed from the influence of spirit." Does this conclusion not tend toward the same direction that Pentecost points? If Saint Francis lived with the marks of the Lord Jesus upon his soul, can we wonder that the *stigmata* appeared upon his palms?

We live in a universe plastic to moral and

spiritual ends. Instead of its being a closed system it is open, utterly open, to the side of righteousness. As Thomson says: "The more we know of the world the more it becomes like a home in which the religious can breathe freely."[1] The early Christians took the hint of Pentecost and were free to use divine power for miracle, physical or spiritual.

At Pentecost life and religion were loosed from a closed and clamped physical universe.

We are now struggling to that same freedom. We have had our souls caught and clamped in an unresponsive, dead universe. Pentecost tells us that this universe is living, that the Power that works in experience is at work in the stars, that it is all one, that the whole is open to faith, and that anything that is right may happen.

This is the atmosphere in which faith can move freely and work freely. We have now a plastic friendly universe and are at home. Miracles can happen and we are invited to make them happen.

The Acts of the Apostles is filled with miracle, both physical and spiritual. But they were never for purposes of show, never irresponsible, never merely to attest their message, never the magician type—they were restrained, worthy, Christlike. The miracles shown were not some-

---

[1] *Science and Religion,* p. 175.

thing extraneous, imported into the account in
a stilted way; they were inherent, a part of the
whole offensive against sin, disease, and death.
The early Christians knew that they could call
on all the Power there was, against all the
wrong there was, in whatever realm it was.

If Pentecost brought them inward personal
unification, it also brought them outward
physical unification. It was all one. The sum
total of things was with them. The Supernatural had become naturalized within the
natural as well as within the spiritual. They
were ready for anything.

No wonder they turned the world upside
down!

Herein lies the difference between us and
them. We don't expect anything, so nothing
happens. The universe is dead because we are.
We utter moral platitudes and hope that in the
realm of the narrow circle of the moral somebody may be improved. But we haven't the
sense of vastness, the sense that a universe
tingling with the Divine is at our disposal, that
miracles, spiritual and physical, can and ought
to happen. Our gospel is not the gospel of Pentecost, for there the gates to all life—physical
and spiritual—were thrown open.

CHAPTER XVII

PENTECOST AND MODERN CULTS

THERE are two facts that sharply differentiate Pentecost from many modern teachings and tendencies.

The account says, "They were all filled with the Holy Ghost." Here there was no division, as is often the case in present-day thinking, between mystical and nonmystical natures, one capable of receiving and realizing God and the other not—"They were all filled." Every person who wanted to find this Divine Gift found it— found it when they wanted it sufficiently to pay the price. If we live with the Spirit as a dimly realized fact, our souls bleached and anæmic, it is because we consent to live this way. The reason must be laid on the consent of the will and not in the structure of our being. All of our defeats, our lack of spiritual power, our spineless spiritual living are will-consented. For all the doors are open to everything we need to make us live abundantly. Pentecost does not argue that; it presents one hundred and twenty persons—all who sought—as the living, flaming testimony to that fact.

The increased study of mysticism in our modern day is a sign of spiritual yearning, but it often leaves an unhealthy impression, namely, that the mystics are a class apart, spiritual Brahmans, and that what they represent is something for analysis and study instead of something to be partaken of and realized. But analyzing water into H_2O quenches no one's thirst. Studying must pass on into seeking if it is not to end in barrenness. Pentecost knows nothing of dilettante prying into spiritual things, it does know a practical, open-to-everybody way of living by the appropriated resources of the Living Spirit. "They were all filled," stands over against the modern dictum of, "A few specially mystically inclined souls might be filled."

It would strike a terrific blow at my faith if I were compelled to accept the notion that certain people by the very structure of their being are incapable of receiving and realizing the Spirit in conscious fullness. Of course the emotional tone will differ in different people, for each will "receive the manifestation of the Spirit to profit withal." But the point is that each will receive the Spirit. The New Testament knows nothing of this modern division between the mystical and nonmystical. One might as well talk of mystical and nonmystical husbands or wives—the mystical being those who love and the nonmystical those who do not. We are all made for love. In the same way we are all made for God.

[166]

This division between mystical and nonmystical seems to me to be an attempt to naturalize the soul this side of Pentecost. And that means tragedy.

The second thing that differentiates Pentecost sharply from modern tendencies is that whatever happened there seems not to have come from within man, but from without. "Tarry ye in the city of Jerusalem, until ye be endued with power *from on high*." "Ye shall receive power, after that the Holy Ghost *is come upon you*." "There came a sound *from heaven* as of a rushing mighty wind." Pentecost presented resources from without to man; it was not merely a quickening and developing of resources from within. A Hindu put the matter to me in this way: "Aren't the roots always in us? Aren't we born from within, instead of from above?" Here he put his finger upon the crux of our modern religious problem. The modern cults of self-culture, New Thought and Christian Science, as well as Hinduism, tend either toward the emphasis on the divinity of man, so that he is to be awakened to grasp the truth of his oneness with the Divine, or to discover that man has latent resources that make him self-sufficient. In either case he is born from within and not from above. "We must awaken the Jesus within us," said a Hindu professor to an audience at the close of one of my addresses one day. Who

[167]

was it that went across Italy crying, "Awake, Awake, O Christ, in Italy"? Others urge upon us the possibility of all of us becoming Christs. "Ye divinities on earth," cried Swami Vivekananda at the Chicago Parliament of Religions, "it is a sin to call you sinners."

All this, with the modern emphasis within Christianity upon Immanence, makes a very definite tendency—is it toward fullness or futility? Karl Barth in Europe has reacted so violently against it that the God he presents is so transcendent as to be almost unknowable. Are we driven to a choice between Barth and modern tendencies? Has Pentecost any decisive word?

The New Testament does teach a very close union of the human and the Divine, so close that Life flows into life, Mind into mind, Purpose into purpose, Being into being. "In him we live, and move, and have our being." "As thou, Father, art in me, and I in thee, that they also may be one in us." "I am crucified with Christ: nevertheless I live; yet not I, but Christ liveth in me." The union seems to be as close as that of the fingers and the hand—the fingers, while retaining their individuality, are nevertheless rooted in the palm and draw their sustenance from it. While this is true, the New Testament cannot fairly be quoted on the side of modern cults. Men are to be born "from above," the power is from "on high," and the Holy Spirit

is to come "upon us," not from within us. It is
distinctly understood that it is a gift fresh and
new, and not something that already belongs to
us. It is true that the fact that we can receive
the Spirit shows how deeply akin to the Spirit
we are. Nevertheless, the attitude of the New
Testament is that we are to be suppliants, not
self-sufficient. This is a terrific blow to modern
pride. And just because it is a blow to modern
pride it impresses r.e with its truth. Can a
deep God-consciousness arise out of or be super-
imposed on self-sufficient conceits? The essence
of the Divine is humility. And the first step in
finding God is to strike a blow at our pride—a
mortal blow, so that we shall be so humbled in
the dust in order that we can be raised to the
highest heaven, so stricken that we can sing, so
self-surrendered that we can be self-assertive.
The spring of our spiritual life will henceforth
be in gratitude—glad gratitude—for in having
nothing we find ourselves possessing all things.

A friend of mine, brilliant and able, had
adopted as a kind of life-declaration these words:
"I am captain of my own soul, I am master of
my own fate." Also these words: "Under the
bludgeonings of Chance my head might be
bloody, but it will be unbowed." Psychological
walls of resistance had been built up against
life, and they seemed sufficient. But life with a
cruel blow struck those walls and they crumbled.

[169]

Amid the ruins pride was still there, though deeply humbled. Sitting in a cathedral, yearning for some words of hope and healing, my friend heard the congregation run through the prayers and, loving reality, turned from it all with these words: "It is all too fluent and easy; they don't mean it." Then Christ appeared and said, "Yes, they will not let me do anything for them; neither will you." My friend knew it was the naked crucial truth. That self had never been surrendered, that pride had never been humbled in the dust, and so the God that would be healing stood helpless, waiting until the end of other resources had been reached so that he might offer his. And when the end was reached there was God, tender, healing, intimate. The end of self was the beginning of God. When pride ceased, power began.

"The cross chastens the world," said a Hindu friend to me one day. It does—but it does more than chasten—it kills! It kills and it makes alive. It sends me to a cross and then gives me an Easter morning. It smites me dumb and then makes me speak the wonderful works of God. It strips me of everything I have and then offers everything that God has. I can receive the Divine because I am not Divine. This way of the cross leads to Pentecost. Its end is fullness.

It leads to fullness because the truth of Jesus' statement holds good: "He that findeth his life shall lose it; and he that loseth his life for my sake shall find it." Lose your life in self-surrender and self-renunciation and you find it again. It is never yours until you give it up. I never truly had a soul until I surrendered it. I had a set of warring, clashing desires, but not a soul, a real soul, until Christ gave it back cleansed, harmonized, found. A great many young people are talking about self-expression who have no self to express. They have chaos and call it a self. The way to self-realization is by way of self-renunciation.

The cults and teachings that begin with self-culture and self-assertion, or assertions about the divinity of the self, end in futility, a vast lifting of oneself by one's own bootstraps. It is quite true that they do seem to offer and give something in the beginning, for a complete self-affirmation seems to give more than the former partial self-letting go. But the end of the resources soon comes, the universe will not approve it and the end is futility.

The Vedanta philosophy is the supreme affirmation of the divinity of man. "Thou art That," "I am Brahma," are its ever-recurring words. Swami Rama Tirath is a supreme example of how the cult of being born from within runs through its resources and extinguishes itself. He is an attractive, joyous soul. Our hearts warm to him. He seems to have caught the

[171]

secret of joyous spiritual living, and he preached
it throughout the world, especially in America.
And he seems to have found it through the
Vedanta. But looking a little closer I find
that he was a student in a mission school and a
professor in a mission college. He was sat-
urated with Christian ideas and his Vedanta
was not Vedanta. He seemed to have lived joy-
ously for years on the gospel—the gospel tinctured with Vedantism. The pundits of Benares
saw this; twitted him that he knew nothing of
Sanskrit and hence nothing of the Vedanta. He
took up their challenge, began to study Sanskrit, and to learn the real Vedanta. His biogra-
pher and disciple, Puran Singh, tells the rest of
the story:

"But this study of Sanskrit killed Swami
Rama; it benumbed his gay, birdlike spirit, it
changed a poet into a moody philosopher. . . .
During this period Swami Rama was imbued
with the spirit of Shankara's great philosophy of
illusion, and this spirit seemed to sap the foundations of that living joy in him. He was now
quite changed; that hilarity had gone. . . .
In those days Swami Rama, quite sensitive to
criticism himself, and in order to suffer no argument from Narayan Swami, asked him to live
apart. I thought and still think that his exegeti-
cal studies in original Sanskrit instead of being
any help to him deepened his depression and

increased his sorrow of Illusion. He was nearing the Hindu ideal of a Vedantic philosopher and would sit cross-legged for days unaffected by the opposites and unconcerned about his body. He would say: 'Who says there is a world? It never was, never is, and never shall be.' And at the same time he would say: 'You people come and make Rama believe in you as realities and forget Him. All relations are means of forgetting the Lord.' The thoughts of death came crowding in on him these days. The languor of his sad mind showed the depression that was upon him which neither I nor anyone else had the insight to diagnose, far less to cure. . . . Swami Rama made frantic efforts to regain himself, but it seems the philosopher overpowered the sadhu in him, and he died searching for the rose that had perfumed him so wildly. . . . But the torch which Swami Rama took up in his hand was extinguished long before its actual and apparent extinction in the waters of the Billing Ganga where he was drowned."[1]

In East and West cults and tendencies that begin with an utter optimism, asserting even the divinity of man, end in disillusionment and pessimism. They soon run through their resources. The East alternates between the assertion of the divinity of man and the assertion of

[1]*The Story of Swami Rama,* Puran Singh, pages 174, 176, 177, 180, 183, 186, 285, 288.

the nothingness of existence. On the other hand, the gospel begins with a demand for a self-letting-go, life's supreme denial, but it ends with a self-finding, life's supreme affirmation. Its word is, "Let go, let God."

I once watched a bumblebee beat itself against a window pane trying to get out. Finally it fell exhausted upon the window sill and, the window being slightly raised, it crawled through the opening and flew away to freedom. It is only when we give up our self-assertions and fall into the hands of Omnipotent Grace that our souls wing their way to freedom.

This is not merely the statement of narrow evangelicism. It is the place to which all life is pushing us. H. G. Wells, one of the most modern of men, says that the psychologist can now stand beside the preacher and assure us that there is no reasoned peace of heart, no balance, no safety in the soul until a man in losing his life has found it, and has schooled and disciplined his interests and will beyond greeds, rivalries, fears, instincts, and narrow affections. Here Wells comes in sight of the promised land, but only in sight of it, not in possession of it, for his words "schooled and disciplined" still have the smack of the old idea of being born from within. There *is* a place for schooling and disciplining, but only after there is utter surrender to the Master—that settled, the schooling and discipling can begin. Until then, there is no losing of one's life, hence there is no finding of it.

This fact of utter self-surrender lay back of Pentecost and precipitated it. One of the things that make Pentecost seem so remote and unavailable is that it all seems so planned out, so sovereign, so impossible for the human to bring it to pass again. On the contrary, when we search beneath the surface we find that the attitude of the disciples was the decisive factor. Up to Pentecost they had been very tentative, very half-way in their self-surrender to the mind of Jesus Christ. They had given up a good deal to follow Christ—loved ones, home, occupations —everything, except themselves. The essential self was still intact, still watchful for rights and first places, still jealous of the position of others. But after Pentecost this was all changed. They had lost themselves, they were no longer tentative, they were abandoned, their interests were fused, they were no longer clashing, they were inwardly free. What had happened? Utter self-surrender had precipitated Pentecost. They had given themselves, so God could give himself. Pentecost was the result. It all waited on that human self-giving. It still waits on it. Pentecost is not merely an event in time, it is a continuing principle in our gospel, and is available whenever the conditions are fulfilled.

But why does God demand self-surrender? Is

he a despot, demanding that he rule over man?
Does he want to bend us or even end us before
he will do anything for us? Hardly. This condition of self-surrender is not arbitrary, it is
inherent in the very facts. Self-surrender is at
the basis of all real love. Where there is no mutual self-surrender, say between husband and
wife, there is no love. Where each holds back
the essential self, love cannot spring up. Now
the Divine Self-surrender to us has been complete. The cross is its sign. God can go no
further; he has gone to the utmost limit. The
one thing lacking is our self-surrender. When
that comes love breaks into being. It is spontaneous, inevitable.

But no one can love God until he surrenders
to him. The devotees of the cults that teach
self-expression and self-cultivation cannot love
God because they do not surrender to him.

It must be remembered that in that love we
both lose ourselves and find ourselves. In a
home where husband or wife, striving for domi-
nation, saves himself or herself by a refusal of
self-surrender to the other, the self is lost. The
home is unhappy. On the contrary, where there
is mutual self-surrender there is mutual self-
finding; fellowship comes into being, the home
is a heaven. There souls grow great and beautiful, for love is their native air.

Souls wither under self-saving. I once saw a

long line of mango trees sprouting from hidden
buried seeds. Alongside the beautifully growing
seedlings were some unburied mango seeds lying
on the surface of the ground. They were saving their lives, they would not pay the supreme
price. The inevitable result was taking place—
they were losing themselves, for they were with-
ering away. They were doomed to futility and
extinction. They refused the supreme law of
life, self-giving, and that law was breaking them.
The other mango seeds had caught the way to
live—they had lost themselves, and were finding
themselves in the growing tree.

Jesus came under this same law. At Jerusalem, Pilate's Judgment Hall, "the Pavement"
has been unearthed. Graven in the slabs of the
Pavement are circles, where the soldiers played
their games of chance. Some soldiers, with a
smile of contempt, handed over to Pilate a
Prisoner. Then they went to play their games
around the circle. They were free. But he was
not. Cords bound his hands, but deeper still,
love bound him soul and body to the needs of a
race. Was it Roman nails that held him upon
his cross? No, love held him there. He lost
himself to the uttermost. But what have the
years and the centuries spoken against those
hours? Their verdict has been this: those soldiers, free, were free only to wither and die—we
would never have known that they lived save as

[177]

they were associated with him. But he, dying, lives! He has found himself—his authority, his moral grip, his redemptive touch are supreme in our moral universe. This law works for God and man. No mere tossing of the dice of chance brought Christ to this moral supremacy. Mill says, "Religion could not have done better than to pitch on Jesus as the moral guide of mankind. Even now no better rule of conduct can be found than that one should live so that he should approve the life." True, but religion didn't pitch on Jesus. It couldn't escape him. It has tried to forget him, to crucify him, to bury him, but each time he comes back. He is simply inescapable.

Pentecost stands for the abundant life because Pentecost stands for the total losing of life. Among the Jews Pentecost was the Festival of the First Fruits of the Harvest. But here in a deeper and more significant way it stood for that beginning of the harvest of victorious human living. The harvest waved because it grew from buried seed-selves.

"I lay in dust life's glory dead,
    And from the ground there blossoms red
    Life that shall endless be."

Pentecost confronts us with a stern demand for self-giving. The meaning here is not emotion, but devotion. Pentecost means plenty of cost.

If lives are here lighted up, the flame comes from their consuming selves.

The Spirit came upon the disciples "like as of fire," the fire typifying cleansing and consuming. They needed both—the old sin-life to be cleansed and the old self-life to be consumed. The Spirit came upon Jesus, not like fire, for he needed no cleansing, but "like as a dove." To the Hebrew mind the dove was not so much the bird of peace, as it is with us, but the bird offered in sacrifice by the poor. It vividly presented to the mind of Jesus the fact that the Spirit's coming meant his being set apart for sacrifice, for self-giving, for a cross. Both in his case and theirs life in the Spirit meant a cross.

On Good Friday we held an open-air meeting on the hillside of Olivet, overlooking the city of Jerusalem. It was at the time when He went forth to die. For two weeks on that mountain-side we had been facing the world's needs, and we came now to enter into those hours when He took those needs upon his heart to let them break it. We were strangely moved and there was not one of us who did not long to go forth and share with him the burden of the world's pain and sin. I saw the significance of the hour, and leaned over to pluck a wild flower to hold it in memory. As I touched it an Inner Voice said, "Not the wild flower—take a piece of this thornbush and remember the hour by it." It was from a thornbush that the crown of thorns had been taken and pressed upon his brow. I protested that the thornbush was not beautiful, that its thorns were sharp, and that I preferred the flower. But the Voice was more imperious, "You should take the thornbush, for there is something there that you do not see now." I saw the meaning of the controversy, turned rather reluctantly from the flower, plucked a piece of the thornbush and put it within the folds of my Bible—and deeper, and in a spiritual sense, I put it within the folds of my heart and I wore it there. After some months I chanced to look at the thornbush I had been wearing within my heart and, lo, it was abloom with the Rose of Sharon. Long after the wild flowers would have withered away the crimson freshness of the Rose of Sharon was continually with me—the living Christ was there.

Some of us have been plucking the wild flowers of the gospel—its art, its beauty, its æsthetics, its music, its hallowed companionships, its self-expressions—and we have wondered why they wither so soon and why the whole thing is so fading and unreal. Pentecost confronts us with the issue of a thornbush, a cross, a self-giving. We reluctantly take it, and lo, we find that we have found not a cross, but an Easter morning, not a fading Christ, but a Christ of eternal freshness.

[180]

CHAPTER XVIII

PENTECOST AND ENVIRONMENT

In a previous chapter we stated that at Pentecost religion had been loosed from specially sacred places, and yet we find Jesus insisting that his disciples should "not depart from Jerusalem," but to "wait in the city" till they were "endued with power from on high." Why this insistence that they stay in the city of Jerusalem? Was he binding up religion with the Holy City? Hardly. In insisting that they stay there he was really further loosing it from places. For at Jerusalem they had failed miserably. Their moral resources and courage had collapsed under the storm and stress of Passion Week. He bade them stay at the place of their failure, that he might make them adequate at that very place. Had they gone to some other place, they might always have felt that the environment was responsible for the transformation.

Here was religion loosed from specially favorable environments.

A good many of us feel that if we were only differently situated, were in some more favorable environment, we might live a victorious spiritual life. But the disciples were bidden to go into the hardest place they knew, the place

[181]

where Judas had betrayed their Lord, where Peter had denied him, and where they had all forsaken him and fled. If they could face these surroundings and be spiritually adequate, then the spiritual life was a possibility anywhere. The spiritual life that Pentecost offers is not a delicate, frail, hothouse plant; it is built to stand storm and strain and stress.

Someone has said that when facing a problem you should raise it in its most difficult phase, solve it there, and you will have solved it all down the line. Jesus here raised the problem of the spiritual life in its most difficult phase, insisting that the disciples stay where they had been most bitterly defeated, where before a whole city they had morally and spiritually collapsed, where a victorious spiritual life seemed on the basis of past experience impossible for them.

Had they found this new life in some mountain retreat, it would have drawn their thinking away from the problems of the city to the peace of the cloister. He taught them in quiet retreats. He transformed them in the city.

It was said of the demoniac who dwelt in the tombs that he was "a man out of the city which had devils." The devils within him were city devils! The devils of Greed, of Lust, of Exploitation, of Unbrotherliness are city devils. When Jesus cast out the devils he commanded them to go into the swine—a fit embodiment for the

[182]

devils of Greed and Lust. Into the city of cruelty, where the cry of "Crucify him!" had scarcely died away, the disciples were sent in order to be made spiritually adequate to meet life there.

And they were to meet it far more profoundly than they at first supposed. The account says that in the interval between the resurrection and Pentecost they "were continually in the temple blessing and praising God." And all the time they were dodging the issues! When one is between Easter and Pentecost the moral nerve is lacking to face up to life. It is possible to be in the temple continually, blessing and praising God, and all the time refusing to face living issues. Their going to the temple, their blessing and praising God raised no moral issues, precipitated no spiritual crises, made no one take a stand. It was innocuous. It is possible for Religion to be in the city, to go to its temples of worship and bless and praise God and all the time fail to confront the life of that city. Religion may take on "a protective resemblance," make terms with its environment, lose its power of moral and spiritual offensive and become patronized, respectable—and futile.

But after Pentecost things changed. The disciples immediately faced about and confronted the System that had murdered the Son of God. They were now on a moral and spiritual offensive.

[183]

They and what they represented became an issue, so living, so challenging that·it was inescapable. The System gnashed on them with its teeth, struck out at them and broke its own arm in the striking. The disciples smiled their way through threats, rejoiced their way through stripes, sang their way through prisons, and triumphed their way through death. And the multitudes watching found themselves wanting the very thing the disciples had. This freedom! This poise! This moral power! Here religion, while on the offensive, was not offensive; it was winsome, compelling. Their weapons were strange indeed—they turned other cheeks, went the second mile, gave the cloak also, refused to do anything but love their persecutors. And they won! Of course they did. What can you do with a thing like that? It never knows when it is defeated, for it turns its defeats into victories and it turns its Calvaries into Easter mornings.

Yet how we have tried to run away from our Jerusalems! Many a pastor asks for "a change" when he should really ask for a change in heart. Many a congregation wants a new minister when it should really seek for a new Master. We are like the fever-tossed man seeking for a cool spot, first on one side of the bed and then on the other, forgetting that the fever is within him. We seek for a change of circumstances when our

need is a change of "innerstances." A pastor
came to one of our Conferences to find out what
was wrong with his church. He found out—
it was the pastor.

In our renewed emphasis on the social we
have often scoffed at the statement that "the
soul of all improvement is the improvement of
the soul," but it is the veritable truth. In our
emphasis upon the social we have truly said that
the home life was impossible in the slums, and
yet after we have abolished the slum sections
through bettering economic and social conditions we find the home just as badly endangered
through selfish divorce. Changing social conditions do not entirely solve the problem. Something deeper is necessary.

When Jesus said, "I make all things new," he
laid his hand upon the human heart. For out
of the heart are the issues of life. Do not misunderstand me, I am not setting the personal
over against the social gospel. They are not
contradictory; they are complementary. We are
to rescue individual drunkards and strike at
the liquor traffic; to attend to the wounded in
war and strike at the war system; to pick up
those fallen among thieves along Jericho's road
and then try to get the thieves. It is not "either
or," but "both and." We are not merely individuals, nor merely social beings. We are individuals in social relationships; and if religion is

to be real, it must begin at the individual and go as far as his relationships extend.

The people called Methodists believe in entire sanctification—at least their standards say they do! Personally I do not think we have sophisticated ourselves away from the need of it. If I am to be Christian, I must be Christian with the consent of my whole being. If I start in to be Christian, I see no stopping place this side of my all. Entire sanctification would be the life of Christ entirely dominant in the soul. I have no quarrel with this. My only quarrel is that the sanctification, as usually presented, has not been sufficiently entire. If it is to be entire, it should begin at the individual man and go as far as his relationships—social, economic, racial, and international—extend. Then, and then only, would it be entire sanctification. I am committed to the personal and the social applications of the gospel, nevertheless we must face the fact that Jesus did not undertake to make Jerusalem a safe environment for their faith before he dared send the disciples into it. He changed them, and they went out to change the whole structure of human society. His method was a man.

Asoka, India's greatest king, set up pillars throughout India upon which he inscribed the message of Buddhism, and yet Buddhism died out in India. Jesus wrote his message not on pillars, but in persons, and it lives on. Pentecost matched new men against the old environment, and they were adequate. "Heal me at the heart and let the world come on," was their cry and ours.

The oldest living city of the world is Damascus. The secret of its long life is in the fact that it nestles close up to the mountains and the river that rises in the mountains is turned under the city so that it reappears in sparkling fountains and in bubbling pools; it becomes, in fact, the flushing system for the whole city. The city is thus being constantly cleansed from within. The river also furnishes power to turn the wheels of the city's industries, both cleansing and power coming from the melting snows of the mountains. The city is thus endued with power and cleansing from on high.

If the will is surrendered and responsive, so that the channels are open, then, flowing from the eternal purity of the divine nature, the life of the Spirit bubbles up within our hearts as a fountain of exquisite joy, cleansing away the impurities of our thinking and acting and providing power by which to live, and to live anywhere.

If our resources are intact, this life can be lived in our Jerusalem. I am not afraid of Jerusalem, but I am afraid of choked channels. I am afraid of the unresponsive will, of prayer-less hours, of living without what Pentecost provides.

"All I could think of as you spoke to-day was an artesian well," said a discerning lady to a minister. But the life of the Christian Church doesn't always make us think of artesian wells, but of very meager hand-pumping. As Doctor Hutton discerningly says: "Every church now is living too much by its wits. It is too much fretted with anxiety and labor. It lacks certain notes of fullness, of peace, of that confidence in God which is the victory over the world. It is not pregnant, overflowing. It has a basic worry and strain. It has enough to do with itself."

Lady —— told me that her little son came home from Eton one day and said, "Mother, why do all these speakers that come to us always talk to us about conduct? Why don't they talk to us about Jesus and what he is to them?" The little fellow sensed the difference between living the life of duty on one's own resources and of living by the resources of the living Christ. One was a hand-pump, the other an artesian well.

But one day he came out of a meeting in which the sense of Christ was living and real and with face aglow said to his mother, "After a service like that a fellow can say snobs to the devil, can't he?"

After the coming of the mighty re-enforcing of the Spirit the early Christians were ready to say "snobs" to difficulties, to persecutions, to loss—to Jerusalem. When the old Jerusalem rose up to break them, the new Jerusalem came down to re-enforce them. The new prevailed.

CHAPTER XIX

PENTECOST AND THE CHRISTIAN WEAPONS

THERE is an element at Pentecost, often overlooked, which gave a distinctive characteristic to those who became Christians. Seeley says that the distinctive Christian spirit is the forgiveness of injuries, the refusal to retaliate. Its method is that of overcoming evil with good, hate by love, the world by a cross.

Up to Pentecost the outlook of the disciples was the very opposite of this. They were still wedded to retaliation, still believed in the use of physical force to gain spiritual ends. James and John, two of the most spiritual of the disciples, were ready to call down fire from heaven on those who would not receive them; Peter struck with a sword when his Master was arrested in the garden; when he rode into Jerusalem in his triumphal entry the enthusiasm of the disciples and of the populace was evidently due to the belief that the Son of David would restore David's throne. When they saw at the cross that he was not going to do this "they all forsook him, and fled." On the very eve of Pentecost the disciples asked if at this time the Kingdom was to be restored to Israel, expecting that restoration to be made by semiphysical force.

This whole outlook and attitude had persisted, in spite of the resurrection, right up to Pentecost. After the coming of the Spirit it dropped away. The disciples faced life with new weapons and overcame in a new way. Their former attitude is nowhere even hinted at in the rest of the New Testament. So deeply had they imbibed this new method of facing life that as soon as a soldier became a follower of Christ in the early church he was expected to give up his occupation as incompatible with being a Christian. Their whole dependence on physical force was gone, swallowed up by a dependence on higher force—the force of unconquerable love. Pentecost was the pivot upon which this whole reversal of the outlook turned.

Here, then, at Pentecost religion was loosed from dependence on physical force, was given new weapons with which to face life—the weapons of inexhaustible forgiveness, unquenchable good will, and limitless love.

The special and most beautiful characteristic of the Hindu is *ahimsa*—harmlessness—the doing of no harm to anyone. The special characteristic of the Christian became *ahimsa*—and more. For the Christian spirit went beyond harmlessness to an active love and an active doing of good even to enemies. The Christian spirit overcomes by a forgiveness that goes to seventy times seven, it wins the man who compels you to go one mile by cheerfully going two, it smites the soul of the smiter by turning the other cheek, it overcomes enemies by turning them into friends.

All this actually came as a direct result of the impact of the Divine upon the disciples at Pentecost. They found that the Divine overcame them in this very way. He broke rebellion by tenderness. His method of omnipotence was the cross. Henceforth they could no longer call the Divine by the name of "Jehovah" and "the Lord of Hosts," for these names seemed to recall too much of the physical and military force associated with him in the old days. Now it was "the God and Father of our Lord Jesus Christ." A new content had come into the Divine. The Spirit that was within them was incompatible with anything but love.

How grudgingly we have taken to this attitude! The soul of "the fighting male of the West" with his inheritance of the centuries of belief in force has become the battle-ground of contending ideals. The coming of this ideal and attitude of Christ has brought an inner contradiction at the center of our Western civilization. We have a religion that believes in overcoming by love, we have an inheritance that believes in overcoming by force. The strain in our Western civilization results from the clash of these ideals. We cannot give up to Christ, we cannot give him up.

The paganism of the past persists, and now and then takes voice in a Nietzsche, who raves against this way of Jesus as slave morality and cries: "The only vice is weakness: the only virtue is strength. Care nothing for anybody but yourself. The race is to the swift and the battle to the strong. Be hard. Be a superman! All is yours: Take it—if you can get it." If you can get it! That's just the point. As someone has said, "The universe sees that it rots in your hands." Nietzsche, with all his ravings, didn't get it, for he died in a madhouse. The nations in the last war didn't get it, for everybody lost. The prizes of war rotted in their hands. Their blustering strength has turned to millions dead, nations embittered and staggering under impossible debts, and the whole of Europe trembling with the palsy of her own hate. Only one came out of the war with an enhanced reputation—Jesus. Out of the welter of things he rises authoritative and regnant. Our struggle to read his mind into League Covenants and Peace Pacts is our tribute to the Silent Commander. We are beginning to have it burned in upon our consciences that our big navies are not the sign of our strength, but the sign of our weakness; the sign of how little we love, of how little we are ruled by good will, of how little we trust.

We are beginning to realize, dimly, that like produces like, that hate begets hate, big navies beget big navies, war begets war. "A war to end war" is an absurdity. Can Satan cast out Satan —can I by acting like the devil cast the devil out of people? Yet war is an attempt to do that very thing. The only possible way to get rid of an enemy is to turn him into a friend, and that is the gospel way.

"What can your Master do for you now?" sneered a tyrant who had a Christian in his power. "He can help me to forgive you," replied the Christian. And that broke the arm of the tyrant. For this new spirit is power.

How reluctantly have we of the West, enamored of the fighting centuries, taken to this new power! "You Christians of the West should have the Bhagawad Gita as your sacred book, for it is founded on war, while we of India should have the New Testament as our sacred book, for it is founded on conquering by love—the exchange would suit us both better," said an Indian to a European at the outbreak of the Great War. There is enough truth in what he said to make it sting.

"Your New Testament teaches you to love your enemies, while our sacred book teaches us to fight, therefore you should set us a better example," said a Moslem to me one day, and I wished from the depths of my heart that I could broadcast his message to our "Christian" world.

For love is our native air. Hate is like acid

to the lungs. It leaves confusion and death. I saw in Vienna the room in which the ultimatum was signed and then sent to Serbia—the spark that lighted the World War. With what confidence in the power of military force those men strode into that fateful room! But when I saw the room it was not being used any more, the carpets were rolled up, the pictures off the walls and the chairs and furniture topsy-turvy. It was all a symbol of what war and hate can do —they turn order into chaos, our world into a hell.

But what healing power there is in love! I sat beside a veteran missionary as he lay dying of a cancer. He told me he had been dictating his memoirs. I asked if he had dictated the story of how he won the pujari, the priest of the temple. With a wan smile he said, "Why, no; I'd forgotten about that."

The story was this: Some Arya Samajists made up a plot in the temple to break up the preaching of our friend and his band of workers. The pujari of the temple heard them making the plot and went the next day expecting to see the sahib fly into a rage. The Arya Samajists poured dust on the head of my friend and then waited for the explosion. Instead he quietly wiped it off and went on telling his message without any signs of anger. The pujari was dumbfounded. A sahib—a mighty member of the ruling race—to act like that! What made him do it? He went to the missionary the next day to find out. He was told that it was the love of Christ. Then said the pujari, "That is what I need." To-day he is a Christian preacher.

The missionary had forgotten the incident. Could the rest of us forget it? We might forget many other things about him—his great organizing ability, his financial genius—but not this. For this was power! His gentleness had made him great.

If the church could again find this power, it would make her great. I know of one church in India that has two characteristics of Pentecost—an adequate spiritual life and touch with the life of the city; in touch with God and in touch with man. If we had a church like that planted in every city and town in India, I would be willing to say, "Now, Lord, let thy servant depart in peace." There is a "Fellowship of Silence" at this place and Christians and non-Christians, mostly lawyers, meet each day for an hour of silence. In this silence one of these lawyers opened his soul to the Spirit and was transformed. After his baptism persecution set in and he was deprived of some hundreds of thousands of rupees by the intriguing relatives. But they soon began to squabble among themselves over the spoils. In their desperation they came to the despoiled man and asked him to be their referee in the division of the money. He actually accepted and did his best to untangle things. When he felt that he had done his part he asked to be excused from further attendance in the case, but they came to him in a body and begged him not to withdraw, "for," they said, "you are the only one any of us can trust."

Their spoil was decaying in their hands. His moral authority was going up by leaps and bounds. He, the loser, was winning; they, the winners, were losing. The universe was with him and against them. His type was the final type of power.

Had we kept this method of facing life clear through the centuries, our gospel would be regnant in the world to-day. But we lost Pentecost and with it this new type of power. So we linked religion with physical force and with the inevitable decay of that force religion also decayed and instead of being regnant, it rotted. We have not yet shaken off this unholy alliance, for in a great religious conference of picked men from throughout the world a judge arose and said, "Of course we must have war, for we must protect our religion from the rise of the colored races." As I listened my universe reeled and I knew I was face to face again with stark paganism; Jesus seemingly had not lived and Pentecost had not given birth to a new race.

When I came back to myself I knew the judge

was the voice of an expiring paganism. Christ has hold of us and his power is the ultimate type of power. It must prevail. Under his sway we are throwing off that pagan past. During the last two hours of the recent Jerusalem Conference there was a debate on the question of whether we should ask the governments of sending countries to withdraw all military protection from missionaries and from mission property. We felt by accepting this protection we were abandoning our own weapons of good will and trust. The decision was made that we should ask for no protection but rely upon the protection of our own good will and service. We thus stripped our gospel of the pagan accretions of the centuries. Two minutes after this decision was made it was Easter morning—in more senses than one! The Christian movement had come back to that new spirit that was born at Pentecost.

For Pentecost means power—power to forgive injuries, to keep an unsoured spirit amid the deepest injustices, to overcome evil with good, hate by love, and the world by a cross.

CHAPTER XX

PENTECOST AND UNITY

THE gospel was intended to unite, to heal, to produce a brotherhood, to make the world one. That gospel has often been so changed that, in fact, it has been used to divide, to wound, to produce innumerable sects and to make the world more disrupted than ever. The curse of religion has been in its divisiveness. All the time there has been at the heart of our gospel the fact that the Spirit founds life in love, therefore brings unity and produces brotherhood. We see this vividly at Pentecost. Here we find men of diverse temperaments, of clashing nationalities, of deeply ingrained prejudices brought together in the deepest and most far-reaching unity that this world has ever seen. "Now there was but one heart and soul among the multitude of the believers."

Here religion was loosed from divisiveness and made into the most powerful unifying force that the world has ever seen.

This unity was not merely in externals, but in the deepest realms of human living—in purpose, in outlook, in the very temper of their minds. Out of confusion fusion had come. Why is it, then, that for centuries Christianity has been divisive? The only answer is that the Spirit has grown faint within our consciousness and the spirit of denominationalism, of jealousy, of rivalry has taken his place.

Before Pentecost the disciples were divisive and disruptive in their attitudes; after Pentecost they were unitive. Why were they divisive before Pentecost? If we turn to Luke 9, we find the root of their difficulty, and as the same thing is the root of our difficulties, we must trace it. In the quietness of the prayer hour (verse 18) Jesus asked the disciples who they thought he was. On the lips of Peter trembled the great confession: "Thou art the Christ, the Son of the living God." It was a great hour. Their minds had arrived. We might well expect that from this moment on their lives would fit into that great fact, and would take on harmony, symmetry, and power. On the contrary, the rest of the chapter is filled with clashes and blunders. Why did not the recognition that Jesus was the Son of God solve their spiritual problems? It did not and it does not solve ours. Why? Because they were living on an utterly different basis from that of Jesus. His was the attitude of self-losing, theirs of self-asserting. They had given up everything except—themselves. Immediately after this revelation that he was the Son of God had dawned upon them, Jesus tried to get the disciples to come over to his attitude.

[200]

They saw that he was the Son of God; he tried
to let them see what was at the center of his
being the Son of God, namely, a cross. He spoke
to them of that cross and invited them to take
up theirs. It stunned them. He immediately
reassured them by saying that if they would lose
their lives as he was asking them to do, they
would find them; but that if they found them as
they were doing, they would lose them.

They did not get the lesson, so he took three
of the most spiritually minded to the mount to
teach them the same lesson in a vivid way. On
the mount he and Moses and Elias "talked of
his decease which he was to accomplish at Jerusalem." As he stood facing that cross he became luminous, transfigured. He tried to let
the disciples see that life would only shine as it
faces its cross; in other words, life that would
be found only as it loses itself. They were trying to shine by self-assertion, so they did not get
the message.

At the foot of the mountain the disciples
fumbled in the casting out of a demon. With a
word Jesus cast it out and gave the boy back to
his father. They all "marveled at the majesty
of God." But "while they all marveled at the
things that he did Jesus said to his disciples:
'Let these sayings sink down into your ears: for
the Son of man shall be delivered into the hands
of men.'" In other words, he was saying to

[201]

them: You think my greatest glory is in physical miracle. It is not. It is in laying down my life —in self-giving. The account adds these ominous words: "But they understood not this saying." Why? Because they understood not this attitude toward life. We understand not by an intellectual act but only by a spiritual attitude. They had the attitude of self-saving, so they did not understand the saying about self-losing.

The next verse reveals their attitude of self-assertiveness working its way out in relationships: "Then there arose a reasoning among them, which of them should be greatest." Christian worker was clashing with Christian worker. The cause? Self-assertion. Fully one half to three quarters of our problems in the mission fields are taken up with the problems of relationships of worker with worker. I have no reason to assume that it is different at the home base. One Christian worker, realizing how difficult it was to get along with his colleague, at the close of a vacation wired to him as follows: "Be much in prayer, I'm coming home." It would be easy to be a Christian worker if we could be one alone. But we are compelled to be related to others, and a Christian is one who gets along well with others in the Spirit of Jesus Christ. The reason we cannot get along well is that we each want to govern (the pagan attitude), instead of serving (the Christian attitude). "Ye know that the rulers of the Gentiles lord it over them, and their great ones exercise authority over them. Not so shall it be among you: but whosoever would become great among you shall be your servant [marg.]: and whosoever would be first among you shall be your bond-servant [marg.]: even as the Son of man came not to be ministered unto, but to minister, and to give his life a ransom for many" (Matt. 20. 25-28). If you want to be "great," be a "servant," but if you want to be "first," then go deeper still, be a "bond-servant." The way to greatness is open—it is by greatly giving. In the apostolic church after Pentecost the order was this: "God has set people within the church to be first of all apostles, secondly prophets, thirdly teachers, then workers of miracles, then healers, helpers, administrators, and speakers in tongues of various kinds" (1 Cor. 12. 28, Moffatt). Here "administrators" (or "governments," as the old version has it) are just about last, and after "helpers." Among us that word "administrators" has climbed straight to the top. Among them the serving type was at the top and the governing type at the bottom, utterly revealing as to where the self-assertive attitudes had been placed. Among us the serving types are at the bottom and the governing types at the top, utterly revealing as to where the self-assertive attitudes have climbed. With what

[203]

result? We are full of jealousies about place, hence full of clash and divisiveness. At the top, did I say? No, not really, for it is true of them as it is true of us: if we save ourselves, we lose ourselves in the very process. The disciples were never so small as when they were most pathetically trying to be big. By taking thought we cannot add one cubit to our stature. We are what we are, and can add to our stature only by refusing to take thought for ourselves and by thinking only of serving.

Here was the first clash among the disciples, on account of their self-assertive attitude toward life. Now take the second. As soon as Jesus said to them the penetrating words, "For he that is least among you the same is great," John felt inwardly convicted about an occurrence and spoke of it: "Master, we saw one casting out devils in thy name; and we forbade him, because he followeth not with us" (Luke 9. 49). The first clash was individual Christian worker against individual Christian worker; the second clash was group of workers against group of workers. Self-assertiveness may be in the individual, it may be in the group. They were ready to quarrel within the group, but they were also ready to assert the claims of their group against another group. Had they been Christian-minded they would have welcomed and rejoiced in the casting out of the devils by others, but since they were denominational-minded they forbade it. They forbade it because they were afraid that the other group would cast out more devils than their group cast out and thus secure a bigger name! They were quite willing that the devils should stay in if their crowd couldn't cast them out!

Denominationalism has become more refined since that day, but the undertone of group-selfishness with its consequent clash is still with us. It is laying its paralyzing hand on the religious situation to-day. The next step in the Christianizing of so-called Christian lands is the closing of competing churches and uniting in the spirit of Pentecost. I saw on opposite street corners of a small town in the United States three churches—a Methodist Episcopal, a Methodist Protestant, and a Methodist Episcopal, South. Denominationalism would keep open all three— Christianity would close two—any two.

The churches that deliberately take the attitude of separation, or only grudgingly give way to the pressure for unity, forfeit their right to leadership in a world where to-day world tendencies are toward unity. In saving themselves they lose themselves.

The disciples as a group were never so small as when they were trying most to be big. They were never so impotent in moral authority as when assuming authority over other groups.

[205]

This law of losing life by saving it was breaking them with almost mathematical precision. Group-selfishness is group-suicide. Had Pentecost not brought unity and fellowship, they would have buried themselves in the grave of their own narrowness. That was the second clash—group against group. Take the third. Jesus sent the disciples to prepare for him in a city of the Samaritans. The Samaritans would not receive them, for the faces of Jesus and his disciples were set toward Jerusalem. This made the Jewish soul of John angry, and he asked Jesus if they could call down fire from heaven to consume them, even as Elias did. Here was the third clash: Jew against Samaritan, race against race. Self-assertion can be in the individual, in the group, and in the race.

John thought he knew how to treat the people of another race. What they needed was fire! And he quoted the precedent of Elias for his attitude—that was the way they did in the good old times. He backed it by religious precedent. The attitude of one people toward the people of another race is usually the same: fire—fire from heaven or fire from guns! And because of this self-assertive attitude of race toward race the world is in a state of tension. This tension breaks out periodically into war, which, by its spirit, methods, and outlook, is the most unChristian thing I know.

John thought he was showing national righteous indignation; he was, in fact, showing himself and his nation ridiculous. John and his nation were never so small as when, by bluster, they were most trying to be big. The law of losing life by finding it is operative among nations precisely as it is among groups and individuals.

Here were the individual, the group, and the race all out of harmony, and clashing. The cause that lay back of it was self-assertion working itself out in individual, group, and racial relationships. What made this self-assertiveness more dangerous was that it was religious; it thereby became fanatical.

With the glorious recognition fixed in their minds that Jesus was the Son of God, nevertheless not a single thing was done right in the rest of the chapter. Christianity to them showed a wonderful revelation, but little result. All their individual, group and race relationships were fundamentally wrong. These relationships were fundamentally wrong because *they,* the individuals, were fundamentally wrong. When their fundamental attitudes toward life were changed at Pentecost, then those relationships righted themselves. When they let go themselves, took toward life the attitude of the cross, then that cross in them reconciled them to others. The cross is the reconciling method between God and man and between man and man, group and group, nation and nation.

Pentecost put the cross at the center of their lives, hence it righted all their relationships. First of all it righted their personal relationships. After Pentecost Peter stood up, not against the eleven as hitherto, but "with the eleven." They were for him, because he was not for himself. The apostles now wanted nothing for themselves, hence men "sold their land and laid it at the apostles' feet." They did more— they laid themselves at the apostles' feet. Before Pentecost the apostles wanted everything and had nothing; after Pentecost they wanted nothing and had everything.

Not only were their personal relationships righted, their group relationships too were righted. So fundamentally had their ideas changed that Paul, the spokesman of this new fellowship, cried out when division showed itself: "Brothers, for the sake of our Lord Jesus Christ, I beg of you all to drop these party-cries. There must be no cliques among you, you must regain your common temper and attitude. . . . Has Christ been parceled out?" (1 Cor. 1. 10-13, Moffatt.)

But so used to "party-cries" have we become that we have naturalized them within our thinking and within our systems until we have elevated them to the status Christian when

[208]

they should have been rightly kept at the status carnal. A return to Pentecost would so cleanse us down to relevancy that it would make many of our denominational differences look absurd and beside the point.

A frontal attack on them very often does no more than drive them deeper. The dead leaves that cling to a tree during the storms of winter are pushed off from within by the rising life of the sap in the spring. A good many dead leaves cling to our gospel in spite of the storms of controversy through the centuries. They will fall off when we find the life of Spirit.

After Pentecost the race relationships of the disciples were also righted. Instead of calling down fire upon the heads of the Samaritans to destroy them we find the apostles in one of their cities laying their hands on the heads of these Samaritans and praying, not that the fire of heaven should destroy them, but that the fire of the Spirit should deliver them (Acts 8. 15). There was some lingering hesitancy in the soul of Peter about other races, but telling about it afterward, he says, "The Spirit bade me go with them, making no distinction." The Spirit in our lives to-day will also bid us go into life making no racial distinctions. If he does not, then it is some other spirit. Peter obeyed and went to open the doors of life to the Gentiles, so he thought, but found instead that he was flinging open the doors to larger life for himself. He lost his Jewish Brahmanhood and found his world-wide Brotherhood.

There is one place, and only one place, where we can find our unity in personal, group, and racial relationships: Christ.

The British Empire is held together around the person of the king. In a far more fundamental way we are united around the person of Christ. If we only knew it, we are the most united people on earth, for whenever we drop beneath our surface differences into experience we talk the same language, we share the same life—the life of Christ.

Pentecost brings unity because Pentecost is Christ-centric. As the wedding processions go through the streets of an Indian city at night the torch-bearers will hold up their torches so that the bridegroom, seated on his bedecked horse, is illuminated. Christ said of the Spirit, "He shall glorify me"—he makes luminous the person of Christ. And because Christ is central and luminous, marginal differences no longer command the situation. They are lost sight of in the glow of this central Fact.

A little girl was trying to fit together the States of the United States in a puzzle game. She was distracted, for it was difficult to fit in the irregular boundary lines. As she was about to give it up in despair she noted that on the other side was the face of George Washington. It occurred to her that she could fit that face together, for she revered the father of her country. After she had lovingly fitted his face together she turned it over and lo, all the States now fitted in. We have been distracted trying to fit in doctrine with doctrine, polity with polity, and denomination with denomination. There is only one place where we can be unified —around the Christ Person. When we realize our oneness here, we then realize that we are not so far away in other things. For Christ brings a sense both of reconciliation and of relevancy.

CHAPTER XXI

PENTECOST AND THE MORALLY FIT

ANOTHER thing that makes the possession of the Spirit seem so remote and unavailable is the fact that it seems only for rare, morally élite souls. For the stumbling multitudes it appears to be out of the question.

Even the great-souled have made us feel the remoteness of possessing God in redemptive clarity. "Who has ever seen Brahma face to face?" cried the Buddha. "I have not seen him, nor do I know him, but I have made the world's faith in God my own," said the great-souled Gandhi. A Prime Minister of an Indian State, chairman of one of my meetings, quoted the Persian poet who said, "We are like the ships that put out for the port of finding God, but none ever return and tell us they have found."

If this is the language of earnest religion, what about the ordinary man? Does not one have to attain to a certain degree of moral excellence before he is eligible for the Spirit? According to the New Testament, NO! Peter makes the astounding statement on the day of Pentecost to the multitudes that surrounded him, "Repent, and be baptized every one of you in the name of Jesus Christ for the remission of sins, and ye shall receive the gift of the Holy Ghost. For the promise is unto you, and to your children, and to all that are afar off, even as many as the Lord our God shall call" (Acts 2. 38, 39). The highest was thrown open to the morally unfit, for the only condition attached was that they turn around—in other words, repent. This offer was made to the very multitudes who had crucified the gentle-hearted Son of God. Yet without a restriction or hesitation Peter announced to them that they could receive the Holy Ghost.

Here was religion loosed from specially morally fit classes and its dynamic made available for the unfit.

Many of us have felt that perhaps other disabilities might not debar, but that this fact of moral unfitness does debar. And our sense of moral unfitness may not come from the outer gross sins of the flesh, but from those inner subtle sins of the disposition, of ill-temper, of selfishness, of mind-impurity. "I cannot get away from the unhappiness in my heart," said a Bengali woman to a Christian friend. Some of us could say that we cannot get away from the uncleanness of our hearts. This is our central plague. Sometimes we are tempted to say of ourselves what was said to Simon Magus, "Thou hast neither part nor lot in this matter: for thy heart is not right in the sight of God."

[213]

But herein lies the deepest note of the gospel: God asks for nothing, either in the case of the outer gross sins or in the case of the mind-sins, but the reversed will, for a turning away from, and lo, the gates to life are open. I say, "turning away from," and this is important, for it is possible to loathe the sins of the flesh or the sins of the disposition, to fight against them, to pray against them, to do everything—except surrender them! But when once the will consents to let them go there is nothing, absolutely nothing, in the way of purity that is not open to that man.

I came away from the Ashram of a great devotee, who, in his search to find God, had not seen anyone for eight months, repeating to myself, "By grace are ye saved through faith; and that not of yourselves; it is the gift of God." This is the distinction between the gospel and all other ways. Other ways are man's search for God, the gospel is God's search for man. He follows us down the years, we turn, and lo, we are in the Arms of Redeeming Love. Does this sound commonplace and trite? Only to the man who has never experienced it. To the one who has experienced it the wonder of the miracle of it will never cease.

One of the greatest saints of modern India was won to Christ by this very fact. Pandita Ramabai went to England as a Hindu to get some ideas and plans for social reform among her sisters of India. In the slums of London she saw pure-faced, devoted women rescuing the fallen girls. When she asked who these women were she was told that most of them had themselves been rescued from a life of shame, and having been rescued they had gone back into the slums to rescue others. And when she asked what power had wrought that miracle, she was told, "The power of the living Christ." She brought back to India not merely social ideas and plans, but this redemptive Person. She became the center of the greatest social movement of the modern day for the uplift of India's womanhood.

While in his sermon Peter seems to link the offer of the Holy Spirit with repentance and the beginnings of the Christian life at baptism, nevertheless, according to my own observation and experience, and according to the rest of the Scriptures, this gift is usually associated with later stages of the spiritual life. It is true that every sincere Christian has a measure of the Spirit, but at Pentecost the coming was measureless. While every Christian has life, here was life abundant. The disciples found this gift not in the beginning of their discipleship but midway. We can see why this was true then and holds true to-day. It might be explained as follows: Someone has said that on any subject the mind always acts in three stages. First, there is the rapid climb; second, a long plateau; and, third, the table-land of discouragement. In the beginnings of the spiritual life there is the rapid climb in conversion. Then there is the long plateau where life is on a permanently higher level. But the third stage is the table-land of discouragement. In this stage we find things in our lives that are still unchristian; we become disillusioned about other Christians and we often lay semi-paralyzed hands upon our tasks. We feel that we are still very partially Christianized. True, there are the heights when the vision is clear and God is a conscious reality, but the valleys ensue. We are on a table-land, alternating between inspiration and depression. This is a Seventh-Chapter-of-Romans experience, and many stop here as if this constituted the Christian life. At this stage a great many fall by the wayside and give up the attempt to be Christian. Others feel the beckoning of the Eighth Chapter of victory and a spiritual crisis is precipitated. They know they must go on or go under. The choice is now between Pentecost and penury. I have watched this crisis come in the lives of young missionaries, usually within a year or so after their arrival on the field. India finds them, discovers the weak spots, and forces upon them a spiritual crisis. They must now go on to spiritual mastery or sink back into spiritual mediocrity. To reach this crisis with a gospel without Pentecost in it as a vital possibility is tragedy; to reach it with Pentecost as the open door is normal Christianity.

In going through the Panama Canal our ship ran into a lock, the huge doors were closed upon us, and from below great fountains bubbled up around us. In just seven minutes our ship was lifted thirty-five feet. The gates opened and we glided out on to a higher level. Then we ran into another lock, the process was repeated, and we glided out on a still higher level into the Gatun Lake. We went through the canal by a series of crises. The soul, too, usually goes onward by just such a series of crises. The gates of decision are shut upon us, we meet the issue and decide God's way; then there is the bubbling of the inner joy, the gates are opened, we are loosed to higher living. Then again we face the question of the halfwayness of our spiritual level, the unsatisfactoriness of being partly Christian. We are driven to another crisis, where we must decide about an utter and unqualified surrender to the Divine Will. We make the decision and again the great deeps are broken up, a peace that often breaks into a bubbling joy is ours, there is the sense of being lifted, the gates to abundant life are open, and we move out on a permanently higher level.

An important thing in our rising from the lower level to the Gatun Lake was the fact that each time we rose it was the water of the lake that came down and lifted us up. We trusted ourselves to the self-giving of the lake and were lifted to its level. This is true in our rising to higher spiritual levels. We rise by God's coming down and giving himself, that he might lift us to himself. It is all of Grace.

This may seem cheap and easy, but underlying it is the greatest demand that can be made of us, namely, the innermost ambition, the secret citadel, our very all. Never was a more costly gift offered—to Him or to us. But no man who takes the Gift ever thinks of the cost; he is overwhelmed at the freeness of it.

Instead of taking this gift and living by it, however, we often do as did the poor man who received from a kind friend a check that was intended to turn his poverty to plenty. He took the check and in gratitude framed it and hung it upon the wall! We take these rich offers of God, his promises, and instead of presenting them as checks to be cashed, we place them as mottoes upon our walls and continue to live in our spiritual poverty. These promises are not to look at, but to live by.

But let no one think that because this is offered freely to the morally unfit there is a moral looseness in it. James says that "the worth of any experience can be judged by its philosophical reasonableness, its immediate lu-

minousness and its moral helpfulness." Judged
by the test of moral helpfulness, this experience
that Pentecost brought shines like the very sun
against a background of Egyptian midnight. In
those early days men sensed at once that the
Spirit that came was the *Holy Spirit.* That
name was given because he brought the sense of
holiness. In this new moral atmosphere lies
withered and died. When we study the case of
Ananias we see that now the disciples felt that
the lie of lies was the offering to God something
less than one's all. The lie on Ananias' lips was
tragic because of the lie in Ananias' soul—there
he offered less than his all.

Harnack says that there was set up at Pentecost a sense of moral tension that sagged and
became flabby only when the living sense of the
Spirit died away and religion ran into stereo-
typed forms and ceremonies.

No; if this gift was offered to the morally
unfit, they immediately became the morally fit.
Their goodness glowed, their purity penetrated.

I once stood in a village and gazed upon the
dazzling whiteness of the everlasting snows of
the Himalayas. At my feet I saw a tiny foul
pool, stained by the life of the village. I said to
the little pool: "I know a power that will lift
you out of this foulness, will purify you and
make you share the whiteness of those everlasting snows. Here is the sunbeam; yield to its

upward pull, trust it completely." The foul drops yielded, were lifted, and I saw them again dropped as pure snow flakes upon the everlasting mountains.

O soul of mine, very like those foul drops, to you is offered this Gentle Power to lift you out of the uncleanness of even your mind-sins to the white purity of God. Let go, let God!

CHAPTER XXII

PENTECOST AND SPIRITUAL CULTURE AND CONQUEST

SOME of the phenomena at Pentecost were transient, but two facts were permanent. Peter, speaking of the Gentiles' Pentecost, said, "God, which knoweth the hearts, bare them witness, giving them the Holy Ghost, even as he did unto us; and put no difference between us and them, purifying their hearts by faith" (Acts 15. 8, 9).

Here was one element common to both the Jews' and the Gentiles' Pentecost, namely, that by the coming of the Spirit their hearts were purified. Purification of heart was a common element in both these outstanding comings of the Spirit and hence seems to be a permanent element in his coming everywhere.

The second was when Jesus said to his disciples, "Ye shall receive power, after that the Holy Ghost is come upon you: and ye shall be witnesses unto me both in Jerusalem, and in all Judæa, and in Samaria, and unto the uttermost part of the earth" (Acts 1. 8). Power to witness for Christ was to be an abiding element, from Jerusalem to the ends of the earth. We have, then, the two permanent elements that the coming of the Spirit brings: purification of the heart and power to witness effectively for Jesus Christ. The one is to supply my own need, the other is to supply the needs of others. One is for Christian culture and the other is for Christian conquest. One goes to the innermost heart and the other goes to the outermost world.

These two things cover our spiritual needs. We need personal purity, we need propagating power. The purity the disciples received was not purity from outward gross sins—these had already been sloughed off. They were purified not from the sins of the flesh, but from the sins of the disposition. Drummond has called our attention to the difference, in the parable of the prodigal, between the younger-brother sins, the sins of the flesh, and the elder-brother sins, the sins of the disposition. The one sinned low down in his flesh and the other sinned high up in his disposition. The sins from which the disciples at Pentecost received cleansing were the elder-brother sins of bad temper, of self-seeking, of jealousy, of unbrotherliness and lack of love. This is the place where religious people need desperately to be cleansed. The sins of the disposition are hurting us far more than the sins of the flesh. Bad-tempered "saints" are hindering the kingdom of God far more than are drunkards. Someone has said that "if we can hold our tongues, we can hold anything else." But religious people often do not hold

[222]

their tongues. There is petty backbiting, tearing each other's character to pieces through jealousy and scandal-mongering. Our Conferences are often filled with jostling for place and honor and power, and the appalling thing is that we often do all this religiously and in the name of principle. Eucken says there is no danger to religion so great as this, that the old life, put out by repentance and conversion, comes back and takes over the new forms in the service of the old self. In that case we are selfish still, but now religiously and piously so. We still quarrel, but now it is over "principle." "Lilies that fester smell worse than weeds," and religion turned selfish and little-souled is exceedingly malodorous.

If Pentecost brings purification from the sins of the disposition, then another Pentecost is long overdue. Someone has said that the parasite, sin, is killed by raising the tone of the health of the organism upon which it feeds. These men at Pentecost found their pettinesses killed by the sense of spiritual health. Their selfishness seemed so irrelevant in the light of this self-giving on the part of God. It was all gone.

But to cleanse them was not enough; they needed power to live and to witness effectively for Christ. We have inherited from those early Christian centuries a vocabulary of power, but not the fact of power. One listening to the ordinary Christian service is struck with how the words used denote power, spiritual victory and mastery, but that much of the rest of the service denotes the opposite. We come under the delusion of words: we use the words denoting power and take it for granted that we possess their New Testament content.

I once dictated to some Chinese students what they should write in their Bibles as their Christian decision. The last line was, "And by His grace I will be His witness." Some of the little girls misunderstood the word "witness" for "weakness," and wrote, "And by His grace I will be His weakness." A good many of our present-day church members could sign that! The supreme problem is to turn this weakness into a witness.

A lawyer friend was in his study preparing an address which he was to give before a religious gathering. His little girl interrupted, wanting him to play with her. He told her that he must have quiet to think about what he would say. Her reply was: "Don't you know what to talk about? Tell them about Jesus— that's what lawyers are for, isn't it?" Yes, that is what lawyers are for, what we all are for— to tell about Jesus, not by word only but by the whole impact of the life. Yet that is the place where we are weakest. Jesus told us of

[224]

four places in which we should not put our light, lest it be snuffed out. He warned against putting it "under a bushel," "under a vessel," "in a cellar," and "under a bed." First, the bushel. A bushel is a symbol of trade, of business, of occupation. Here he warns us against putting our lighted lives under our business, so that the business becomes uppermost and snuffs out the lighted life. In a commercial age this is our chief sin. But it is possible to make the bushel into a candle-stand so that the light is on top of the bushel and not under it. In that case the bushel is lighted as well as the surroundings—the business becomes the medium of a message. This is Christian. But the gospel of being a success in business has so gripped our age that the gospel of being a success as a Christian is often overshadowed by it—the light goes out. We become the people of a bushel instead of the people of a blessing.

Again he warns against putting our light under "a vessel." This may refer to a household vessel or to a temple vessel. In the former case it would mean household duties, which in many a woman's life become paramount, and the business of being a Christian witness becomes secondary. And the light goes out. But Jesus' reference may be to a temple vessel, in which case it would mean that overshadowing of religious duties, rites, and ceremonies which keeps the minister so busy with the things of religion that he has little time or disposition for immediate contact with individuals to lead them into conscious fellowship with Jesus Christ. He is more religious than Christian. His light goes out under a temple vessel. The third warning is against hiding the light "under a bed." The bed is the symbol of the flesh life, and properly so, as far as the thought of rest is concerned. To all too many, however, it symbolizes either laziness or licentiousness. Sexuality, even in the legalized marriage relationship, will snuff out the spiritual. Thus many a lighted life has been snuffed out and spiritual darkness and inefficiency have resulted. And this may come not only from lack of self-control, but by making sex a feverish center of thought. If the sex-life is not a sacrament it is a stumbling-block.

The last warning—that the lighted life should not be put "in a secret place," or "in a cellar" (R. V.)—covers most of our difficulties, for it stands for the fear that paralyzes. We are afraid, so we keep our lighted lives "in a cellar." Our fears come out of our lack of resources to meet life. Herein lies the boldness of the disciples after Pentecost. They were bold because they had inner spiritual resources to meet life. They matched their souls against the situation and they were adequate. They had what we call spiritual power.

Spiritual power is seldom found because it is so often sought. It cannot be found if sought directly. If sought directly for itself, the seeking will be tinged, most likely, with desire for spiritual power for purposes of personal success in religious work, for the acclaim that comes to anyone who spiritually excels. This introduces a fatal element.

Spiritual power is a by-product of something deeper. It comes out of inward fellowship with God and abandonment to his purposes. Most of us have no spiritual power because we are not abandoned. "Blessed are the pure [literally, the single-minded] in heart: for they shall see God." We are not single-minded, hence we do not see God in inner fellowship and in outward power. It is not that we do not love him but that we do not love him completely. We give to him, but do not give up to him. The difference between a river and a swamp is that one has banks and the other has none. The swamp is very gracious and kindly, it spreads over everything, hence it is a swamp. Some of us are moral and spiritual swamps. We are so broad and liberal that we take in everything from the shady to the sacred. Hence we are swamps. A river has banks—it confines itself to its central purpose. The civilizations of the world organize themselves not around swamps, but around rivers. There are those who refuse to tolerate anything that cuts across their central Christian purpose. They decide that there must be "the utmost for the highest," they cease from the divided will, become the pure in heart, the single-minded, and hence see God—see him work in and through them. Around such lives the lives of groups, of cities, of nations begin to organize themselves. They become centers of power.

Gibbons' account of the Emperor Gallienus is instructive: "He was a master of several curious but useless sciences, a ready orator, an eloquent poet, a skillful gardener, an excellent cook, and a most contemptible prince." This might describe many of our spiritual lives. We are everything and nothing—everything, and "most contemptible" Christians.

Someone has said that "the danger of shallow education is oversophistication, the false tolerance that is essentially indifferentism, because the great fundamental convictions and ideals have lost their hold on the man." The danger of shallow Christianity is that same oversophistication, the false tolerance that is essentially indifferentism. We tolerate everything in our lives, and hence must finally tolerate our own spiritual paralysis. Paul said, "This one thing I do;" we would have said, "These forty things I dabble in." He was a river. We are swamps. There lies the difference.

We must bring in the scattered will and center it upon God's purposes. When two charged electrodes come together light breaks out between them. Bring together the charged electrode of the surrendered seeking human will and the charged electrode of God's redemptive will, and at the junction light and power break out. All of the divine resources are back of the surrendered will. If you do what God says, he will do what you say. "If ye abide in me, and my words abide in you, ye shall ask what ye will, and it shall be done unto you." You can command God because you utterly obey him. When this merging of interests takes place then you can say, "I can, because God can." A wire attached to a load can be used to pull it only to the degree of its own strength, but that same wire attached to a dynamo transmits power not to the degree of its own strength, but according to the might of the electricity within it. One is impressed that after Pentecost an Almighty Will was working within hitherto weak wills. No wonder they turned the world upside down, for the Power that had made the world was remaking it through them. Streeter says that the Spirit is "The Beyond that is Within." But this is more than being spatially the Beyond—he is the Beyond what we are and can do, and yet that Beyond becomes the Within. Through him we can do anything we ought to do. Pentecost is the Sermon on the Mount become practicable.

Here the ideal is fused into the real. Pentecost is power.

The saxifrage is, literally, "the rock breaker." It puts its roots down into the cracks of a rock and breaks it to pieces. Soft rootlets rend rocks, because there is higher life in the roots. The early Christians put their tiny rootlets of thought and act down into the cracks of great pagan systems of religion and life, and before men knew what had happened these systems had crumbled to ruins. The magnificent ruins of the Roman city of Jerash can be seen in Transjordania. The city was founded upon the incense trade with Arabia, the incense being used in the pagan temples. The Christians changed men's minds about God, the incense ceased to burn on pagan altars and the great city crashed into ruins. What a tiny soft rootlet it was— the change of men's thought about God—and yet it smashed not only that Roman city but the whole Roman empire. These men and their message were spiritual saxifrages, the rockbreakers.

In these days of big business and big successes religion has caught the contagion and has been pursuing hugeness. It has been moving away from those simple elemental forces that lie at the heart of our gospel. That hugeness has turned to hollowness.

Chalmers, eloquent and persuasive, attracted

great audiences. He thundered from his Sinai against the sins of Scotland and tried to bring the Scotch to an obedience to the commandments. They went away saying how great Chalmers was. They took the man and forgot the message. It sickened Chalmers, both in soul and body. He lay helpless upon his bed, feeling that he was a failure. He was at the end of his resources. Here God met him and offered him the resources of the Spirit. He took them. He went back to his pulpit a new man. Now the crowds no longer went away to talk about the greatness of Chalmers, but about the greatness of Chalmers' gospel. He wrote the Ten Commandments on the soul of Scotland. A personal Pentecost had turned him into an effective witness.

I have watched the peasants of India laboriously lifting water into their rice fields by a basket suspended on ropes. It is hard, slow work. But I have also watched the sunbeams come and quietly and gently lift the water and drop it down upon their fields. It was done without strain. Some of us have tried pathetically to lift the level of the life amid which we labor, but it is hard, strained, and heart-breakingly meager in its results. It is all lifting by hand. It is strain, hence drain. Pentecost offers to struggling ineffectiveness the gentle but effectual Power of the living Spirit.

Two things remain in Pentecost as permanent —power for living, power for life-giving. Someone asked a very able and successful minister why he did not smoke. He replied that probably it would do him little harm personally, but, said he: "I follow a calling that makes it necessary for me to be called in very suddenly to see sick people. For this reason I must have nothing about me that would in the slightest prove offensive to anyone in the most delicate state of health. Every moment I must keep myself aseptic."

The Spirit in the life does the twofold work of making the life aseptic and the witness acceptable.

CHAPTER XXIII

IT IS WONDERFUL!

As we have made our way through Pentecost and its meaning the words of a Chinese teacher have lingered in my mind like a benediction and a challenge. I asked her whether she was a Christian, and she answered that she was. Then she looked out across the fields toward the hills in the distance as if in deep thought, and suddenly turning toward me she said, very slowly and earnestly, "I think it is wonderful to be a Christian." So do I! For these simple words gather up the impressions that one has when he thinks about the possibility of human living as the doors to the Upper Room swing open. They are the very doors to life.

It *is* wonderful to be a Christian. It is wonderful to have a Character in human history whom you can utterly trust and to whom you can utterly give your heart. A Hindu said to me one day that he had once looked at a picture by Rembrandt, a picture of a face, a face very luminous, but around it were dark clouds. That luminous face amid the clouds stood, he said, for Jesus. Around him are clouds. There are many things that are so distracting, so puzzling about

[233]

our world, but in the midst of things there is one luminous Face—the face of Christ. "That one Face, far from vanishing, rather grows and becomes my universe that feels and knows." I can wait till the clouds that surround him render up their meaning, whether they are clouds of wanton destruction or of beneficent rain, but in the meantime I have a Spot in my universe that is luminous and utterly trustable. If that Face should fade, my universe would turn to midnight. It is wonderful to have a Place of which you are always sure and to which you can turn in a distracting world.

It is wonderful to be a Christian. It is wonderful to have a world in which the cross is at its center. Now we know that standing back in the shadows is a Love that will not let us go. God not only means well, he means to make us well. His wounds answer our wounds. The cruelest, hardest, most wicked word that life can speak has been spoken—spoken at a cross, and God turns that cruel, hard, wicked word into a word that heals our race.

It is wonderful to be a Christian. It is wonderful to have a world with an Easter morning in its history. Suppose there had been none, and that the universe's last word had been a cross instead of an Easter morning; then on that cross the sons of men would have been forever tortured with the Son of man. But now, since life's last word for me is to be Easter, I do not mind if life's latest word is a cross. What can life do now, what is left for it to do, since Life has done everything?

It is still more wonderful to be a Christian when all of this becomes actualized, concreted, available at Pentecost. Here this Jesus of history becomes the Christ of experience. The seemingly Nowhere becomes the Now-here. And that heals us.

I asked a Hindu one day what was the matter, for he seemed to be in distress. "There is nothing the matter with me except that I have not found Him," he replied. But isn't that all that is the matter with the world—it hasn't found Christ? Underneath all our restlessness is this inner pain—we have not found him. But at Pentecost they had found him—rather, he had found them.

"There are very few people who can swank the finding of God," said a European lady who had turned Hindu. She said it to break the force of my contention that outside of Christ I did not see people finding God. Swank the finding of God? It is the very last attitude that one feels like assuming if he finds God. When God finds us, as he does in the gospel, then all idea of attainment is gone and obtainment takes its place. We are lost in wonder, love, and praise. It is wonderful to have the gospel of the seeking God. That is the pledge of my finding him. And Pentecost knows no stinted finding. It means finding in fullness, in overflowingness. We are inundated with God. Have some of us not known what it is to ask that the Divine Hand be stayed? There seemed no capacity to hold more; it seemed that the vessel would break.

This sense of the Divine Spirit within becomes the fountain of the purest and most exquisite joy that the human heart is capable of knowing. The word "joy" runs like a refrain through the New Testament. So much so that one could almost say that the New Testament way is "salvation by joy." It was a joy that ate up the lesser joys of the flesh. They seemed irrelevant in the light of this new joy. No wonder Clement of Alexandria exclaimed, "The Holy Spirit is a glad Spirit." There is gayety in the Gospels. Jesus says, "My joy might remain in you, and that your joy might be full." My joy, your joy. The joy of the Gospels comes from finding something that is congruous to our nature. Said a Hindu, "The thing that strikes me about Jesus Christ is his congruity with our souls." When the soul finds Christ, after trying the incongruities of evil, immediately there is the rhythm of adjustment, of symmetry, of inner harmony. Integration is the modern word. It is the joy of the eye that sees, of the æsthetic nature that senses beauty, of the intelligence that has found truth, of the heart that knows love, of the life that has found Life.

It was the joy that Pascal knew. He had one of the most brilliant minds of Europe, wrote a treatise on conic sections at sixteen, laid the foundation for the calculating machine, and though he died at thirty-six, left an amazing impress. Brilliant in mind, he was dissatisfied in soul, sought for peace, found it when a verse of Scripture became suddenly luminous. When he died they found sewed in a piece of cloth above his heart these words: "Certainty! Fire! Joy! Peace! I forget the world and everything but God. Righteous Father, the world hath not known thee, but I have known thee! Joy! Joy! Joy! Tears of Joy! Jesus, Jesus, I separated myself from him, renounced and crucified him, but now I submit myself absolutely to Christ my Redeemer." Written over his heart it was a symbol of what was written deeper. His soul had found its congruity—Christ. This joy of the brilliant Pascal is not different from the joy of the Negro woman, who, while the minister was unfolding the glorious gospel, kept exclaiming her "Glory," and her "Hallelujah." Someone tried to keep her quiet, but she exclaimed, "I can't, for I's overcharged!" The early disciples were "overcharged," hence irrepressible. To the discomfiture of every one, they listened to false accusations in council halls while their faces shone like those of angels; they departed from judgment halls with bleeding backs, rejoicing that "they were counted worthy to suffer for his name;" they rejoiced their way through prisons, and saluted death with a smile. The Spirit's *ananda* (the beautiful Hindi word for "joy") kept their souls above the storm and strife.

This joy of the Spirit is no cheap joy. It has scars on it—radiant scars. It is joy won out of the heart of pain. Those who know it have found one of life's deepest and most transforming secrets: the transmuting of pain into a pæan. Sorrow becomes not something to escape; we can make it sing. We can set our tears to music, and no music is so exquisite, so compelling. The early Christians learned immediately and at once the truth which the philosopher Royce puts in these words: "Such ills we remove only as we assimilate them, idealize them, take them up into the plan of our lives, give them meaning, set them in their place in the whole." When their heartstrings were stretched upon some cross of pain and the winds of persecution blew through them, then from this human Æolian harp men heard the very music of God. They did not bear pain, they used it.

James says that "this active dealing with sorrow gives a new dimension to life." Life in the Spirit opens up to us in very truth a new

[238]

dimension to life. Other men live with the possibility of happiness through the three dimensions of prosperity, pleasure, and progeny; the Christian adds the fourth, through pain. When the outlook is not good, they can always try the inlook. They have "private reasons for being happy," for their happiness is not dependent upon happenings, but upon inner undisturbable-from-without relationships. If "we are only safe when we can stand anything that can happen to us," then the Christian has found the only safety there is, for, by his active dealing with sorrow, he has learned not merely *to stand* anything that can happen to him, but *to advance* by means of that very happening. Mrs. Lee lost all of her six children through a landslip, and I heard her rise and say, "I thank God for every sorrow that has ever come to me." It was not cant, for there were radiant scars on every word she said. The subsequent beautiful years of service have said so. The point is that Mrs. Lee traces back to a quiet personal Pentecost, found on shipboard, the discovery of this wonderful secret.

May I add a word of personal testimony? No one in public work can escape criticism. I have had my share. It used to cut me to the quick. But now when criticism comes I find myself asking, Is it true? If so, I will take it, will profit by it. My critics thus become "the unpaid watchmen of my soul." If the criticism isn't true, I can still use it. I can make these fires of unjust criticism serve to burn up my fetters and make me free.

In a Friends' meeting in Vienna I found myself rising and saying: "For many years I have worn a cross upon my heart, and this cross has made me. But recently it has been lifted and I miss it and I find myself asking for another cross." "What a terrible prayer to pray!" said a friend as we walked out of the meeting. Yes, it was, but it would have been more terrible not to pray it, that is, if we want to know the fourth dimension of life. I found myself praying recently, "If wounds must come, I have only one request to make about them—let them be clean wounds." If we can keep away from our wounds the infection of complaint and sourness of spirit, they will heal quickly and leave glorious scars.

It is "the joy of the Spirit" that is the antiseptic. His presence keeps our wounds clean. But it does more—the Spirit becomes vitality to soul and body. As Romanes says: "A prolonged flow of happy feeling does more to brace up the system for work than any other influence operating for a similar length of time." Men who live in the joy of the Spirit can do an incredible amount of work because inner frictions are eliminated. Most people do not break

[240]

down from overwork but from under-being.
Many of us are at civil war with ourselves, hence
we have no vitality or resources left to prose-
cute a foreign war against life and its evils.
If, as Captain Hadfield, the nerve specialist,
says, "we are only as tired as our minds," then
nothing, absolutely nothing, rests us so much as
that sense of inward poise, of adequacy to meet
life, that comes from the Spirit's presence in
the depths of one's being. I know this to be true,
for I have lived on power not my own for many
years. On arrival in India I was told that I
would break down within a year if I kept that
pace. This would have been true had there not
been the rejuvenation that comes from the fellowship of the Spirit. His life is energy on the
plane of the body, and spiritual power on the
plane of the spirit.

Someone has put it this way: "Joy increases
vitality. Greater vitality gives a stronger sense
of reality. This means stronger convictions. Of
convictions purposes are born. And conviction
and purpose make influence certain." So out
of this inner joy comes physical energy and spiritual power.

As I write these lines I look out upon the
terraced hillsides of the Himalayas. I see a
great crowd of villagers who have come for the
day to weed the fields. One of them is beating a
drum and they are all singing. They are work-

ing to music. Blessed is the Christian who has learned to work to the music of the Spirit.

A delegation of three women had invited me to address the students of a Latin-American city. One of the three was an atheist, another a Theosophist, and the third a Roman Catholic. After the address the brilliant atheist turned to me and said, "The reason we come to hear you is that you have a song in your heart, and Latin America dearly loves music." I can write that because it wasn't my song, it was the song of my Guest. One can honor a Guest when he dare not honor himself. I had no song until he came. My heart is like my canary, which would not sing until after it had its bath. When Jesus brought his cleansing, then, and then only, did my heart learn its song. I once said to a Hindu audience that when I found Him I arose from my knees and felt as though I could put my arms around the world and share this with them. They applauded. Of course they did, for we are made for this and recognize our life when we see it. "You Christians have something I haven't —joy," said a Brahmo Samajist preacher. He had beautiful precepts in his religion, but no Pentecost. Hence the Brahmo Samaj movement, lacking the vital Divine Spark, has passed into high-minded religious respectability, but with an undertone of unsatisfied wistful yearning running through it.

[242]

Modern Christianity, wherever it lacks that Divine Spark, has run into that same gentility and that same sterility. The prayer of the man at the close of the service unconsciously illustrates our attitudes: "O God, if any spark of divine grace has been kindled in this meeting, water that spark." We have thrown the cold water of rationalism upon our gospel until the divine glow has turned to ashes. "I want to see some of you Christians mad after Jesus," said a Hindu to me one day. After Pentecost these men were "mad" after Jesus. We are only mildly interested in him. They were Christian. We are religious.

It is wonderful to be Christian. But it is not wonderful to be merely religious. The world is filled with religion—it lacks being Christian. I saw in London the original document that formed the basis of the organization of the Y. M. C. A. When the little group headed by George Williams drew up the document they first wrote at the top, "Young Men's Religious Association," but they drew a line through the word "Religious," and above it wrote "Christian." That was one of the most decisive lines ever drawn in human history. They decided that their movement would not be vaguely religious, but definitely Christian. That has been the driving power back of the Y. M. C. A. It was founded in the passion to lead young men into definite relationship to Jesus Christ. When it loses that and passes into being vaguely religious, it is doomed to sterility.

It is a great, decisive day in any man's life when he decides no longer to be merely religious, but to be definitely Christian. That decision will lead him face to face with Pentecost, for you cannot be a Christian in any real sense unless you have in some real way experienced the power of the Spirit.

Christianity is at the parting of the ways. It is now at the point of decision where it must decide in a larger way to be definitely Christian or vaguely religious. The whole pressure is toward a syncretism. In East and West the demand is that we draw a line through the word "Christian," and put in "Religious." This is in the supposed interests of universality. In reality it leads to "a mush of amiability." You cannot be more universal by being less Christian. Whenever you strike a truly Christian note you strike a universal note. If we want universality, then back to Pentecost! For here the universal Christ becomes universal in experience, and this experience breaks into universal forms.

It costs little to be religious. There is no cross in it. It costs your very all to be a Christian. But in the words of the Chinese teacher, "It is wonderful to be a Christian."

CHAPTER XXIV

THE TECHNIQUE OF FINDING

THE famous words of Livingstone come to mind: "The end of the exploration is the beginning of the missionary enterprise." The end of the exploration as to the meaning of Pentecost should be the beginning of the inquiry as to what Pentecost can mean to us personally. The end of the inquiry is to become an inquirer.

How can the Spirit become operative in our lives? To use a modern phrase, what is the technique of our finding the Spirit and of living through his power? What are the terms upon which he offers himself? This is most important, for, as Professor Hirsch says: "The vital point in our knowledge of the gospel lies in our answer to the question, How is the Holy Spirit given?"

When I turn to the New Testament to trace out the technique of the finding of the Spirit at Pentecost it seems to be absent. There seems to be nothing blocked off or very definite in the steps to be taken. The account says that they "continued with one accord in prayer." And the Spirit was given. It was all very natural and seemingly devoid of technique. But under this naturalness there is a technique, and it does not differ essentially from the technique of setting up close human relationships.

Someone has described being a Christian as "a long falling in love with God." If love is to be the center of our relationship, then how do we fall in love with God? Well, how do we fall in love with anyone? The first step is a drawing near, for, as has been said, "Propinquity is the soul of love." Nearness seems to be necessary to love. Nearness, then, leads to mutual self-surrender. Nothing has been weighed out or measured, but heart has been given to heart and each knows that he or she belongs to the other person. Out of that self-surrender faith emerges. The atmosphere becomes one of trust. Trust, then, becomes the medium through which life and thought can be communicated to each other. Finally, in addition to the initial self-surrender, there is a continuous adjustment of mind and purpose and life. The steps, then, seem to be these: A Drawing Near, Self-surrender, Trust, Continuous Adjustment.

When I turn to Pentecost I find, underneath the simplicity of the account, these four stages. They were steadfastly in prayer for ten days. Prayer brought a drawing near to the Divine. In that nearness they found themselves gradually letting go one thing after another, until finally the self-surrender was complete. Out of that self-surrender faith came into being—

[246]

an active, appropriating faith. Then faith closed the circuit. It became the medium through which the human and the Divine were fused into one. "They were all filled with the Holy Ghost." After this there was set up a process of constant adjustment of the human to the Divine. "It seemed good to the Holy Ghost and to us," was the phrase used to express the constant attitude. The outcome of these four stages—prayer, self-surrender, appropriating faith, constant adjustment—was victorious spiritual living.

The technique of finding the Spirit at Pentecost is thus not arbitrary, imposed, unnatural. Rather it is natural, growing out of the facts. It is valid to-day. The first step is prayer, and through prayer a drawing near. There can be no great spiritual awakening either in the individual or in the group unless and until the individual or the group give themselves to prayer. Dr. John R. Mott says that wherever, throughout the world, he has traced a spiritual awakening to its cause and center it has always been found in a prayer life that was beyond the ordinary. But herein is our weakness—our prayer-lives are very ordinary, hence our spiritual impact is very mediocre. While in the West I stated publicly that the ministry was not praying. I did not mean that ministers do not pray —we all do—but I did mean that we are not praying in a way that brings self-abandonment, that self-abandonment in turn bringing a venturous faith that appropriates divine resources, and leads to our receiving the Spirit as a mighty working Fact in life. There are wonderful exceptions, but on the whole we are using oars when we might use the power of steam. We are trying to organize life into being instead of being organisms imparting life. In these modern days we feverishly run about on the surface in automobiles, and that surface running is symbolical of our surface living. We have lost the depths. Very often we are feverishly busy doing nothing, but being feverishly busy. When we feel there is something wrong and that it is all ending in futility, instead of giving ourselves to prayer we—appoint a committee! If a monument were erected over the dead situations in Christendom, we might inscribe on it, "Committeed to Death." We call a committee instead of calling to prayer, and the one is often an "alibi" for the other. The fact is that our taste for prayer determines our taste for God.

It has been said that the Reformation was born in Luther's prayer closet. All reformation, individual and collective, begins in some one's prayer closet. I find myself better or worse as I pray more or less. It works with almost mathematical precision. We find, sooner or later, that in prayer we either abandon ourselves or we abandon prayer. Prayer will keep us from self-withholding or self-withholding will keep us from prayer. I find God fading out of my life to the degree that prayer fades out. The fading out of the God-consciousness is the greatest tragedy and loss that this generation has sustained. Prayer will rediscover it.

I do not argue the question as to whether anything happens in prayer—I simply testify: It does. It works. It was said of Jesus that he prayed all night upon the mountain, and when he came down in the morning "the power of the Lord was present to heal." Of course it was. The power of the Lord will be present to heal through us if we give ourselves to prayer. "The streams that turn the machinery of the world have their rise in solitary places." Those who move this age toward God have moved out of this age to the solitary places. Then they come back with power. It was said of the man in the Scripture, "If he be alone, there is tidings in his mouth." No man has tidings, unless he takes time to be alone and apart with God. There he listens to what God says, and men listen to what he says.

But let it be noted that in prayer I do not bend God to my will, but I blend my will with God's. He can therefore do things through me that he otherwise could not have done. If in our universe some things are left open contingent upon the human will, so some things are left open contingent upon prayer. Prayer digs the channels from the reservoir of God's boundless resources to the tiny pools of our lives. Through prayer we begin to live by his power.

Since prayer is the very breath of the life of the Christian it is befitting that it should be made the first step in receiving the Spirit. Prayer precipitated Pentecost. Those ten days in prayer brought the disciples face to face with two things: themselves and their Resources. In the increasing clarity of those prayer hours they saw that the chief stumbling-block in the way of their living the Christian life was just themselves. They saw that they could never appropriate God's resources until they had abandoned themselves. That leads us to the second step of self-abandonment.

In John's Gospel it is said that the reason the Spirit had not yet been given was that "Jesus was not yet glorified." When he went to the throne then the Spirit was given. It is not different to-day. There is only one thing that keeps us from receiving the Spirit—Jesus is not on the throne of our lives. Something else is. When he becomes Lord of all he offers us all. It is only empty hands that can grasp a whole Christ. When we are sure we are withholding nothing we may be sure that God is withholding nothing. The Gift of the Spirit may then become ours.

We are now ready for the next step—that

delicate but decisive step of faith. Many fail to go boldly in and possess the land. At this juncture we must talk faith with God. We must hold fast to the fact that God has not brought us along so far only to let us down at the decisive moment.

Jesus said, "Receive ye the Holy Ghost"; the word "receive" is active voice, so that it might be translated, "Take ye the Holy Ghost." We are not to wait, supinely and passively; we are to reach out and take the offered Gift.

"Faith is an affirmation and an act
That bids eternal truth be fact."

Jesus said, "What things soever ye desire, when ye pray, believe that ye receive them, and ye shall have them." This is not a deceiving of the mind into believing something that is not so. For here faith turns to fact, and fact to feeling. I remember distinctly that, after living the Christian life for some time, I met this demand for my all. I responded as far as I knew. I determined that Christ could have me without reservation or qualification. After having said this to him and having meant it, I quietly arose from my knees and walked around the room, inwardly affirming that I believed God was as faithful as I was, that when I offered my all I believed he offered his all and I would take it. Very vividly do I remember that doubt closed in on me and that I pushed my hands away from me as if pushing doubt away. This continued for some minutes, when faith took hold and the quiet sense of the purifying and illuminating presence of the Spirit went through every portion of my being. I could do nothing but walk the floor, my heart welling with thanksgiving. For days I seemed possessed with an unearthly bliss. The most beautiful thing was that this coming of the Spirit seemed not to be a transient, fugitive thing, but the coming of an abiding Guest. It had the "feel" of permanency. "He may abide with you forever," were the words of Jesus about it. And it has been so. Underneath the overtones of changing emotion and feeling there has been the undertone of the sense of the permanent Divine within the depths of the life. Feelings change, facts abide.

Faith, then, is the venture that dares. It seems to be walking out upon a void, but that void will turn to solid rock beneath the feet. The tendency just here will be to look at our own unworthiness instead of at his faithfulness. If we look in we shall be discouraged, if we look around we shall be distracted, but if we look up we shall have peace. If we were compelled to wait until we were lifted by our own worthiness, we should be forever in the mire. An unfortunate man, ragged and hungry, was given a check by a business man, and was told to get himself some clothes and food. Some days later the business man met him on the street, still ragged and hungry. He accosted him, remonstrated with him that he had used up the check in drink, instead of getting clothes and food.

"No," said the unfortunate man, "here I have the check with me, but when I went to the bank to get it cashed, I looked at my clothes and then at the well-dressed clerks within and I said to myself that they would never give me the money. I felt unworthy."

"But," replied the business man, "it is not your clothes or your worthiness that decides the question. It is my name on that check."

This whole thing is backed by the integrity of the character of God. He signs his offer in the blood of his own cross. I repeat what I said above: he not only means well, but he means to make us well. Faith is simply taking what in all sincerity God offers.

If I seem to be running into what will be termed by some the language of an outworn orthodoxy, I cannot help it. I can do no other. I do not use it because it is new or old, but because it works. This is the way over which I have traveled, and I find it works. I had nothing to offer but my bankruptcy, and, to my amazement, He took it and gave me all the resources of the Divine that I would take.

One of our aged saints, an artist with a rare

streak of humor running through both her art and her saintliness, looked at a wonderful sunset while in a small station in India. As she gazed at the riot of beauty on the monsoon clouds she exclaimed: "What a wonderful sunset, especially for such a little place!" Spiritually I have had that same feeling about this whole matter: As I have gazed upon the wonder and beauty and redemption of it all, my feeling has been, What a wonderful redemption for such a little heart to hold!

But faith is not merely an act that takes the proffered Spirit once for all—it is more, it is an act and an attitude. We pass out of that whole paralyzing, pessimistic attitude of doubt and pass into that creative, initiative, abounding attitude of faith. Doubt paralyzes, faith creates; faith, therefore, is the normal attitude of the soul. Doubt is the "No" to life, faith is the "Yes." When one has the faith-attitude, there sets in what may be called spiritual initiative. Things happen around such lives. They become morally and spiritually contagious. For the end of the finding of the Spirit is not an experience but an expression. Pentecost is not a terminus but a starting point. It is not an end in itself.

One of the tragedies connected with Pentecost is that because it is usually accompanied with exquisite emotion, the emotion becomes an end in itself, the life becomes ingrown. At my feet as I write is a bleeding root sticking out of the ground. The little knoll here in the Himalayas had to be leveled off so I could pitch my tent, and in the leveling the shrubbery was cleared away and the root left. It is alive after some weeks, but it is still bleeding. The life that should have gone into flower and fruit is ebbing away. Some of us have had the root of the matter in us, but it has not passed on into fruit. So we are inwardly and spiritually bleeding to death. If our roots are in Pentecost, our fruits must be in the ends of the earth.

That leads to the fourth stage: a continuous adjustment of the human to the Divine. The spiritual life is both a gift and a growth.

One of my friends whose moral and spiritual influence is felt in many parts of the world was leaving India discouraged and broken—both in soul and body. In the darkest hour of his life he took hold of this verse: "Whosoever drinketh of the water that I shall give him shall never thirst." He began to drink. He was transformed. Years later he said publicly, "Since that time, thirty years ago, I have not had a dark, discouraged hour." The secret of his continuously victorious spiritual life is found in the fact that he recognized that the word "drinketh" is a word in the Greek expressing completed but continuous action, and might be translated,

"Drinks and keeps on drinking." The crisis leads to a continuance. We give our all once and for all, but there will be a continuous unfolding of that "all" as we apply it more and more widely to oncoming life.

We can find no experience that is proof against prayerlessness. If the finding of the Spirit is begun in prayer, it is continued and ended in prayer. By watchfulness and careful living we are to guard "that good thing which was committed unto" us; we are to keep it "by the Holy Ghost which dwelleth in us."

Life in the Spirit must no longer be lived on the unit principle, but on the co-operative plan. We supply willingness and he supplies power. There is more and more a merging of interests, of thought, of purpose, of life. We become more and more sensitive to the Divine and to the divine leading.

One of the most difficult things about life in the Spirit is the matter of divine guidance. It is difficult, for our wires often get crossed and we hear the voices of our own desires, instead of the voice of the Spirit. The reason we cannot depend upon divine guidance in a crisis is because we do not train ourselves to daily obedience. Only those who are sensitive to the Divine can sense the Divine.

When I was deciding the question of my life's work I received a letter from a college president saying, "It is the will of the faculty, the will of the student body, the will of the townspeople and, we believe, the will of God that you should teach in this college." At the same time I received a letter from a trusted friend saying, "I believe it is the will of God that you should go into evangelistic work in America." Then a letter came from the Board of Missions saying, "It is our will to send you to India." Here was a perfect traffic-jam of wills! These were all second-hand, and I felt that I had a right to first-hand knowledge in such a crisis. Not that I would despise the opinions of friends in spiritual guidance, for God often guides through them. But obviously here they could not be depended on. So I took the letter from the Board, went to my room, spread it out and said, "Now, Father, my life is not my own and I must answer this. Lead me and I'll follow."

Very clearly the Inner Voice said, "It is India."

"All right," I replied, "that settles it—it is India."

I arose from my knees and wrote at once, saying I was ready. The Inner Voice did not fail me then. It has never failed me since. In many a crisis, too intimate to spread on the pages of a book, I have looked to him to give me a clear lead and I would follow. He has never failed to give me that lead sooner or later, and when

[257]

he has given it, it has always turned out to be right. He has never let me down. I have let him down, time and again, but I find him utterly dependable. I am sure that outside of that Will I cannot succeed; inside of that Will I cannot fail. The words of George MacDonald to Keith Falconer, as he went to the East, have been appropriated as my own: "This is a practical working faith: It is man's business to do the will of God; God then takes on himself the special case of that man; therefore that man should be afraid of nothing."

No two persons experience the Spirit in exactly the same way. There is a broad sameness of fact, but an infinite variety in phenomena. "Each receives his manifestation of the Spirit for the common good" (1 Cor. 12. 7, Moffatt). It would not be for the common good if the Spirit were to manifest himself through all in the same way. It takes many differing instruments to make up a symphony. We must let the Spirit pull out all the stops and play every key of our personalities. We must be utterly ourselves. We must be natural. But we must also remember that we need other Spirit-played instruments to complement and complete our partial tones. The one who most differs from us may have most to give us. The Spirit comes not to uniform us but to unify us.

There is no magic in any of these steps. They

are simply an unfolding of the human to the Divine. There is no magic whatever in Pentecost. The day of Pentecost was the occasion of the coming of the Spirit, but not the cause. There are those who think it was the cause, that God waited deliberately to give the Spirit on that particular day. Rather it is more possible to think that when that particular day approached, the disciples, who, after all, were Jews and believed implicitly in divine festivals, had their expectancy increased, and this led to letting go that last thing—themselves. When that was done faith received the offer on the part of God, the gift of the Spirit.

I remember on one occasion we were in a mission station where they were preparing for the visit of the governor of the province to the school. The missionary who was doing most of the preparing for the governor was inwardly setting her house in order to receive the Divine Guest, the Spirit. Her heart was panting after the Spirit as the hart panteth for the water brooks. I was standing on the veranda watching for the governor to come around the hill. When he did so, I called out to those in the house, "He has come." The lady, whose deepest undertone was this craving for the Spirit, thought, for the moment, that I meant that the Spirit had come. Her faith at that moment closed the circuit. He *had* come! She went

THE CHRIST OF EVERY ROAD

quietly to her room, closed the door and knelt
and thanked God that he had come. When she
came out to meet the governor some of us saw
a sparkle of the eye and a radiancy of counte-
nance that does not come from merely meeting
governors! The governor's visit and my statement had precipitated the crisis that brought
the acceptance of the Spirit, but they had not
caused his coming. So with Pentecost. We must
loose the Spirit's coming, even from that festival
day. God did not sovereignly give the Spirit on
that chosen day. That would make it mechanical and far away from us. Rather did the disciples choose to offer themselves and to take God's
gift that day. That makes it vital and very near
to us. For we can do the same.

There is only one thing predetermined in the
matter of finding the Spirit. John, commenting
on Jesus' statement about "the rivers of living
water," said, "But this spake he of the Spirit,
which they that believed on him were to receive:
for the Spirit was not yet given; because Jesus
was not yet glorified" (John 7. 39). Note the
phrase "were to receive." The receiving of the
Spirit was deliberately put in the divine program for them. Here is something predetermined for every follower of Christ—we are to
receive the Spirit. If we do not receive the Spirit, then we deliberately cancel the divine program for us. If we have not the Spirit, it is

because we do not want him—do not want him sufficiently to go through the necessary steps.

This finding of the Spirit is what the Scriptures call an "open secret." It is open to all, but it is secret, so secret that only those who bring to it the price of their all and an appropriating faith will have it opened to them.

We may well close this chapter with a simple but moving narrative from one of the great souls of India, Miss Sorabjee. Her school, into which the sons of princes and wealthy people of Western India come because of the character training and the thorough education they receive, is one of the most remarkable in India. It is a school with a soul. And the soul of that soul is Miss Sorabjee. The secret of her consistent and constant spiritual impact is to be found in this narrative, which she writes at my request:

"It was in the summer of the year 189—(I think 1896) that Miss Grace Wilder wrote me a letter, quite unexpectedly (for though we were well acquainted we used not to correspond), asking, 'Have you received the Holy Spirit?' The question surprised me not a little, for I knew that she was aware that I was a Christian. I pondered over it and then decided that I was a Christian. I had a wonderful blessing at the confirmation, was a regular communicant, and an active worker for Christ, so I must have received the Holy Spirit. I therefore put away the letter, deciding to explain matters when I should see Miss Wilder again. This was in May. In August of the same year I attended a meeting of the Poons Missionary Conference, where Mr. Robert Wilder spoke on what he called that 'Verse of Contrasts' in Saint Luke 11. 13: 'If ye then, being evil, know how to give good gifts unto your children; how much more shall your heavenly Father give the Holy Spirit to them that ask him?' He contrasted 'Ye (being evil)' with 'Your heavenly Father'; 'Know how to give' with 'Give'; 'Good gifts' with 'The Holy Spirit'; 'To your children' with 'Them that ask.' He spoke of the necessity for the baptism of the Spirit, and the results that would ensue if every worker claimed this as his right. He read us a letter from a missionary in Calcutta who described the wonderful things that were taking place in her school since she had claimed and received this Power from on high—how the Bible classes, which up to that time had been lifeless, had suddenly grown full of life; how long-concealed misdemeanors among the girls were confessed by them, and pardon sought; how old quarrels were set aside, and peace and love took the place of anger and hatred. Then Mr. Wilder went on to say, 'God has no favorites, that power can be yours. Remember "the Holy Spirit to them that ask!" '

"I went home and up to my room. I knelt down and prayed, 'Lord, give me this gift.' But though I prayed till past midnight, the heavens seemed as brass. For three days I went about my work like one in a maze, doing my duties, but with one thought always uppermost: 'Oh, if I could only get the Power!' On the Saturday following, the Missionary Conference held an all-day of prayer, and Mr. Wilder was one of the leaders. During one of the intervals I went into the office of the head of the Mission and said: 'You people are all talking of the gift of the Holy Spirit, and you tell of having received it, but I have discovered that God has favorites. I have prayed and prayed and he does not hear me, nor answer my prayers by giving me what he has promised.'

"He took up a little Almanac from the table, and, instead of answering my anxious remarks, said, 'Will you accept this?' I was hurt and showed my disappointment, taking the proffered calendar without a 'Thank you,' while I continued what I had been saying by remarking: 'I have held out the hand of faith in vain; God has no gift for me.'

" 'Have you got that gift I gave you just now?' asked Mr. R——. 'How did you get it?' 'Why, I just took it,' I cried, as the meaning of his words dawned on me. 'Oh, is it as easy as all that? Am I only to take his gift?'

"Then I wanted to know how I could be sure, sure beyond doubt, and my kind friend said, 'Reckon on having received it, and the next time he tells you to do anything, do it.'

"The bell rang for the next session, and I went into the big hall, and knelt near my mother and sisters. Mr. Wilder was leading the Intercessory Service, and read out a certain petition. God's Spirit whispered, 'You pray for that.' I had never prayed aloud in public, extemporaneously, and was overcome with shyness, but, 'Reckon on having received the Power' was ringing in my heart and ears. I lifted my voice and prayed a little prayer which I feared only my mother heard, but oh, the peace and joy that filled me! I walked on air for days after that. My work was revolutionized. I had been asking God to help me in *my* work, now I let him pick me up and use me for *his* work. He used me for winning others. Everything was now changed."

Everything was changed because she was changed.

CHAPTER XXV

THE CHURCH AT ITS BEST?

IN conclusion, let me say that with the impact of my faith upon the systems and soul of the East I have been forced to change many things. My faith has been simplified. Many things have dropped away as irrelevancies. But one thing has remained unchanged during these years. I came to India with this conviction and the years have done nothing but verify it. It is this: Pentecost is not a spiritual luxury; it is an utter necessity for human living. The human spirit fails, unless the Holy Spirit fills.

I have watched up-standing young people come to the East out of our universities with a fine social passion and a wonderful human touch. They really did want to serve. Then as difficulties and discouragement closed in on them I have watched that social passion grow faint, that humanism grow sour and cynical, that desire to serve wither, and they have gone home again wondering if it were worth while. The reason for this lies in the fact that there was not sufficient inward personal realization of the Spirit's resources to sustain the social passion, the human touch, and the desire to serve. They tried to live out the implications of Pentecost without the power of Pentecost. The Sermon on the Mount is beautiful—with Pentecost; without it, it is paralyzing. It is not unkind to say that I have seen parlor reformers grow weary in the dull drudgery of the kitchen.

On the contrary, I have watched men and women consistently and continuously stay by their tasks through thick and thin and keep an undiscouraged and unsoured spirit, an unquenchable hope, a faith in God and in people, and the secret has always been that they have lived upon resources not their own. They have found an adequate dynamic in the living presence of the Spirit. They never know when they are defeated, for they are not defeated within. There they remain intact. But it is not merely defensive power; it is gloriously, hilariously offensive. They win because they are winsome. They have learned the way to live.

The words of a Chinese teacher illustrate what I mean. In one of our Round Table conferences it came the turn of this teacher to tell what his faith was meaning to him in experience. He said in simple, straightforward, sincere fashion: "Some time ago I wrote out in my New Testament what my faith was meaning to me. At the top I wrote, 'It works!' Under that I wrote, 'You ask me for this, that, or the other definition or explanation and I may not be able to give it, but it works. I put my faith under sorrow, and it learns to sing; under life, and it learns to live. Thank God it works!'" As my Chinese brother talked on I found my heart beating in unison. I could say from the depths, "It works!"

A very able friend said to me one day, "I read your book on the Round Table conferences the night when the famous prize-fight took place, and the thing that struck me was that there was a deeper bruising of spirit taking place in your Round Table conferences than there was the bruising of the body in that ring. Aren't there scars on your faith?"

"Yes," I replied, "there are some very deep scars on my faith, for the skeptical and the non-Christian have smitten it for twenty-two years, but the more it has been smitten the more it has shone. Yes, there are scars on my faith, some very deep ones, but underneath those scars there are now no uncertainties. There is a way to live. And this is the way. It works!"

It works to the very degree that we will work it. And the world situation is calling us to work it as we have not worked it in the past. The East now knows what it means to be a Christian and is demanding that we be Christian. The West, in its eagerness, has pushed along many roads that have ended in dead-ends and, suffering from disillusionment and cynicism, is asking if there is a road with an open vista. The situation looks

to us for a solution. The fact is that we, as
Christians, at home and abroad, have come to
the parting of the ways. The strain on our
Christianity is getting greater and greater. The
growing complexity of our civilizations is increasing the complexity of demand for an adequate spiritual dynamic. We must give it or
fail to function as Christians. The extent of
the projection of our gospel into the soul of this
age will be determined by the depth of our own
experience of that gospel. We cannot go further than we have experienced.

This is vividly illustrated in the history of the
Evangelical Revival, a revival that cleansed the
springs of the national life of Britain and saved
her to the moral leadership of the world. Wesley describes the memorable Watchnight Service
in his *Journal:* "About three in the morning, as
we were continuing instant in prayer, the power
of God came mightily upon us, insomuch that
we cried out for exceeding joy and many fell to
the ground. As soon as we had recovered a little
from that awe and amazement at the presence of
his Majesty, we broke out in one voice: 'We
praise Thee, O God; we acknowledge Thee to be
the Lord.'" Out of this formative hour the
Evangelical Revival really began. Up to this
time the preaching of Whitefield and Wesley had
been attended with meager results; after this,
amazing success attended their work. They

could go further now, for they had gone deeper.

This is further illustrated in the experience of a very dear friend. We were on the banks of the Beās River in the Punjab when a spiritual crisis was precipitated in his life. Alexander the Great had come as far as this river in his conquest of India. He had crossed the four rivers of the Punjab and now he had come to this fifth; beyond it lay India—the prize he had come so far to gain. It was September, when the Punjab is hot and muggy. It was laying a paralyzing hand on Alexander's soldiers. He tried to whip them up into a fighting mood by a great oration, but it fell upon deaf ears. They were weary and homesick. The inertia of the East had conquered them. Alexander saw it was of no use, turned sadly back, poured out a libation to the sun, sailed down the Indus River, up the Persian Gulf and died in a drunken brawl at Babylon. He got as far as the Beās and there the East turned him back.

My friend had also come to the Beās. And the East was getting him too. He had come to spend a year with me in evangelistic work. He was able, well-read, devoted to India. But the whole thing was laying too heavy demands upon him. While we were at this river in a conference he came to me and said: "I can't go on unless I get something. I can teach comparative religions in America, but this is demanding some-

thing of spiritual experience that I haven't got
to match against it." He told me not to wait
breakfast for him, for he was going out on the
banks of the river to settle matters. He was
gone for some hours. Of course God met him—
he was waiting for him. He came back another
man. He was then ready to cross the Beās and
go into the soul of India. He could go further,
for he had gone deeper. When, throughout
India, the groups of students thronged about
him, I saw the adequacy of his spiritual experience. He had something to share.

When he returned to America a young minister, sensing the fact that my friend had found
a joyous spiritual adequacy, came to him and
said: "I have been preaching things that are not
operative in me. I refuse to perjure myself any
longer. I am not going to preach again unless
I can preach reality. I'll give God until Sunday
to do something for me, and if he doesn't do
anything for me before Sunday, someone else can
preach; I won't." Here was spiritual honesty
and desperation that was bound to lead somewhere. He too saw that he was at his Beās. He
could go no further until he had gone deeper.
He took Saturday off as "a day of retreat." He
came forth from those prayer hours a changed
man. He had a new dynamic—the Spirit. He
went to his pulpit the next morning and the
crowd filed in and settled back in their seats

to listen to the old words. He hadn't been talking ten minutes before they saw they had a new minister. There were undertones in his quiet words they had never heard before. The WORD was throbbing in his words. Before that morning was over almost the whole congregation was seeking what their young minister had found. He was going further now, for he had gone deeper.

The church, at home and abroad, has come to its Beãs. As I said in the beginning, the world-ground is being prepared for a spiritual awakening on a widespread scale. We are on the verge of something big. But we cannot capture these latent yearnings for Christ unless Christ captures us more completely. Materialism and inertia will close in on these spiritual yearnings and smother them, unless we can meet them with a gospel adequate in breadth and in depth. Pentecost gives both. We are therefore shut up to the alternative of Pentecost—or failure.

We cannot go further until we go deeper.

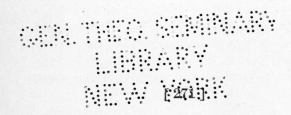

HERE LIES ARTHUR

HERE LIES ARTHUR

PHILIP REEVE

SCHOLASTIC

First published in 2007 by Scholastic Children's Books

An imprint of Scholastic Ltd
Euston House, 24 Eversholt Street
London, NW1 1DB, UK
Registered office: Westfield Road, Southam,
Warwickshire, CV47 0RA
SCHOLASTIC and associated logos are trademarks and/
or registered trademarks of Scholastic Inc.

10 digit ISBN 0 439 95533 5
13 digit ISBN 978 0439 95533 1

A CIP catalogue record for this book is
available from the British Library.

Printed by CPI Mackays of Chatham plc

Papers used by Scholastic Children's Books
are made from wood grown in sustainable forests

1 3 5 7 9 10 8 6 4 2

www.scholastic.co.uk/zone

For Geraldine McCaughrean

NOTE ON PRONUNCIATION

Before English existed, people in Britain spoke a language similar to Welsh. At the back of the book, there is a guide to how some of the names and place names in *Here Lies Arthur* might have been pronounced.

HIC IACET ARTHURUS, REX QUONDAM REXQUE FUTURUS
Here lies Arthur – King that was, King that will be again.

Sir Thomas Malory, *Le Morte d'Arthur*

SOUTH-WEST BRITAIN

AROUND AD 500

Even the woods are burning. I plunge past the torched byre and hard into the shoulder-deep growth of brambles between the trees, but there's fire ahead of me as well as behind. The hall on the hill's top where I thought I'd find shelter is already blazing. I can hear men's voices baying like hounds on a scent, the hooves of horses on the winter earth like drums. I see their shadows long before the riders themselves come in sight. Fingers of darkness stretch from their raggedy banners, reaching through the smoke which hangs beneath the trees. I duck sideways into a brambled hollow and wriggle deep. Thorns tug at my dress and snag my hair. The ground's frosty. Hard and cold under my knees and fingers. Fear drags little noises out of me. I squeak and whimper like a hunted cub.

But it's not me these horsemen are hunting. I'm nothing to them. Just a lost girl-child scurrying across the corners of their war. They thunder past without seeing me, the firelight bright on spears and swords, on mail and burnished helmets, on shield bosses and harness buckles and fierce faces lit up like lanterns. Their leader's out in front on a white horse. Big, he is. Shiny as a fish in his coat of silver scales. The cheek-guards of his helmet ripple with fire-gleam and his teeth between them are gleaming too, bared in a hard shout.

You've heard of him. Everyone's heard of Arthur. Artorius Magnus; the Bear; the *Dux Bellorum*; the King that Was and Will Be. But you haven't heard the truth. Not till now. I knew him, see. Saw him, smelled him, heard him talk. When I was a boy I rode with Arthur's band all up and down the world, and I was there at the roots and beginnings of all the stories.

That was later, of course. For now I'm still a snot-nosed girl, crouched in the brambles, giddy with the thump and stink of horses and so still that you'd think I'd been turned to a stone by my first glimpse of the Bear.

I didn't know then who he was, nor why he'd led his fierce, shiny riders to burn my home. All I knew was it was unnatural. Wrong as snow in summer or the sun at midnight. War's a thing for autumn, when the harvest's in and the rains not yet come to turn the roads to mud. When men can be spared to go harrying into other lands and carrying off other men's grain and cattle. So what do these horsemen mean by coming here in winter's dark, with the trees bare and the hay-stores half empty and cat ice starring and smashing on the puddles they ride their horses over? Are they even men at all? They look to me like Dewer's Hunt. They look like the Four Riders of the world's end I've heard the monks talk about up at

Lord Ban's hall. Though there's more than four of them. Five, seven, ten, more than I can count, heaving uphill on a steep sea of horse-muscle.

Uphill, and past me, and gone. Their wild voices blur into the crackle of burning brush and the steady bellowing of scared cattle from the byres. I sneeze on the smoke as I make myself move, slithering across the flank of the hill, over the knuckles of tree-roots, over the granite boulders furry with moss, through sinks of dead leaves in the hollows. Don't ask me where I'm going. Away from the burning. Away from those angry riders. Just away is good enough for now.

But then I reach the road, down at the bridge where it crosses the river, and there's another of the raiders there. His horse has come down in trampled mud at the bridge's end and the battle has left him behind. He's on foot, furious, flailing at the horse with the flat of his sword. A young man, his white face framed by wings of red-gold hair, a thin beard clinging to his jaw like fluff the wind has blown there. His eyes are full of angry tears and a desperate hunger for blood. Even the blood of a girl-child, I realize, as I somersault out of the scratchy undergrowth and land thump on the path before him. He forgets the horse and comes at me. With his blade in front of me, the steeps and fire behind, I turn, looking for a way out.

Ways out are all I have been looking for this evening, ever since I woke in my master's house to find the thatch ablaze, the women screeching, the men scrambling sleepily for staves and spears and sickles. I remember how the shadows of horsemen flicked past the open doorway. How my master had run out shouting and how a sword came down on his head and made the women screech louder. How I scrambled between the horses' legs and over a fence the pigs had trampled down in panic. Gwyna the Mouse they call me, and like a mouse I always have the sense to scurry out of trouble.

Except that now all my quickness and cunning have brought me to this: a dead end, cut off short by a shouting boy.

And for once I'm more angry than afraid. Angry at myself for running into his way, and angry at him and his friends for their stupid, unseasonal war. Why couldn't they stay at home, wherever their home is? I dart at the boy, and he flinches back, as if he thinks I mean to fight him. But mice don't fight. I duck by him quick, feeling the wind of his sword past my face, hearing the hiss of sliced air. I run towards the bridge, where his terrified horse is heaving up, mud and white eyes and a smoke of dragon-breath. I go sideways to avoid it, and lose my footing on the ice, and fall, and keep on falling.

And I leave the fire and the noise behind me, leave everything, and dive down alone through darkness into the dark river.

The first shock of that cold water jarred my teeth and made my lungs go tight. I surfaced in the shadows under the bridge, and heard the boy above me, screaming curses at his horse. I turned circles, paddling with my hands. This mouse could swim. Raised near the river, I'd been in and out of it as long as I could remember. In summer me and the other children of the place came down at evening when the day's work ended to splash and shout until the light died. In autumn, master had me dive in to set his fish-traps. Open-eyed in the hubble and swirl below the rapids, I'd wedge the long wicker creels in place, then lift them out later full of plump, speckled fish.

So I took a deep breath and dived, kicking out hard, letting the river drag me away from sword-boy. Gritty water pressed against my eyes. I could see only darkness, with here and there an orange fire-gleam slanting down. It was easier to find my way by touch. I pawed over slimy boulders to the first bend below the bridge and came up for air, yelping and gasping in the clatter of the rapids. The current tugged at me, reminding me of all the things that haunt rivers, ready to drag unwary children under with their long, green hands. I was scared of them, but the raiders scared me more.

I slid down into a calmer pool and trod water there, listening for the sounds of battle. There was nothing, only the voices of the river and the woods. Far off, the farm where I'd grown up was burning like a dropped torch. I wondered if all master's household were dead. There had been no love between me and them – I was just a hanger-on, the whelp of some dead slave-woman. But still that farmstead was the only home I'd known. Out of pity for myself I cried and cried, adding my tears to the river till the cold clutched and shook me and set all my teeth a-rattle.

At last, just to keep warm, I started swimming again. Downstream, letting the river do the work. I kept my head above the surface this time. If you'd been watching from the bank you'd think you'd seen an otter, scared from its hole by the fighting upriver and heading for quieter fishing grounds. I swam until the trees parted above me to let the sky show and the river widened into a deep pool. Another river joined it there, coming down off the moors and tipping into the pool in a long fall, pale in the moonshine like an old man's beard.

There, cold as a ghost, wet as a drowned dog, I came ashore, heaving myself out by the tangle of tree-roots that reached out of the bank. I flopped into the litter of beechmast and dead leaves between the trees and made a little ball of myself, trying to hug some warmth back into my juddering, shuddering limbs. The noise of the water filled my head. Where would I go now? What would I eat? Who would I serve? I didn't know. Didn't care either. There was no more feeling left in me than in a hearthful of cold ashes. When feet came scuffing through the fallen leaves and stopped beside me I didn't even look up, just knelt there, shivering.

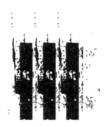

It was dark under those trees. I couldn't see the man who lifted me and carried me away from the pool. I couldn't see his waiting horse, though I felt it snort and stamp when he hung me over its saddle like a blanket-roll. I didn't see him till we reached shelter. It was an old building from the Roman times, big and pale in the owl-light, half sunk in furze and trees. He led the horse right inside, and small, loose tiles slid and scraped beneath its hooves as if the place was floored with teeth, or knucklebones. He lifted me down from the horse's back and laid me in a corner. I was too scared to look at him. He moved about quietly, kindling a fire. Big shadows shifted across the walls. Traces of paint clung to the plaster. Ivy hung down thick through the rotted cage of rafters overhead, rustly and whispering. I squinched my eyes shut. I thought if I was small enough, and still enough, and quiet enough, he might forget me.

"Hungry?" he asked.

I opened one eye. He was crouching by me. He wore

a shabby black travelling cloak fastened with a flashy, complicated brooch. A jangle of charms and amulets hung round his neck. Horse charms, moon charms, paw of a hare. Magic things. In the shadow of his hood his face gave away no secrets. Sallow, sharp-nosed, beardless. Was he a priest? He wasn't dressed like one, but I'd never seen a man clean-shaved who wasn't a priest or a high-born warrior, and this was no warrior. Fine-boned like a hawk, he looked. Quick and birdy in his movements too. And his eyes were hawk's eyes, patient and clever.

What did he want with me?

"Hungry?" he asked again. He stretched out the palm of his hand towards me and suddenly a hunk of bread was between his fingers. I shuffled backwards, pressing my spine against the wall. I was afraid of him and his magic bread.

He laughed. "It's only a trick, girl. Look close." He folded his hand over the bread and when he opened it again the bread was gone. He waggled his fingers and the bread was back. It perched on his palm like a baby bird. He held it towards me again but I closed my mouth tight and turned my face away. I didn't know much but I knew to fear magic.

Another laugh. A ripply sound, like water running in the first thaw of spring. "Scared it'll make you sleep a thousand years? Or witch you away to my kingdom under the hill?" He pushed the bread back inside his clothes and went about his business. He took a saddlebag from his horse and opened it, pulling out a cooking pot, a sack of food, a stained old blanket that he wrapped around me. All the time he talked to me softly, the way a farrier whispers to a scared horse.

"I'm as mortal as you, girl. I am Myrddin. The bard Myrddin. You know what a bard is, don't you, girl? A traveller and spinner of tales. There's my harp, bundled in oilcloth, see? It was *I* who thought *you* came from the otherworld. Creeping out of the lake like that. You must swim like a fish. I thought you were the lake-woman herself, come up from her home under the waters to steal my heart away. But you're a little young yet, aren't you, to be stealing anything but apples and barley cakes? How many summers have you seen? Nine? Ten?"

I managed a shivery shrug. Nobody had ever told me how old I was. Nobody had ever asked before.

"And have you a name?" He crouched down again on the far side of the fire and watched me. He threw back his hood, baring cropped, greying hair. The flame light stroked his face and gleamed in his eyes. He wore a look you could have taken for kindness.

"Gwyna," I said.

"So you can speak! And where have you come from, Gwyna?"

"From my master's farm. Up that way." I pointed with my head. My voice sounded very small and dull compared with his, as though the river-water had washed all the colour out of it. But it made the lights in his eyes flare up like embers when a breeze catches them.

"You've come from Ban's place?"

I nodded numbly. Ban was my master's master: lord of the fort on the hill above my burned home, and all the lands you could see from that hill.

"But it must be miles from here. . ."

"Not so far by river," I said. "I swam all the way."

"Like a fish." He was looking at me different now. I started to feel pleased. Nobody had ever cared much what I was or did before.

"I swum under water half of it," I said. (I didn't know it then, but I was sealing my fate with that silly boast.) "It's my job to set the fish-traps at fall-of-leaf. The cold don't worry me. I can open my eyes down under water and I can hold my breath. . ."

"How long? Show me?"

I gulped in a great breath and sealed my lips tight behind it. I watched him, and he watched me. Blood thumped in my neck, and the back of my head. I felt proud of myself. It was easy. I couldn't see why people bothered breathing, it was so easy to get by without. And still this Myrddin watched me. After a while the breath I'd taken started to grow stale inside. A bit of it seeped out my nose. The dam of my lips cracked, letting out more. I gasped, and the game was over, and still he was watching me.

"Better and better," he said. "Perhaps the spirits of the lake did send you to me, after all."

"Oh no, sir! It was the burning, and the riders. . ."

I stopped. Here by the warmth of his fire the battle seemed far off and strange, like a dream I'd had. But I hadn't dreamed it. Outside, the sky was turning pale above the bare branches. Birds were stirring. Day was brewing. "Oh sir!" I said, "They came with fire and swords and horses! They came killing and burning and hollering!"

13

Myrddin wasn't worried. "That is the way of the world, Gwyna. It has been so ever since the legions sailed away."

"But they'll come here! We must hide! We must run!"

"Peace, child!" he said, and he laughed. He caught me by both shoulders as I tried to scramble to the door. His horse sensed my fear and whinnied softly, stirring its tail, wafting a smell of dung towards us. Myrddin said, "You've nothing to fear. Not now. Not if you're with me." He sat me down again, shushing and crooning to calm me. "You know who those riders are, Gwyna? They are the war-band of Arthur. You've heard of Arthur, haven't you?"

Well of course I had. I never thought to meet him in my own woods, though. Arthur was someone out of stories. He fought giants and rescued maidens and out-foxed the Devil. He didn't ride about burning people's shippens down.

I said, "It can't be. What would he want here?"

Myrddin laughed and scratched his chin, as if he was trying to work out the easiest answer to that one. At last he said, "Arthur offered your Lord Ban his protection, in exchange for gold and other tributes. But Ban thought the price too high, and refused. That was foolish of him. Now Arthur has come to take Ban's holdings for himself. And he looks to me to help him do it. I ride with Arthur's band, see. I spin tales for him, and about him. I parted from him a few days since and came here by a different way, scouting out the land. If you know how the land lies a battle can be half won before it's started. Sometimes there's no need for a battle at all."

14

I took a moment to understand what he'd said. When I did, I was scared of him all over anew. What had I done, to make God deliver me up to a friend of the raiders?

"You've turned paler than porridge," he said. "But you've nothing to fear from me, and nothing from the Bear either. It'll make no odds to you who your lord is. Except that if I can make Arthur strong enough there might be peace again, like our grandfathers' fathers knew back in the days when Rome held this island. Strength like Arthur's could be used for good, see, just as the strength of old Rome was. That's why I help him, Gwyna. And I have a sense that you can help him too."

He talked and talked while I sat drying out beside his
fire, and the grey day brightened grudgingly above the
woods. He was in love with words. He found his own
conversation so interesting he didn't notice that he was
the only one talking. I just sat watching, listening, while
he spoke of places I'd never heard of: Elmet and Rheged,
Ireland across the sea, Din Tagyll where the ships from
Syria put in. Oh, I snatched a few familiar names out of
the word-storm. I'd heard of bad King Gworthigern,
who let the heathen Saxons settle in the east, and how
they rose up and tried to steal the rest of Britain too.
And I knew a song about Ambrosius Aurelianus, who led
the armies of the Britons through battle after battle until
he smashed those Saxons flat at Badon Hill. But mostly
Myrddin's words flowed past my ears like water.

"When Ambrosius died," he said, "there was no man
strong enough to take his place. The army he built to
fight the Saxons came apart into a hundred different
war-bands. Now they fight each other, and leave the

Saxons sitting tight upon the lands they stole in the eastern half of Britain. Some of those war-bands serve the small kings of the hill-country. Some serve the big kings of Dumnonia and Powys and Calchvynydd. Some are landless men, loyal only to their captain, grabbing loot and territory where they may. Arthur's band is like that. But Arthur's is the best, and one day, with my help, Arthur will be leader over all the rest as well. Then he can finish what Ambrosius started: push east and drive the Saxons into the sea."

I was only half listening. I was more interested in the stew Myrddin cooked up while he talked. I'd never thought I'd see a nobleman cook his own food. It was watery stuff, flavoured with onions, and dry meat a-bob in it. I ate all I could and then fell asleep, propped up in a corner with my head on my scabbed knees. In my dreams the woods were still on fire.

Woken by voices, I jumped up. I'd slept the day away. Afternoon sunlight bled down through the mat of weeds and wormy rafters overhead and made patches on the floor. The horse was half asleep, head down. Out among the trees two men were talking. One was my new friend, or master, or whatever he was. The other I did not know.

I crept past the horse and peeked. In the shade of the trees that grew around the old house's door stood another horse, a white one with a mane the colour of old snow. A man sat on it, looking down at Myrddin. The newcomer was a warrior, with a leather breastplate, and a sword at his side. His thick, red cloak had run in the rain, dribbling pink stains down his horse's rump. His helmet was off, and his sandy hair stirred in the breeze.

I went closer. I didn't think I'd be noticed. Noblemen don't notice people like me, any more than they notice the stray dogs and cats that flit around their halls. I heard the newcomer say, "The Irishman is on his way. He'll bring all the men he can muster, and ours are tired after the fight. If it comes to a battle. . ."

"It will not come to that," Myrddin promised. "Don't you trust me, Cei?"

"Not an inch," said the rider, laughing. Something made him glance my way, and he started as he caught sight of my face watching him from the shadows. Then he kicked his horse's flanks and turned it away. It looked strong and fast, that horse. It had been well looked after, and well fed on other people's hay.

"We meet at the river, then?" I heard the rider shout.

"The pool above the ford," called Myrddin, one hand up, waving, as the rider went away between the trees. "Where the waterfall is."

As the hoof beats faded he turned and saw me watching. He came towards me smiling, and I was still so little used to being smiled at that I just stood there basking in it till he reached me. He took me by one arm and pushed me back inside. "There is work to be done, Gwyna."

I looked at the dark loaves of dung his horse had dropped on the floor. I wondered if he wanted it cleaned up.

"Didn't I say you'd help me help the Bear?" he said. "Arthur needs a sign. There's an Irishman who rules those wet moors that rise up south of here. He's Ban's man, and if he chooses to avenge his overlord it will be a hard strife, and a waste of good men. Better for everyone if he can just welcome Arthur as his lord in Ban's place. Arthur could use an ally here in the west.

I've spoken with the Irishman, and he's agreeable. But his people won't trust a man who carries the sign of Christ on his shield. The ways of the new God lie thin in those hills of his, like first snow. Just a pretty coverlet. Dig a little and you soon find old ways and old gods underneath."

I shivered. It must be bad luck, I thought, to talk so carelessly about gods. I crossed myself, and made the sign against evil. I didn't want to anger any gods, not new nor old.

"So the old gods are going to make Arthur a present," Myrddin went on, fumbling among the furs and cloths behind his saddle. "A sign to show they are on Arthur's side."

"What sort of sign?" I asked, afraid.

"I'll show you."

His quick hands undid the fastenings on a long bundle of oilcloth. Something golden caught the light. A sword hilt. I'd not seen many swords, but I knew enough to know this one was special. The pommel and the crosspiece were red gold, inlaid with swirls and curls of paler metal. The hilt was twisted round with silver wire. The blade shone like water in the folds of the cloth.

"Swords are important to the Bear," said Myrddin. "And not just for fighting with. They mean something. A sword thrust through a stone was the badge of Artorius Castus, who saved us from the Picts and Scots in olden times, and from whom our Arthur claims descent. The gods will send this sword to Arthur from the otherworld, to show that they love him as they loved the old Artorius."

20

He was holding out the sword to me as if inviting me to touch it. I drew back.

"It has a name. Caliburn."

"Is it really from the otherworld?"

"Of course not, child. I bought it from a trader down at Din Tagyll. But we can make men *think* it is from the gods."

If I'd been a man, or even a boy, I might have said, "What do you mean, 'we'? I want no part in enchantments." But I was only Gwyna the Mouse. It was my lot to do as my elders told me, even if I didn't understand.

Myrddin tousled my matted hair. "And maybe some god *is* watching over us," he said. "Something sent you to me, that's for sure. I had planned to have the Bear row out and find the sword on a ledge beneath that little waterfall, hid among the rushes there like Moses in his basket. Spin a story afterwards to explain it. But now I have a better notion. And now I have you, my little fish. . ."

21

He left the horse tethered there, and hustled me away
through the woods. All he took with him was the sword,
bundled in its roll of cloth. The air was growing cold.
Myrddin nodded and said, "There will be a mist upon
the water."

How could he know such a thing? What demons told
him so?

"You'll be wondering how I came into Arthur's
service, I suppose?" he asked, striding ahead of me
through the thickets.

I'd been wondering no such thing. It was no place of
mine to wonder about his life. But I knew that he was
going to tell me all the same. I sensed he was nervous,
and that talking for him was a way of keeping fear at
bay.

"It's a good story," he promised, talking at me over his
shoulder as he went stalking through the wood. His
breath fumed in the cold air, wreathing him in smoke.
"You should hear how the men tell it round their

campfires. They say I worked for Arthur's father, that old villain Uthr, who was captain of Ambrosius's cavalry. It seems this Uthr had an eye for the girls, and one spring it lighted on one called Ygerna, that was wife to some small lord down in Kernyw. Lust lit up his brain like a gorse-fire. You could see the smoke pouring out of his ears. But what to do? Ygerna's husband was jealous. Kept her penned in his fort and let no man come near her.

"So Uthr called on me, and on my powers. One night, when his rival was off raiding some neighbours' cattle-runs, I transformed Uthr by magic into his image, and he slipped into the fort and into Ygerna's bed without anyone guessing. And the child conceived that night was Arthur, and his victories outshine old Uthr's as the sun outshines the moon."

Shoving my way through dead bracken at the magician's heels, listening to all of this, I wished I could just make a run for it, and take my chances with whatever wild beasts and wicked spirits lived in this maze of trees. Running had always served me well before. But running from Myrddin would be different, wouldn't it? If he had the power to transform one man into the likeness of another, then he could surely catch me and transform me into anything he chose. A frog. A toad. A stone.

"Of course, it's all nonsense," Myrddin said. "You'll have to learn that, Gwyna. Just because someone tells a story doesn't mean it's true. I have no magic powers. I'm just a traveller who has picked up a few handy conjuring tricks along the road."

"Then how did you change Uthr into another man?"
I asked.

"That's what I'm telling you, girl. It never happened.
Old Uthr took that fort by force, and carried off Ygerna
along with all his other trophies. Probably tired of her
within a week. There's no difference between Arthur and
any other of Uthr's landless bastards, except that Arthur
has me to spin stories like that one about him. You see,
Gwyna, men do love a story. That's what we're going to
give them this morning, you and I. A story they'll
remember all their lives, and tell to their children and
their children's children until the whole world knows
how Arthur came by the sword of the otherworld. And
here we are!"

We had reached the pool. Late afternoon sun lit the
oak-tops on the far shore, but the water lay in shadow,
and a faint silver breath of mist hung above it, just as
Myrddin had promised.

How had he known? He had just said he could not
work magic, but how else could he have seen into the
future?

A horn sounded, away downriver. Myrddin hurried
me along the shore. We pushed through undergrowth.
The armoured leaves of a holly-tree scratched my face. A
narrow ledge of rock led to the waterfall. Ferns grew
thickly here. The spray rattled on their leaves. Fleshy
and pointed they were, like green tongues. Among
them, almost hidden, I saw a faint path snaking in
behind the water's white curtain.

Myrddin turned and put the swaddled weight of the
sword into my hands. Then he took me by both

24

shoulders and stooped to stare into my face. Dark as good rich earth, his eyes were, and a quick to-and-fro flicker in them like the dancing of candle-flames as he watched me, searching, expectant.

"They are coming. I'll tell you what you must do, little fish, and you must listen well."

The sun crept west, and the tree-shadows shifted on the far shore. I crouched alone on the damp, narrow shelf behind the waterfall. The shout of falling water filled my head, but the spray barely touched me. It was a magic place. From a few paces away I must be invisible, yet I could look out through the water-curtain and see Myrddin quite clearly as he paced about in the sunlight on the eastern shore.

His face turned suddenly in my direction. He was too far off for me to make out his features, but I guessed it was a warning look. I looked at the trees behind him, and after a moment I saw light on metal, and the shapes of men on horses. They came out of the woods in a line, wary. Round white shields with the symbol of Christ on them, ☧, in red. Arthur's men. I looked for the sandy-haired one called Cei who had come to Myrddin earlier, but I could not tell which was him. The riders had their helmets on, and most rode white horses, and all wore red cloaks.

I knew Arthur when I saw him though. A red horse-tail fluttered from his helmet, and between the cheek-guards his teeth flashed in a white grin as he urged his horse down the shingle into the shallows. He was talking to Myrddin, but I could not hear their voices.

Then someone pointed across the pool towards the western side. More riders were coming down through the trees on the steep hillside there, and men on foot ran lightly between them. Spears and hunting bows. A big man with a black beard riding ahead of the rest. He stopped, and his men with him. They looked at Arthur's band. Some waved their weapons and shouted. Insults, I suppose, now I think back. Men stand taunting each other for hours sometimes before a fight begins.

But there was to be no fight. Myrddin was holding up his arms, shouting something back over the water. He swept his hand across the pool, reminding the Irishman's men that this was a magic place, a gateway to the otherworld. Telling them that that was why Arthur had come here, to pay his respects to their gods.

Now Arthur was dismounting, handing the reins of his horse to a boy who came running forward to take them. I could see men on both shores looking at each other in surprise as Arthur walked into the pool.

I said little prayers under my breath as I slipped off my old wool dress and wadded it into a crack of the rock behind me. I gripped the sword Caliburn in its oilcloth wrapper and took deep breaths. I didn't think I had the courage to do what Myrddin had ordered, but I hadn't the courage to disobey him, either. The air was cold. The water would be colder. I shuffled on my bottom to the edge of the rock shelf and let myself drop into the whirl of foam under the waterfall.

"They'll all be watching the Bear," Myrddin had said.

26

"Not every day you see a great warlord take a bath in all his gear. Or out of it, for that matter. No one will see you."

I hoped he was as right about that as he had been about the mist.

I surfaced cautiously under the fall. Water drilled down white all round me. For a moment, confused by the swirling and the noise, I didn't know which way I was facing. Then I saw Arthur pushing across the pool towards me. He was up to his chest; up to his shoulders. In the middle of the lake he had to half swim, which he did awkwardly, weighed down by his armour, his red cloak spread on the water behind him. Then, as he entered the tongue of rippled, roiling water that spread from the foot of the fall, the pool shallowed again and he rose up standing, waves lapping at his chest. Just as Myrddin had promised me he would.

I ducked under water, as I'd been told to. It was easy to stay down with the weight of the sword in my hands and no clothes to float me up. My bare feet sank into the thick dough of leaf mould on the bottom. I blundered forward with my eyes open, scrambling through the crown of an old drowned tree, slithering in its slimy, rotted bark, stirring up such a tumble of peaty flakes that for a moment I could see nothing at all. And then, close ahead of me, I saw the square gleam of Arthur's belt-buckle, the tower of his armoured torso. I blinked the grit from my eyes and looked up and saw his head and shoulders high above me, out in the air. For a moment our eyes met. His were wide under the iron

27

eyebrows of his helmet. Wide and filled with wonder and something that I did not recognize, because never in my life had anyone been afraid of me before. Then my own long hair swirled up over my head and hid him. My lungs were drum skins, and my heart was pounding on them.

"Do it slowly, gracefully," Myrddin had told me. But when I tore the oilcloth wrapping from the sword it almost floated free, so I had to snatch it down and stuff it between my knees and poke the sword up with my spare hand. I felt it break the surface. My hand, out in the air, felt even colder than the rest of me. The sword was too heavy. I could feel it wobbling. My fingers were so numb that I knew I couldn't keep a grip much longer on the wet hilt. Why didn't he take it from me? Bubbles seeped from the corners of my mouth. Why didn't he take it?

He took it. I snatched my empty hand back into the world of fishes and used it to clinch my nose shut, holding the air inside me until I had swum back under the plunge of the fall, where I could surface again. I gulped down a mix of air and water and scrambled to the rock shelf, not a bit like a fish or an otter or any other water-thing, but frantic and graceless. I was too cold to care if anyone saw me or not as I climbed up into my hiding place. But when I looked back through the falling water, they were all watching Arthur slosh ashore, holding Caliburn high over his head so that it burned with sun-fire. Some waved their arms; some ran about. Their mouths wide open in their beardy faces, shouting things I couldn't hear.

28

I found my clothes and crawled into them, and felt no warmer. I lay down on the damp stone behind the waterfall and hugged myself and shuddered, and my teeth rattled, rattled, rattled.

I must have fallen into a shivering sort of a sleep. When
I woke, the light beyond the waterfall was almost gone,
and someone was pushing towards me along the hidden
track among the ferns.

A voice called softly, "Girl?"

I'd not thought to see Myrddin again. Why would he
even remember me, now I'd served my purpose? Yet
here he was. He must have thought of further uses for
me.

"I'm sorry to leave you cold here, and such a time!
You played your part well. You should hear the stories
they're already telling, our men and the Irishman's. How
the lady beneath the lake gave Arthur a magic sword. . .
That hand rising out of the water. . . If I'd not known
better, even I might have thought. . . For a moment
there, with that sword shining against the shadow of the
rocks. . . Even Arthur believes it! He's used to my tricks,
but he really thinks I conjured up the lady of the waters
for him. . ."

I wondered sleepily how anyone could have been fooled by my dirty, trembling hand, holding up a sword too heavy for it. I did not know then that men see whatever you tell them to see.

He wrapped me up in his cloak and carried me gently back along that precarious path to the shore, where his horse was waiting. Unused to gentleness, I let myself relax. By the time he heaved up me up on to the horse's back I was half asleep again. He rode with me along the forest track, holding me in front of him like baggage. By the time I woke we were passing the burned timbers of my home and starting uphill towards the fort Arthur had captured the night before. The huts that had ringed it were gone. Only their black bones remained, dribbling ghosts of smoke into the twilight. The gate was smashed open. Strangers stood on the walls. The church and the house where the monks had lived were burned and broken too, and the stones were cracked and crumbly from the fire. Dead men lay about. Outside Ban's hall the dragon banner blew, dark against the bat-flicked sky. Shouting came from the open door, and laughter. Myrddin dismounted and boys ran to take his horse. They didn't notice me as he lifted me down. Bundled up as I was, I suppose they thought I was a bag or a blanket.

He carried me in his arms along the side of the hall. It was a long building, with stone walls that tapered at each end and a steep thatch towering above. I could hear sounds like the roaring of wild animals from inside, where Arthur and his men were celebrating their victory and sharing out Ban's treasure and his women.

31

At the end of the building a narrow doorway led into a honeycomb of small rooms. There in the half-dark Myrddin dumped me on soft bedding and left me, tugging a curtain closed across the doorway as he went out. Through a high, tiny window the first stars showed. Firelight shone in around the edges of the curtain. I sat up and looked about me. Straw scrunched inside the plump mattress as I shifted. This must have been Ban's wife's room till last night, and some of her fine things were still in it, though they'd been tumbled and overturned as if a storm-wind had swept through the place.

A puddle of light showed on the floor near the doorway. I crept to it, and found a mirror of polished bronze. My own eyes blinked up at me, like a spirit looking out of a pool. I'd never looked in a mirror before. I saw a flat, round face, a stubby nose. My hair, which was normally the hopeless brown of winter bracken, hung in draggles, black with lake-water. I was a nothing sort of girl, no sooner glimpsed than forgotten. Why would Myrddin care what became of me? Maybe he planned to kill me, seeing as I was the only one who knew the secret of the sword from the water. . .

I started to think of escaping, but just then shadows moved across the spill of light beneath the curtain and I heard a man's voice quite clear outside, saying angrily, "You brought her *here*?"

I threw myself back on to the bed and pretended to be asleep. With eyes half shut I saw the curtain drawn open, then quickly closed again when the two men were inside. The newcomer was the man called Cei. He carried an oil lamp. He knelt beside me, but Myrddin stayed near the doorway.

"So this is the truth behind your trick," Cei said. I saw his ugly face in the lamplight turn to Myrddin.

"A good trick, too," said Myrddin. "Even you might have believed it if you'd not seen the sword and the girl before.

Cei still looked angry. He stared at me as if I was a wild cat that Myrddin had smuggled in. "Myrddin, Arthur himself believed what happened at the river! He is out there now, telling anyone who'll listen about how he saw the lake-woman. If he learns it was this child he'll kill you. If the Irishman finds out. . ."

"Then we must make sure that Arthur and the Irishman don't find out," said Myrddin. "But I must do something with her. I won't smother the girl like a kitten. She served us well."

Cei gave a shrug. I heard his armour creak. He said, "Then let her loose somewhere. She's nothing. Even if she does tell, no one will believe her."

"She deserves better than that," said Myrddin firmly. "After what she did for us? Our lady of the lake? You've seen the way the Irishman and his friends look at Arthur; as if he's half a god himself."

"So what do you mean to do with her?"

"I'll keep her by me. She'll be a useful servant."

"And men will say, 'The trickster Myrddin has taken a girl-child as apprentice,' and they will remember that white hand rising from the lake and the long swirl of hair and sooner or later the brighter of them will put

33

one thing beside another and work out that today's spectacle was just another trick. And you will be finished, and Arthur too, maybe."

"Then what if she was not a girl?" asked Myrddin, and turned to look at me. I don't think he'd been fooled for an instant by my play of being asleep. "What do you say, child? How would you like the great Myrddin to transform you into a boy?"

I sat up and stared at him. I thought he was about to change me by magic, like he had the Bear's father. But that had been just a story, hadn't it?

He came closer and took the lamp from Cei and held it so the light shone on me. "Look. There's nothing girlish about that face. And no shortage of dead men's cast-offs to clothe her in. With her hair shorn and leggings and a tunic on she'd look like just another of the boys who hang round Arthur. She needn't even change her name, much. Gwyn will do."

"What do you say, child?" asked Cei.

Well, what would you say? Better a boy than a frog, or a stone-cold corpse. That's what I reckoned.

"Of course," said Cei, glancing up at Myrddin, "when a few more summers have passed there'll be no mistaking her for anything but a maiden."

Myrddin waved his words away like midges. He liked the thought of pulling this new trick. Outwitting everybody with his foxy cleverness. He said, "When a few more summers have passed, Cei, the story of the sword from the lake will be rooted so deep that nothing will blow it down, and then young Gwyn can become Gwyna again. Or maybe by then your brother will have

34

outrun his luck and led us all into our graves, or your Christian god will have returned in glory and declared his paradise. So don't lurk there fretting like an old woman. Go and find clothes for my boy here."

Cei left, grumbling that he did not care for being ordered off on errands by a godless mountebank, but I guessed he did not mean it. The way he and Myrddin threw insults at each other told me they were old friends. When he was gone Myrddin said, "He's a good man, Cei. Arthur's half-brother. But he hasn't Arthur's ambition. Old Uthr's blood doesn't burn so fierce in his veins. A follower, not a leader."

I didn't say anything. It wasn't my place. I listened to the voice of my heart instead. It was busy asking me what it would be like to be a boy. Would I have to fight? Would I have to ride? Would I have to piss standing up? I was sure I couldn't do any of those things. No one would ever take me for a boy, would they?

But they did. Cei returned with a woollen tunic (oaten-coloured it was, with red borders) and scratchy homespun trousers which hung down to my ankles, bound round my shins with ribbons of soft leather. My shoon were leather, too, the first I'd worn. They made each foot feel like a fish in a trap. Then Myrddin took out a wicked-looking knife and cut my long hair so that it spiked up on end like hedge-pigs' prickles, and when he had brushed the trimmings from my shoulders I went out with him into the hall.

It was so full of noise and smoke and men that I could hardly see anything at first. Arthur's shield-companions were feasting with the Irishman's warriors, celebrating their new alliance in beer and meat. Wherever I looked some man's broad back was in my way, and all I could hear was their great bull voices bellowing. But the men drew aside when they saw Myrddin coming, and soon we got near the big fire where one of Ban's captured cows was roasting. There stood Arthur, with a knife in his hand and grease on his tunic, carving honour-portions for his favourites, slinging their meat to them along with jokes and laughter.

It was the first time I'd seen him without his helm and fish-scale armour on. He was less like a god than I'd expected. A solid, big-boned man with a thick neck and a fleshy face. His cropped, black hair was thinning at the front, and his scalp shone with sweat in the firelight. His eyes were small and dark, set deep, and they had a sleepy look, but they could become sly and thoughtful all of a sudden, or twinkle with merriment like a boy's. I guessed they might narrow easily with rage. A dangerous man, I thought. A bear of a man.

"Myrddin!" he shouted, seeing my master through the smoke and waving the meat-knife at him. "Where have you been? Get out your harp. Give us the story of our victory!"

Myrddin grinned at him, and said, "A good story is like good mead, or good beer. It needs to brew a while."

Men turned to look, and some shouted "Myrddin!" too, and gestured with cups, or hunks of meat, or upraised hands. I watched the way they looked at Myrddin, and I guessed that he was someone they joked about when his back was turned, but someone they feared too. After all, had he not called up the spirits of the waters that very afternoon?

"What's this?" asked Arthur, pointing at me with his knife. "You have a son, and never told us?" Laughter from the men about. Arthur laughed too, and shouted above the noise of the others, "Let's pray he doesn't take after his granddad!"

Myrddin claimed to be the son of a bard, but there was another story, too: that his mother was a nun and his father the Devil himself. I didn't know that then, mind. I thought all their rough laughter was at me. It battered me backwards like a storm of wind till I was pressed against my master's robes.

Myrddin laid a hand on my shoulder. "Gwyn's a kinsman of mine, come to be my servant. He travelled with me from Din Tagyll. Can't I have someone to fetch and carry for me just as you fighters do?"

Arthur's bright eyes were on me, spilling tears of laughter at his own joke. I thought he was sure to see the truth about me, and I felt myself shrink and blush, waiting for him to bellow, "That's no boy." But I was only a servant. Why would Arthur waste a thought on me? After a moment one of the Irishman's captains said in his moss-thick moorland accent "This is Myrddin? The enchanter?"

Arthur turned to him, and I was forgotten. "The greatest enchanter of the island of Britain. Did I not see her face myself when she gave me this sword? The lake-woman. He called her up. Summoned her like I summon a servant-girl. What a face! Beautiful she was! And a swirl of golden hair, like. . ."

Words failed Arthur. He moved his hands around, sketching a swirl of white-gold hair in the smoke. His listeners were entranced. How could anyone doubt his story? Myrddin might lie to them, but Arthur was an open man; like him or not, you could see the truth shining out of his big face. "Naked she was, down under the water, and white as doves' down. . ."

A knot of men closed round him, and round Myrddin who stood beside him. They shut me out. A wall of backs. Thick belts and hanging swords. I turned away, and the talk of other men washed over me, full of unknown names, coarse laughter, talk of dead enemies and stolen women. I pushed among their tree-trunk legs, invisible to them as the dogs that truffled for scraps in the rushes on the floor. Then a hand touched mine, and I turned to find a face on a level with my own.

I started back, stepping on one of the dogs, which yelped and growled low. For a moment I'd thought the boy I was facing was the same one I'd met in the woods, the red-haired, angry one with the fallen horse. But when I looked closer I saw that this one was younger, closer to my own age, and grinning.

"I'm Bedwyr," he said. "My uncle Cei told me you're in need of a friend."

I nodded nervously, glad of Cei's kindness, yet fearful in case this lad could see through my disguise more easily than full-grown men.

"Come on," he said, "I'll take you to the horse-lines."

"Why?"

"So we can see that our master's horses are safe for the night," he replied, still friendly, but looking surprised at how little I knew. "You are new to Myrddin's service, then? But you'll know how to groom a horse. . ."

I nodded again, but I didn't know. I knew that food went in at one end and dung came out the other, but that was all my knowledge of the tribe of horses. "I come from over the water," I told him. "From Armorica, that people call the Lesser Britain. My father was rich, and we had servants to do everything for us. But everyone was killed by Saxon pirates last spring, and now I am just a servant."

I don't know where the words came from. They seemed to have been waiting inside my head for a time when I would need them. I remember wondering if I would be struck dumb or dead or mad for telling such appalling lies. I remember thinking that Bedwyr was sure to know that I was lying. But I survived, and Bedwyr didn't question me. He felt sorry for me, and his eyes filled with tears. He hugged me in a brotherly, bearish way he'd copied from the fighting men and said, "How you must hate the Saxons. I hate them too. I'll kill hundreds and hundreds of them when I'm older, and a warrior like my brother."

He pulled me past a knot of men and pointed through the greasy smoke at where the lad who'd nearly killed me in the woods was stood, laughing too loud at some older man's joke. "That's my brother Medrawt," he said. "Our mother's Cei's sister, Arthur's half-sister. Medrawt will lead a war-band for Arthur one day. Me too, God willing. For now I'm Medrawt's man, in charge of his horse and his weapons. Medrawt fought in the battle last night, and killed a dozen of Ban's men."

I guessed I wasn't the only person who had been spinning tales about himself, but I looked astonished and impressed, which was what Bedwyr seemed to expect of me. Now that I could see them both I realized they weren't that alike, except they had the same red-gold hair and the same pale skin. Bedwyr was stocky and freckled and he had a friendly, laughing face, but

Medrawt had the look of someone who'd grown fast and lately, and still wasn't sure how to move inside his tall new body.

Bedwyr hugged me again. I tried not to shrink from his touch. I wasn't used to being touched, except by my old master's boot or the flat of his wife's hand. "We'll avenge them," Bedwyr said. He thought I was still moping about the poor murdered family I'd just invented. "Next summer," he said, "we'll ride side-by-side and wash our swords in Saxon blood! We'll be brothers, Gwyn."

"Brothers," I agreed, and wondered what he'd do when he found out I was more suited to be a sister. I trailed after him out the big door at the hall's end, trying not to walk too oddly in those odd, uncomfortable clothes. I didn't think I wanted to ride with a war-band, or wash my sword in anybody's blood, but I was glad of Bedwyr all the same.

Outside there was ice on the puddles and the sky was enormous with stars. The sentries talked softly on the walls. Frost made a fuzz of white fur on the helmets and shields piled up outside the hall. We passed a thicket of spears set butt-downward in the earth, where the heads of Lord Ban and his men had been spiked. I suppose it should have grieved me to see my own lord brought down like that, and the houses of his shield-companions roofless and his hall in the hands of Arthur's gang. But I didn't feel anything, except my leggings chafing and my new shoes nipping my toes. I followed my brother Bedwyr downhill in the dark to the horse-lines.

On the whole, I preferred being a boy. The things boys do – even the chores – are better fun than women's work. Even the clothes are easier, once you grow used to them.

There's more to being a boy than wearing trews and cutting off your hair, of course, and don't let anyone tell you different. There's ways of moving and ways of standing still you have to learn. There's a way of looking at things as if you don't care about them, even when you care about them a lot. There are grunts that mean more than words. Boys have all sorts of rules among themselves, just like dogs. Rules about who leads and who follows. They don't talk about them, they just seem to be born knowing these things. I had to pick them up as best I could, by watching Bedwyr and the others.

There were about two score boys in Arthur's band, acting as servants and grooms, learning the ways of war from the older men. They sensed there was something different about me, right from the start, but I think they put it down to me being servant to Myrddin, who wasn't a soldier like their masters but a poet and maybe a magician. That made them too scared to bully me, which was good. And Bedwyr had decided to be my friend, which was better. Bedwyr wasn't the oldest or the strongest of the boys, but the rest looked up to him because he was Arthur's nephew and his brother was already one of Arthur's warriors. So they accepted me for Bedwyr's sake. They mocked me when I was too shy to piss beside them and burrowed off into the bushes on my own, but mockery is all part of how boys talk to each other. None of them ever guessed I was a girl. Myrddin was right. People see what they expect to see, and believe what you tell them to believe.

The war-band waited most of a month at Ban's fort, till the green spears of Easter lilies started jabbing up through the mud at the lane-sides. Then Arthur left the Irishman to hold Ban's lands in his name and rode away, taking with him a dozen hard warriors the Irishman had pledged to Arthur's war-band. As well as those men, the Irishman had promised to pay yearly tribute to Arthur: three ingots of tin from the mines in his hills, three loaves as broad as the distance from his elbow to his wrist, a tub of butter three hand's-breadths across and three deep, and a sow three fingers thick in her hams. It was less than he'd paid when Ban was his overlord. But he was a wily Irishman. As I helped my master mount his horse in the shadow of the gate I heard Arthur grumbling that he'd never see any of that tribute.

Myrddin said calmly, "It doesn't matter. At least the

43

Irishman won't move against you. That leaves you safe to turn your eyes east to the lowlands, where men will pay you taxes in gold, not butter, if they think you can keep trouble from their door."

Arthur looked sideways at him, thoughtful. He wasn't a clever man, Arthur, but he was clever enough to trust my master's judgement.

We rode downhill and turned east on the river-road, and the bare green branches of the woods soon hid the fort and the hill it stood upon. Two standard-bearers went in front, carrying Arthur's banners: the red dragon of Britain, like a long red sock with the foot cut out, and his own flag, a flat square stitched with the symbol of a sword thrust through a stone. Behind them rode Arthur, and his captains, and his sixty warriors, gorgeous in their red cloaks on their ghost-white horses. We boys followed, with pack-horses and spare mounts. By noon I was further from home than I had ever been, yet still we kept going. Britain was bigger than I'd thought.

Days went by. I got used to seeing the world from horseback. I rode a pony called Dewi that had been taken as plunder from Ban's pastures. Arthur had given him to Myrddin, and Myrddin gave him to me. The first time I got up on his back I fell straight off the other side into a dung-puddle and the delighted crowing laughter of the other boys. But I learned fast. Second time I stayed up, swaying, and Bedwyr showed me pityingly how to grip the reins, how to tug Dewi's head round to steer him, how to control him with the pressure of my knees and heels against his hairy flanks.

Strange, it seemed, to think I owned something so big

and beautiful and alive as Dewi. He was white with a hint of grey-blue dapple at his hind-end, strong in the leg and well muscled. I got to love the way his mane tufted, wood-smoke colour, and how he would put his big head down to nuzzle me when I was trying to bridle him. The squared ridge of his long nose, hard as a shield. His steady walk, the quiet power of him. Sat on Dewi's back, I felt like one of those creatures they have in Greece that Myrddin told us of one time; half man, half horse. I'd look down from his saddle at common people who could only stand and watch as Arthur's band went by. Now and then I'd catch sight of some little dirty girl-child with scabs on her knees and think, wondering-like, "That's what I was, till master changed me."

But though I knew it was true, it grew harder and harder to believe it. My new life was so different that the old felt like it had never been at all. Even I was coming to think of myself as a boy.

We rode through a land that was a patchwork of small powers. Strong men had hacked territories for themselves out of the carcass of old Britannia, and then they had had sons, and their sons had had sons, and each son had taken a portion of his father's holding till what remained were countless tiny kingdoms. Some were combined under the heel of a single overlord, Maelwas of Dumnonia in the south, or Cunomorus of Kernyw in the far west, or the kings of Gwent and Calchvynydd northward. But among the smaller kingdoms, and in the borderlands, a man might still forge territory of his own.

The country we travelled that spring wasn't exactly Arthur's, but the men it did belong to weren't strong enough to argue when he came riding up to their holdings with his band behind him and my master Myrddin at his side, shouting out words as fine as banners: "Make way for the *Imperator* Artorius! Make way for the *Dux Bellorum* of the island of Britain! Great Arthur will protect you from the Saxons!"

In truth, the Saxons had been beaten so soundly by old Ambrosius that they'd kept meekly to their lands in the east ever since, and the few small war-bands who came raiding over their border sometimes had never reached this far west. But if anyone dared voice that thought Myrddin would scowl like an owl and say, "Are your memories so short in this country? Don't you remember the terrors of the Saxons' war? The houses and churches on fire? Women and children snatched away as slaves? Bodies strewn in the streets, red with blood, as if they'd been crushed in a wine-press? It was men like Arthur who protected us then. And it's Arthur who will protect us again, when the Saxons return. Why, it's only the fear of Arthur that keeps them from swarming west and murdering you all! What do you think will happen to your homes and your children if you don't give Arthur the little he asks, to keep his brave fighters fed and clothed and mounted?"

I think Myrddin really believed what he said about those Saxons. You could see his fear for Britain's future in his eyes when he spoke of them. You could hear it in his voice. But I don't know what Arthur thought. Sometimes it seemed to me those Saxons were just a threat he used to make men part with their belongings. He would sit on his white horse while my master made his earnest speeches, and the people would look at him, and at his gang behind him, and go scurrying to bring him tribute and offer us shelter in their houses and food for ourselves and our hungry horses.

Once we ran up against a rival war-band, led by another man who also called himself *Dux Bellorum*, and there was a battle at a ford. I didn't see it, for I was back with the wagons. I heard the noise of it roaring and crashing like a far-off storm, and once the shrill screaming of a wounded horse. I couldn't understand what it was at first, but Bedwyr tensed like a hound that hears the hunt go by. When we crossed that ford later there were dead men in the water either side, leaking long ribbons of blood downstream.

Medrawt killed a man in that fight. It filled him with a shaky sort of laughter. He came and hugged Bedwyr and promised him a share of the stuff he'd taken from his dead enemy. I'd never seen him show kindness to his younger brother before. He was so conscious of being a man that he barely let himself look at us mere boys, except when he was barking at Bedwyr to clean his gear or tend to his horse or find him something more to eat. But Bedwyr loved him, and when I watched them laughing together I could see why.

"This is my friend Gwyn," said Bedwyr, tugging Medrawt towards me. "Gwyn's Myrddin's man. We're brothers in arms."

"Gwyn," said Medrawt vaguely, looking me up and down. Just for a moment I saw a little shadow of confusion pass across his face, as if he recognized me but could not remember why. Then it was gone. I was just a boy, and his brother's friend, and his blooding had put him in such a good temper that he threw me an iron bracelet he'd taken from the dead man's wrist.

Arthur hung the head of the rival *dux* from his saddle-girth till the stink and the flies grew too much. Then he lobbed it into a pool beside the road. I don't think he meant anything by it, except to be rid of the thing, but it pleased the war-band. They took it for a tribute to the old gods.

I'd learned, by then, the ways of all the different gods and spirits who watched over Arthur's band. Outwardly, most of the men were Christians, and their shields carried that red ☧ to show it. Crosses and tin medallions with Christ's alpha and omega sign jangled round their necks, in the hope that God would notice, and turn away the blades of enemies in battle. Some were earnest. Cei prayed every night, and looked sour and disapproving when Arthur threw that head into the water. But most were wary of the old gods too. You can't live in this land of mists and rivers and not know they're there: the lake-lady in her waters, the small gods of trees and stones. The new god has hushed and shrunk them, but he can't quite drive them away. And some of the band, like red-haired Gwri and his men from the wild uplands of Gwynedd, scoffed at Christ, who seemed weak and womanish compared to their own god, Nudd, the hunter.

And Myrddin? He had no gods. His head was full of

tales of magic and wonders, but in his heart he didn't believe any of them. He told me once, "There are no gods, Gwyn. No ghosts, no spirits. Nothing but our own fears and hopes. Gods are tales for children. They're tricks we play upon ourselves, to make it seem there's some sense in our lives."

"But you must believe in something," I told him, staring at all the charms and talismans that hung round his neck.

He laughed. "These? They're just for show. Simple people see them, and think I'm closer to the gods than other men. Men I meet on the road are afraid to rob me. But believe? I suppose some hand must have set this world moving. But I don't believe any god is watching over me, ready to help me if I make the right sacrifices and stamp me flat if I don't. It's a freedom, not believing. It gives me the power to look clear and hard at what other men believe, and use it to steer them."

Well, I'd seen the truth of that, hadn't I? But I didn't think it'd suit me, that sort of freedom. It seemed to me that going through the world without a god would be like going through midwinter snow without a cloak. I went on saying my prayers to Christ and his saints, and if they didn't answer them I'd sometimes try the old gods, too. I kept it to myself, though. It pleased my master to think he'd turned me to his own cold way of thinking.

"And Arthur?" I wondered once. "What does he believe?"

"Arthur's different. He believes in gods, both the old and the new. He welcomes their help when it comes. But he won't grovel for it. He thinks he's their equal, and better than most of them."

The roads led us at last to the old legion fortress that was Arthur's base. A rampart high as the highest tree, and a wall upon the rampart, and a palisade upon the wall, and a tall gate with watchtowers. It held me spellbound as we rode up to it. How could men have built anything so *big*?

Inside the walls were scores of huts and some bigger, boat-shaped buildings hunched around a feast-hall. A smell of cooking fires, and animals wandering about the houses. Some of the men had women and families there. Cei's wife was a squat, cheerful, barrel-shaped woman, who had given him a daughter, Celemon. It was strange to see his hard face soften as he picked the girl up and swung her round him. Arthur had a wife, too: Cunaide, red-haired and beautiful as summer. I remember staring at all the gold she wore. She didn't look so very much older than me.

I expected my master would have a wife, or a woman, or at least a home, but he had nothing. While we stayed there we slept as we had slept on the road, bundled up in blankets at Arthur's fireside. Turned out Myrddin owned nothing but the things he carried bagged on the saddles of his horse and my pony. "I like to travel lightly through the world," he told me, when he saw my disappointment. "If you have nothing, no man can take it away from you."

There we left the war-band for a time and rode on alone, stopping at villages and hill-top halls. Without Arthur's army my master was able to travel easily into the territory of other lords, for a harper is welcome everywhere. It was that time of spring they call Blackthorn Winter, when blossom lies white on the hedge-banks like fresh snow. Sunlight dappled us. Over our heads the trees were putting on new leaves of fresh, shy green.

We travelled sometimes on old Roman roads which looked like God had made them, for what mortal could build roads that wide and straight? The going was easy there despite the weeds and bushes that had grown up between the slabs of stone. Now and then we went into some old town where men still tried to act like Roman citizens, despite the trees that were sprouting in their streets and the tiles that took flight from their roofs each time the wind blew. And each night Myrddin unwrapped his harp and told his tales of Arthur.

He wasn't much of a harper. It wasn't much of a harp, to be fair. I got to know it well, for a part of my duties was tightening its strings and carving new pegs for it, and oiling the wooden frame, and making sure it was tightly wrapped in lambskin and oiled linen when we went a-travelling. But however well I wrapped it, the damp of the road crept in somewhere, and it was a warped, battered, crack-voiced old thing. The sounds Myrddin plucked from it weren't beautiful, nor meant to be. They were just a stream of sound for him to set his words afloat on.

And what words! To people who had never left the valleys they were born in, Myrddin brought news of the wide world, and tales of the wonders of Britain. There was a lake in Brechiniog where Arthur had seen islands that floated on the water, and never rested twice in the same place. In the tin hills stood a stone which turned at dawn to warm each face in the rising sun, till Arthur hugged it in his arms so tight it couldn't move, and told him its secrets so he'd let it go. Arthur had stolen from the King of Ireland a magic cauldron which was never empty, and always full of what you wanted most to eat.

It was funny to see the way people bathed in his stories, believing every word. Funnier still when he told them of the lake, and the hand that had reached up out of it to offer Arthur his wonderful sword. And funniest of all was the feeling I had that even if I'd told them the truth, they would all have believed Myrddin's account over my own. "Everyone loves a story," he always said. And whatever Arthur did, Myrddin could turn it into a story so simple and clean that everyone would want to hear it, and hold it in their hearts, and take it out from time to time to polish it and see it shine, and pass it on to their friends and children.

"There's nothing a man can do that can't be turned into a tale," he used to tell me, as we rode from one hall to the next through the hills of summer. "Arthur can do nothing so bad that I can't spin it into gold, and use it to make him more famous and more feared. If the tales are good enough even the poor man who goes hungry from paying Arthur taxes will love him. I am the story-spinning physician who keeps his reputation in good health."

The stories kept changing, too, but that didn't seem to matter. Some people knew a different tale about a sword. They'd seen the symbol stitched upon the war-band's battle-flag, and a story had grown up about a sword wedged in a stone, and how Arthur had freed it to prove that he was Uthr's son, and heir to old Ambrosius. "Ah, that!" said Myrddin, when someone reminded him of it one night in a hall hard by the Usk. "That sword was broken, in Arthur's fight with the giant of Bannog, so the lake-woman gave him a new one, see? What, have you not heard about the fight at Bannog?" And he was away, spinning a tale of giants so rich and fierce that all his listeners forgot they'd never heard before about the sword-from-the-stone being broken, and Arthur needing a new one.

It started to seem that there were two Arthurs: the hard man who had burned my home, and another one who lived in Myrddin's stories and spent his time hunting magical stags and fighting giants and brigands.

I liked the Arthur of the stories better, but some of his bravery and mystery rubbed off on the real man, so that when we came back to Arthur's place in the harvest and I saw him again, I could not help but think of the time he had captured that glass castle in the Irish Sea, or sliced the Black Witch into two halves, like two tubs.

Myrddin said he was not an enchanter, but he worked magic all right. He turned me into a boy, and he turned Arthur into a hero.

XI

Here's a story Myrddin told that year, while we sat around the hall-fires, me and Bedwyr reunited, and the other boys and men of Arthur's band. He'd been talking to the Irishman's kin, and he'd got from them a tale their grandfathers had brought across the sea from Leinster. It was all about some old Irish god, but Myrddin took the god out and put Arthur in his place and when he told it by the harvest fire even the Irishmen listened rapt, as if they'd never heard of it before.

One Christmas, Myrddin said, Arthur gave a feast here in this very hall for his loyal companions. And as they feasted, the big door there blew open, and in roared the wild west wind, all filled with snow, and with the snow a giant dressed in green. Green cloak, green tunic, green boots, green leggings, and an armour-coat of long green scales like laurel leaves. A green sword at his side, green hair, green beard, teeth green as summer acorns in his green head. "Where's the governor of this gang?" says he, looking round (and I dare say his voice was as green as the rest of him). And when Arthur stands up he says, "I've heard of your bravery, Arthur. The courage of your shield-companions is known all across the world. Even the emperor in Rome has heard of them, and quakes at night with the fear that they might come and pluck his rotten empire like an apple." (Cheers, of course, at this bit.) "Well," says the green man (only the way that Myrddin has him say it makes his listeners stop cheering and laughing and lean towards him big-eyed, waiting). "Well, I'm here to test your famous courage."

And he takes out a great axe, its haft green with moss, its blade shining that silver-green of a spring lake reflecting new birch leaves. He lays it on the flagstones by the fire. *Chink.* He gazes round at the guests with his green eyes. "Any one of you," he says, "may strike my head off. Here, I'll make it easy for you. . ." And he goes down on one knee and bows his head, and pulls his green hair aside to bare his green neck.

Up jumps Medrawt, ever eager to show his strength and courage. "I'll meet that challenge!" he shouts. "I'll cut off your old green head with such a blow it will fly out of that door you've so rudely left open and all the way back across the sea to Ireland!" And he takes his stance beside the kneeling green man, and lifts up the axe, all sharp and shiny in the firelight.

"Just one condition," says our green friend, before the blade comes down. "If you cut off my head today, you'll have to let me cut off yours tomorrow. That's fair."

Medrawt hesitates. (The listeners chuckle, imagining the look on the young man's face.) He senses a trick. In tales like this there's always a trick, and nothing is ever what it seems. The gold you bring back from the otherworld turns overnight into dry leaves. The pretty lady is an old hag in disguise. Medrawt lowers his sword. His face is almost as green as the stranger's. (Listening to the tale, he laughs uncomfortably, and accepts the friendly blows and laughter of his comrades. He's pleased he has a part in the story, but he wishes it had been a braver one.)

Now up steps Arthur, and the listeners go quiet again. They know the real business of the story is beginning. "I won't let my men face dangers I won't meet myself," says the Arthur in the story. And he takes the axe from Medrawt and, quick as lightning, strikes off the green man's head. *Thump.* It rolls across the floor. A spatter of green blood comes out of the severed neck, sticky as sap.

Then the headless body stirs. It stretches, and rises to its feet. The guests gasp and stare in horror. (And Myrddin's listeners gasp and stare along with them.) The body walks to where the head lies and picks it up. The head's green eyes look about it. The green mouth grins. "I'll be back tomorrow night to take my turn," says the head. The body takes up the axe in its other hand, and the green man strides out of the hall and vanishes into the snowy, midwinter dark.

A long day of worry passes. Next night, the gates and doors are barred, and a guard is set all around the fort. But sharp at midnight the green man appears in Arthur's hall, as whole and sound as when we first saw him. Arthur's men rage and his women wail and weep, but Arthur stands up, brave to the end, and says, "I've made my bargain, and I'll keep it" (or something such – Myrddin put it better, and included a lot of stuff about how much Arthur cares for his men, and how he'll miss them). Then he kneels down, and bares his neck, and the green man raises his axe.

Crash! The blade smashes a flagstone in half. (That one there, between your feet, Sagranus.) Arthur is unharmed. He springs up, whole. The green man kneels to him. "Artorius Magnus," he says, "you're as brave as they say. I'll go back to my own country and tell them of your courage, champion of Britain."

In the silence as the story ends, I look about. I see their faces, and I feel the same look on my own. An enchanted look. It's not that we believe the story. We all know no green man really came here, or walked around with his head held in his hand. But we feel we've heard a kind of truth. Even Arthur feels it, lounging in his big chair with Cunaide at his side and his hound Cabal at his feet. For a moment, the real Arthur and the story Arthur are one and the same, and we know that we are all part of the story, all of us.

A year has passed. It's my second summer as a boy. I've almost forgotten that I ever was a girl. The oak-tops in the cleaves below the fort are a green sea, stirring and shushing in the wind, and the hills beyond them reach away in hazy veils of green and blue to the real sea, which is a distant silvering along the joining place of world and sky. I've never seen that real sea close, but I'm about to. Arthur is taking a band of men south to gather taxes from fat farmers. And Myrddin is to go with him, and so am I.

I remember making the horses ready, the work of loading the pack-ponies, hanging their saddles with bags which we hoped would be full of gold when we came home again. I remember stopping nights at thick-walled halls where sulky headmen glowered at us as they grudgingly handed Arthur his tribute. The sky was blue, and the sun was golden, and the roadsides bloomed with meadowsweet and foxgloves. People in the farmsteads said Arthur had brought the summer with him, and that pleased him, though they'd have said the same to any great man who rode by with a gang of warriors behind him.

And I remember a villa in the hills, a Roman-ish place, with slaves to run it still, and plump red cattle grazing the pastureland. Gorse popping in the sunshine as we rode to it along a white track, dust clouding from our horses' hooves like smoke, and a hawk pinned on the sky high up. The owner of the place looked even sulkier than the rest when Myrddin told him that great Arthur was guarding this land against the Saxons. He said this was the territory of Maelwas, King of Dumnonia, and he had already paid his tribute.

"If this is Maelwas's land, where is he?" asked Arthur, smiling, looking puzzled. The men behind him laughed. Maelwas was a joke to them, the old king of a land too big for him. Arthur rode on their laugher, laughing himself as he went on, "I don't see Maelwas hereabout. We crossed into his country days since, and never a welcome have we had. I think Maelwas's lands are shrinking like the last patch of hair on an old man's head. I reckon you need someone else to guard you against those Saxons."

The landowner looked grim, and said he had already paid tribute.

"Then you'll pay it again," said Arthur, and he jumped down off his horse and walked past Myrddin and knocked the man down. He didn't draw his sword, just kept kicking and stamping until the man's face was one soft mask of blood and his teeth were scattered all about in the dry grass, yellow as gorse-flowers.

The man's servants and family looked on without

speaking or trying to help. Children snuggled into their mothers' skirts. When Arthur was finished some slaves came forward to drag their master away. "You see what can happen?" Arthur asked the rest, wiping blood-spatter off his face with a corner of his cloak. "You never know when a war-band might ride up here to burn your huts and take your cattle and your women and your gold. You need a strong friend to keep trouble at bay."

And Bedwyr and me going round with the bags while he spoke, and the servants running indoors to fetch gold coins and pewter dishes and a set of silver spoons with the symbols of Christ on the handles, and that hawk still circling high up.

After that Arthur pointed us east towards a rich church he planned to plunder. But at a ford along the road we met a band of men sent out by Maelwas, who had heard of our coming at last. Insults and arrows went to and fro across the water all through a sweltering day, but it was too hot to fight, and come the sundown we drew back into the woods on our side of the river, and the Dumnonii drew back into theirs. "Arthur doesn't need a fight with Maelwas," Myrddin said. "He has made the old man notice him. That's a start."

So we turned downriver to the sea, where there was a place that had been held by one of Arthur's old shield-companions once, a man called Peredur Long-Knife. He was ten years dead, this Long-Knife, and all his sons with him, but his widow was supposed to hold his lands still, and Myrddin reckoned she'd pay well for Arthur's protection.

We came at evening down a long combe, following aimless sheep-tracks through bracken and bilberries and the scratchy, purple ling, and there was the sea, all shiny pewter and as wide as the world. I'd thought it would be smooth and clear, like a great pond, but it was dark and rough and hummocked, heaving up in white-topped hills. I had to hide my surprise, for Bedwyr and the other boys thought I'd been across it in a boat when I came from Armorica to be my master's servant. I couldn't see how anybody could venture out on that restless greyness in a boat. I couldn't stop glancing at it, for fear it would rise up when I wasn't looking and drown the land. I didn't trust that sea one bit.

We rode down to the beach, and our horses snorted and jerked up their heads at the salt air. The sky was a wet slate, scratched all across by the hard voices of the gulls. There was a smell of rot from the tideline, and a village of round huts straggling up to a stronghold on a cliff-top. Door-curtains flapped in the damp air, and a few fishermen's children ran to hide among the drying nets as we rode by.

"Looks poor," said Arthur grumpily, as we came up the track to the stone-walled hall. "This was a wasted ride."

"Maybe they'll spare men, at least," Myrddin replied.

"Looking for more men from this place will be like groping for coins in an empty purse."

Around the rampart of the hall ran a gap-toothed palisade, with dead gulls strung up on it, perhaps in an effort to scare off their friends, who kept screaming overhead, daubing the place with white dazzles of shit. Inside the fence a rash of huts had sprouted. A chapel hunched low in the hall's lee with its back to the weather. A pack of men with half-shaved heads and flapping, crow-black robes spilled out of it to stare as our horses came through the unguarded gate, clip-clopping on the warped boards that made a roadway there. The tallest barred our way. Thistledown hair, he had, and fierce eyes. His robes stuttered round his skinny limbs, cloth so thin you could see his white flesh through the weave. His nose was red, though, and his words ran together, like a man who liked his wine. He held up his shaky hands in front of Arthur's horse.

"Turn back!" he shouted. "You are men of the sword, and the sword will devour you! Your hands are red with blood! I, Saint Porroc, command you in the name of the Lord of the Seven Heavens, turn back and leave this place!"

The sea-wind took his words and whisked them over the wall and away through the dry dunes and the shivering sea-cabbage. But not before we'd had time to hear them. All down the line of horsemen, riders reached for their swords. No man told Arthur to turn back. Not if he wanted to keep his head on his shoulders.

"But he's a saint!" I said, nervous.

"A self-appointed saint." Myrddin gave a soft, scornful laugh. "Britain teems with them."

Arthur, up at the head of the column, leaned on his horse's neck and grinned. "And does the lady of the place hire you and these other beggars to be her guards?"

(I looked at the hall. In the doorway, like a ghost, a woman stood watching us.)

"God guards this place!" the old man in the roadway bellowed. "And I am God's servant. You'll find no warriors here. No swords, no weapons. Nothing but the love of God."

I winced, expecting any moment to see Caliburn flash from its sheath and cut the thin, straining stalk of his neck. But Arthur's moods were always hard to guess. He just laughed.

"Out of my way, old man," he said.

A kind of mumbling howl went up from the black huddle of monks. Saint Porroc shouted shrilly, "If you kill me, God will whisk me up to Paradise, but you will whirl and scorch for ever in the fires of Hell!" But he didn't look happy at the prospect of martyrdom. He let slip a strangled shriek when Arthur urged his horse forward, and let it push him awkwardly aside. He stumbled and sat down hard in the gritty sand, where he held up his arms and started shouting Latin. His followers all copied him and their psalms and spittle blew past us on the salt gale as we went on our way up to the hall and dismounted outside.

Peredur Long-Knife's widow was a small woman with frightened eyes. A big driftwood cross hung round her neck on a rough cord which had made red weals in her flesh. Everything else about her was a shade of grey, as if the tears she'd shed for her lord and all his sons had washed the colour out of her. But she knelt before Arthur, and kissed the hem of his cloak, which I think pleased him after the welcome we'd had in the hills.

"I have no gold to offer you, and no warriors," she whispered. "This is a place of women. All the men went to the wars, and God did not see fit to send any of them home again. I have no sons now, only my daughter. Saint Porroc guards us. He has been kind enough to build his hermitage here upon my land. It is his prayers that protect us from sea-raiders and horse-thieves."

Arthur cast his eye over the daughter, who stood further back, staring at us from behind a fence of waiting-women. She was pretty enough, but only a child, no older than me. His gaze slid off her like water off metal and went roving among her older, prettier companions.

"We'll take no gold from you," he said, talking to the lady of the place, but with his eyes on one of the serving women. "A bed for the night, and straw for our horses, and a day's hunting. That's all we ask of Peredur Long-Knife's widow."

Peredur Long-Knife's widow looked past him to her saint, as if expecting help. None came. She seemed to gather herself, leaning for a moment against the doorpost while she struggled to recollect the right words and ways for greeting war-lords. With a watery effort at a smile she said, "You are welcome, my lord Arthur."

That night she served a feast for us. Killed and roasted a pig she probably couldn't spare (though I noticed that Saint Porroc's monks had pigs a-plenty in pens behind the little chapel). She was so frightened of Arthur that just looking at him seemed to hurt her. Arthur could have helped himself to her place without a thought, and everybody in the hall knew it; you could see it in the wary, watchful looks they gave him through the smoke. The monks outside knew too. When I slipped out to piss I saw a dozen of them standing outside their hump-backed huts, eyes on the hall. They knew they and their angry saint would be booted out if Arthur took the place.

But Arthur had no use for this drab, sandy holding, so far from his other lands. Anyway, he was in a giving mood. He ate the stringy pig and called it good, and drank Peredur Long-Knife's memory in gritty, vinegarish wine. He nodded approval when the widow's blushing daughter picked out a tentative, tuneless air upon her harp. He grabbed the serving girl who'd snagged his fancy and sat her on his lap and shouted to my master for a story.

So Myrddin, who'd seen the hunting-spears being sharpened ready for tomorrow's sport, told us the tale of another hunt that Arthur had ridden out on, and somehow the real hunt merged into a magical hunt where Arthur and his companions took the places of the old heroes, and the boar they were hunting became Twrch Trwyth, the great boar of the island of Britain, and they chased him deeper and deeper into dark old thickets of story until Arthur speared him and snatched from between his two ears the magic comb.

And we slept by the fire that night, wrapped in our cloaks, dreaming of riding through ancient woods, with the white tail of Twrch Trwyth flashing ahead of us and the spears in our right hands so sharp we heard the air sing as the blades sliced it.

I woke to a booming, sunlit morning. The doors of the hall were open, and a sea-wind was whisking up the ashes in the fireplace. The light kept dimming suddenly as a cloud masked the sun and bursting out again, golden, world-filling. Even the gulls sounded happier.

The men and boys of Arthur's band were waking up around me, scrambling to their feet and shaking the wine-fog from their heads. Bedwyr, all tousle-haired, tugged me away to ready our masters' horses for the hunt. He was itchy with excitement at the day ahead. "A hunt's not like war," he said earnestly. "In a hunt we're the equal of the grown men. Speed and wits may take the quarry, where weight and strength mean nothing. I hunted often in my father's lands when I was younger."

I nodded, trying not to show how I really felt about the idea of riding our wiry little ponies fast across those hummocky, tussocked cliff-tops. I tried to look as if I had hunted before, too; as if I'd spent my summers chasing the boar Twrch Trwyth instead of dipping for minnows in the withy-ponds. And when I thought about the tales Myrddin had spun for us in the firelight I found it wasn't so hard, after all, to imagine myself a great hunter. You could see the same thing in Bedwyr's face, and in the faces of the other men as they got ready, shouting for spears and calling dogs to heel. The spell of the story was still at work in us, and were we all eager to prove what heroes we were.

My master, stepping out blinking into the sunlight, tipped cold water on my imaginings. "You'll stay here with me, Gwyn."

"But your horse is ready, master," I said.

"Unready her, then," snapped Myrddin. "Do you really think I would risk my neck galloping through those tangle-woods? I leave hunting to the horsemen. Besides, they say that dragon's teeth and giant's bones may be found along this shore, and I mean to look for some. Fetch a bag, and come with me."

I blushed hotly, half relieved and half ashamed at being kept from the hunt. Other boys laughed as I tramped back to the hall. One of the men – Owain, maybe – called out, "Let the boy come, Myrddin," but of course my master would not relent. I knew what he was frightened of. Injuries are common on the hunting field. What if I fell, and someone tried to tend me, and discovered what I really was?

I could hear the horns sounding as I climbed the stairs to the chamber where Myrddin had been quartered (no blanket by the hearth for Arthur's enchanter). As I rummaged through his things for the old sack he wanted I could hear the clatter of the departing horses. I felt as if they were taking something of mine away with them as they rode along the cliff-road, through the gorse.

Coming back down I found no sign of my master. Started for the beach already, one of the women told me. I went round the hall's corner and saw Peredur Long-Knife's daughter stood alone in a little sad garden which someone had planted in the lee of the wall: half a dozen salt-wizened shrubs, ringed by a fence of white driftwood shards like the ribs of drowned sailors stuck upright in the sandy soil.

I could have gone by, but something drew me to her. I think I sensed that she was like me somehow. Set apart from other people. I wanted to know her, so I went towards her. She still didn't notice me. She was shading her face with one hand while she stared at the distant shapes of the huntsmen riding up the green cliff-side into the furze.

"Not seen their like?" I asked. I remembered how she'd stared and stared at them, the night before.

She looked round, startled to find me there, then smiling. "Never! They're so shiny! So beautiful! Is Arthur as brave as they say? He looks brave! When I saw you all coming up the hill yesterday I thought it was God's own angels come down to earth. . ."

"But weren't your father and brothers fighting men?"

"Were they? Were they? I never knew them, see. I never thought to ask. My mother doesn't talk of them. They died before I was born. There used to be a few old men with spears to guard us against sea-raiders, when I was little. But when Saint Porroc came he made my mother send them away, and burn the spears. He said God would guard us." Her eyes couldn't settle on me; they kept being dragged back to the cliff-top, and the far-off brightness of the riders' cloaks. "Saint Porroc says that men like Arthur are outcasts of God, and have no power over him. But Arthur just pushed him aside! I never saw anyone dare disobey the saint before."

I'd forgotten about Saint Porroc and his monks. They'd not seen fit to join us in the hall the night before, and by the time I woke they'd been hidden away in the chapel, which buzzed like a bee-skep with their angry-sounding prayers.

"Who is he, this Porroc?" I asked.

The girl looked shocked. "*Saint* Porroc!" she said

earnestly. "He is a great man of God. He came here two summers back, with his disciples. We are so blessed that he chose our hall! He is very close to God, you see. He punishes his body in all manner of ways to keep himself godly. He flays himself with brambles, and he never lies down on a bed to sleep but rests himself upon a heap of fresh-cut nettles."

"You've seen him do that?"

"No, no. But I heard him tell my mother."

I grinned. I'd already guessed, see, what kind of man this saint was. The Myrddin kind. Only difference was, he spun stories about himself, not Arthur.

"He has nothing," said the girl. "He urges my mother to be like him, so that she can come to God. He had her give away all our fine things, all her gold and silver that was left from Father's time, and all the best wine from our cellars."

"Who'd she give them to?"

She frowned, as if she'd never thought about that. "I don't know. Saint Porroc and his monks took them. He said they'd use them for the glory of God."

I squinted along the side of the hall. Now that the hunters were gone, Saint Porroc's monks were setting off to their work in the miserable straggle of fields below the rampart.

"Saint Porroc doesn't go with them?"

"He's too busy at his prayers."

"Ever been inside that church of his?"

"Oh no! Saint Porroc would not permit it! He talks to God and angels there!"

I thought about the wine-jars I'd seen in the ditch

70

behind the chapel. I could guess what manner of angels Porroc chatted to, while his hangers-on were weeding their bean-rows.

"Let's look," I said.

"What?" The girl took a step backwards, so as not to be caught by the thunderbolt that must surely strike me down. Looked up nervously at the sky, but it stayed blue. I could see the wickedness of what I'd suggested excited her. Living the way she did, all holy and prim in this hard-scrat place, the thought of wickedness was as sweet to her as honey. But she said, "Oh, you mustn't, no, no. . ."

I didn't listen. My year as a boy had primed me for mischief. My time with Myrddin had taught me enough that I wasn't scared of men like Porroc. If Myrddin won't let me go to the hunt, I thought, I'll have a hunt of my own, and flush out Porroc's secrets. I took my new friend by her hand. "What's your name?"

She hesitated a moment, and colour came to her cheeks, as if she was ashamed. "Peri," she said.

"Well, Peri," I promised, "we're going to give the Blessed Saint Porroc an angel to talk to."

Peri had to act the angel, I decided. Angels have long hair, don't they? And they're tall, like she was, and graceful. Anyway, I wasn't stripping off in front of her. Like Saint Porroc, I had secrets to keep.

"But he'll know me," she said, when I explained what we were going to do.

"He's half blind," I told her, remembering the way Porroc had screwed up his eyes to peer at us the day before. "Anyway, he'll not see your face. You'll have the sun at your back. The glory of God will shine about you."

"Don't talk about God that way! Oh, we shouldn't do this. . ."

She was as scared as I'd been the day Myrddin made me play the part of the lake-woman. Her fright made me feel braver. I snatched the dress she'd taken off and stuffed it into Myrddin's bag before she could change her mind. Slung the bag across my shoulders. Under her dress Peri wore a long, sleeveless, white shift. I untied her plait so her hair tumbled down. Dark, springy hair, gingery where the sunlight touched its edges. Hair I'd have envied, if I'd been still a girl. There was nothing else girlish about her. Her chest, under that white shift, was flat as a slate. Her jaw had a boyish squareness to it, too. But that fitted our purpose. Angels aren't girls.

They have wings, though. I fetched one of the gulls that hung along the rampart-fence and took its big white wings off with my knife. It didn't take me long to lash them to my belt and loop it round under Peri's arms, hiding it under her shift at the front. The wings were skewed, and at the back the belt and all the cordage showed, but from the front, with those white feathery points poking up over her shoulders, she looked. . . Well, angelic.

We went down to the church, me keeping watch for passers-by, Peri hugging herself against the chill of the wind. She was giggling nervously with the thrill of it. This was the most exciting thing that had ever happened to her, I suppose. I warned her to keep quiet. "Angels don't giggle," I said.

"How do you know?"

"The sort of angels Saint Porroc thinks about don't giggle, and that's the sort we've got to give him. Remember to keep quiet. He'll know your voice. He's never heard mine."

Saint Porroc had built his church without windows, but high on the wall above the door there was a hole to let smoke out and the light in. I scrambled up the roof and hung over the edge of the thatch to peer through it.

Upside-down, I saw the chapel's dim innards. An altar, with a swag of reddish cloth hung up behind it, and Porroc down on his knees in front of it.

That surprised me. I'd thought him a play-actor, pure and simple. Thought to find him sitting in a soft chair, sipping wine. But maybe there was some truth in his religion after all. Maybe he really did think he was God's servant. Maybe he'd been honest once, before he understood what a living he could make with his prayers and prostrations.

For a moment then I felt the huge peril of what we were doing. What if God was looking down on me, and didn't see the joke? But I couldn't go back now without looking a fool in front of Peri, and I didn't want that. I remembered what Myrddin had said. Porroc was a charlatan. God wouldn't care what tricks we played on him.

Down below me, my pretend angel stood outside the door, her long shadow stretching out from her bare feet. Her worried eyes upturned to mine. I nodded, and made faces at her till she gathered up her wits and nerve and shoved the door open, like we'd agreed.

Saint Porroc turned from his praying, and stuffed a cup of wine behind him somewhere. There was a scowl on his face as he swung round, but it dropped off him quick enough as the light from the open doorway hit his face.

What did he see? A dazzle of sunlight, and in the heart of it a white robe, and the light shining through two spurts of white feathers. His face went empty and amazed. He tried to shade his eyes. And I leaned close to my spy-hole and shouted through my cupped hands, "Porroc!"

74

There was a good echo in that high-roofed place. His name seemed to come at him from all around. He went down on his face, whimpering.

"God's lost his patience with you, Porroc!" I yelled. Not very angelic, but the best words I could find, and they seemed to work. Porroc writhed, a long black worm trying to burrow into the flagstone floor. "You love wine more than prayers," I told him, "and you rob the poor widow who gives you shelter!"

All that shouting was making me want to cough. I paused, swallowing, while Porroc wailed apologies at the floor.

"Go from here, Porroc!" I yelled. "Punish your body! Go to the cold sea and clean yourself!"

I looked down at Peri and hissed for her to move aside. She left the doorway and scrambled nimbly round the corner of the church. She'd barely made it when Saint Porroc shot out through the open door, like God's own boot had kicked him up the arse. Wailing, he ran through the rampart gate and away down the board-road towards the beach, and his monks in their fields left their work and hurried after him.

I slid down the thatch and flumped on the ground next to Peri. Coughing and laughing. Peri looked as if she still half expected God's finger to reach down and rub us into the dirt like two gnats.

"Come on," I said, when my cough had gone. "He's out of our way. Let's see what he hides in that hole of his."

Peri shook her head. Her bravery was all used up. She was fumbling with the belt, trying to drag off her heretical wings.

75

"Keep watch, then," I ordered, and ran into the dark of the church. Black as a pit, it was, after that sunlight outside. No wonder poor old Porroc had been dazzled when the door burst open. His wine-cup rolled across the floor, and the curtain behind the altar flapped in the breeze. I lifted a corner and looked behind it. And there, of course, among the cobwebs, I found all the things he had persuaded Peri's mother to part with in the interests of her immortal soul. Fine gold dishes, and bags that had a money-full look about them, and gold neck-rings and other jewellery in a well-made casket, and a whole crowd of those tall Gaulish wine jars in a corner, leaning together like drunks.

I laughed at my own cleverness, and went back outside. Peri had managed to get the gull-wings off, but she was looking at her shift in dismay, and wouldn't even listen to my story about Porroc's treasure. There'd been some blood left in the wings, and somehow in working herself free of them she'd smeared some across the breast of her white shift.

"The servants will see," she cried. "They'll tell my mother! Oh, what am I to do?"

"Take it off," I ordered.

She seemed fearful. "Look away."

I turned my back on her, and busied myself tugging her bundled-up dress out of the bag I carried. Behind me I heard her hiss at the cold as she pulled the stained shift over her head. "My mother said I must never let anyone see me unclothed," she said.

What was it made me look round? Just mischief, maybe. Just a desire to go against whatever Peri's godly mother said. Anyway, I glanced over my shoulder, and caught sight of her in her nakedness. Only a flash, like something glimpsed by lightning. But enough. It drove all thoughts of Saint Porroc and his plunder from my head and blew them away on the wind.

I'd known all along there was something strange about her. I'd not known what it was that kept pulling my eyes back to her face, to the line of her jaw and the set of her features. But I saw it now, and once I had, I couldn't imagine how I'd been so stupid not to see it sooner.

Peri wasn't a girl at all.

I looked away quick, before Peri caught me peeking, and held the dress out behind me with one hand. When I turned, she'd pulled it on. It looked all wrong on her, now I knew her secret. *His* secret.

"Why do you dress like that?" I asked.

"Like what?"

Could it be he didn't know? I saw nothing but honest confusion in those long-lashed eyes. No, this wasn't some quick disguise. His mother hadn't seen her guests coming and said, "Quickly, son, put on a gown, or they'll have you for their war-band." It takes time to grow your hair long enough to sit upon. It takes a better actor than Peri could ever be to mimic the movements of a well-born maiden; those downcast eyes and shy tilts of the head. This boy must have been treated as a girl his whole life long, and it had never occurred to him that he might be anything else.

I waved the bloodied shift at him, lost for what to say. "I'll wash this with my master's stuff. Bring it to you later."

"What about Saint Porroc?"

"My master Myrddin will know what to do with him."

We walked back towards the hall, side by side, a little apart. I said, "That name of yours. . ."

"It's Peredur," said Peri. "My real name's Peredur. "I know it's a man's name, but it was my father's, and as there are no men left to take it, my mother said it must be mine."

"It's a good name," I said, and mumbled something about looking for my master, and left him there. Hurried to the shore with my head full of questions. Why would Peredur's mother do such a thing? And how long did she mean for her son to live as a girl?

Down on the shore where the grey waves broke, Saint Porroc was tumbling like driftwood in the cold white surf. His monks stood on the sand, calling out prayers and praising God for this new sign of their master's holiness. I crunched past them along the top of a shingle bank towards a place beneath the cliffs where another black shape leant into the wind.

Myrddin looked round sharply as I drew close. "You took long enough," he said. "What mischief have you been making?"

I didn't want to tell him. I could imagine too well the storm that would break over me if he found out the trick I'd used to snare Saint Porroc. Anyway, I'd other things on my mind. "The widow's daughter is a boy," I said.

"And it has taken you all this time to notice?" said Myrddin. "Have I taught you nothing? I don't expect Arthur and his men to see more than the widow wants us to, but I didn't think you'd be fooled." He chuckled, kicking his way through the stinky hummocks of seaweed. "The lady must be as great a magician as I am, to work such a transformation."

"But this is different!" I blurted. "I'm not like Peredur! I'm just *dressed* as a boy. He really thinks he is a girl. She's let him think it all his life!"

Myrddin didn't seem to be listening. He crouched beside a stone and traced a raised shape he found in it, a flinty whorl. "What is this?" he asked. "What *is* it?"

"I don't know master. It looks like a ram's horn. Or a snail."

"A stone snail?" He shook his head. "The Creator is keeping secrets from us, Gwyn."

He looked up at me. He'd heard my question after all. "You can see the widow's reasons, surely? Imagine being her. All her life sons have been dropping out of her belly and into battles. One after the next cut down, and then their father. And while she's still stupid with the news of his death, she finds there's one more child in her. If you were her, wouldn't you do anything to stop this last lad from hurrying off to the same death as the others? Bring him up to know nothing of riding, weapons, hunting, any of the war-games young men play? Keep him safe at your side always?"

"But it won't work, will it?" I said. "Not for ever. He may fool people now, but once he grows a beard and his voice turns gruff, people will think it odd. Even he will notice that he's not like other girls! We should tell him the truth."

My master shook his head. "No, Gwyna." (He still called me Gwyna sometimes, when we were alone, as if to remind me of what I really was.) "The only way she'll keep that boy out of the wars is if we put an end to wars. Raise up one strong man who'll stop this petty squabbling. Bring peace back, and in that peace boys will be able to grow to manhood without learning how to butcher one another, and men of wisdom will turn their minds to greater matters, such as snails entombed in sea-stones."

He frowned, looking back at the hall, considering Peredur as if he was another freak of nature; another stone snail. "Yes. That boy has a strange road ahead of him, but he must find his way alone."

We walked back along the beach. Porroc was still in the sea. "Saint Porroc has all the fine things of this place heaped up behind a curtain in his chapel," I said.

I felt Myrddin's eyes on me. "And how do you come to know that?"

I shrugged. Myrddin looked at me, and then at the hermit, bobbing half drowned in the breakers. There was a laugh in his voice. "Perhaps you have learned something from me after all. . ."

When I got back to the hall that evening Peredur's mother watched me nervously, as if I frightened her as much as Arthur himself. Peredur was a good daughter, and must have told her about the strange questions Myrddin's boy had asked. Peredur did not join us that night to eat the venison that Arthur and his men brought back with them.

Next morning, while I was saddling our horses, Arthur and a few of his men went into Saint Porroc's chapel. The saint and his monks stood shouting curses at them, and warning them that Porroc had been sent a vision by the Lord only yesterday, and that the earth would open up and swallow Arthur shoulder deep if he defiled the hermit's holy place. Arthur paid them no heed. He came out with armfuls of gold, and his men behind him the same. He said, "These things we shall take as tribute. Henceforward, this place is under our protection."

As we rode away I looked up and saw Peredur watching from a window, gazing wide-eyed at the splendour of our cloaks and horses and our shiny swords. I waved, and he waved back, and I rode on, glad that I was not quite alone in the world.

XV

I thought often of Peredur on the long ride home, but once we reached Arthur's stronghold I soon forgot him. There was work for us boys in the fields below the ramparts, helping reap and stack the hay for winter silage, cutting and threshing the wheat. And harvest was barely in the barns before a messenger arrived. He was a nervous, chinless man, sent from a town called Aquae Sulis that prided itself for clinging on tight to the old Roman ways. He had come to ask for Arthur's help.

I wasn't there when he said his piece to Arthur and Myrddin, but word of what he'd come about soon spread. A Saxon raiding band was moving west, burning and looting. Aquae Sulis's hired soldiers had deserted, and now it lay defenceless. The council had demanded help from Maelwas, since the town lay on the fringes of his lands, but no help had come. So they begged Arthur to bring his war-band and save them.

It was the chance that Arthur had been waiting for. He needed a town under his protection if he was ever to be taken seriously as a power among the little kings of Britain. Aquae Sulis wasn't big, but it had been important once, and it was still rich.

I listened to the men talking about it as Bedwyr and I and the other boys got the horses and the weapons ready. The way they spoke made you wonder if the poor old citizens wouldn't be better off just letting the Saxons in.

North-east along the old roads, in autumn sunlight, with the dusty blue sky above and a line of white cloud on the horizon like the foam of a wave that never broke. Sleeping in the open, in the golden woods. Myrddin with his harp beside Arthur's fire, spinning us tales of victories gone by, and reminding us that it was near Aquae Sulis that Ambrosius had routed the Saxons in our fathers' time.

Aquae Sulis waited for us in a loop of silvery river, at the bottom of a green bowl of downland. A wall ringed the main part of the town, thrown up hastily during the Saxon wars, with fragments of old pagan tombs mixed in among the brick. There were gates in it, and people coming and going. Coming, mostly; packing into the town out of the rumour-haunted countryside. The guards were men in Roman gear. Big four-cornered shields with the sign of Christ on them. Rusty armour patched and mended. Their leader rode a bay horse, and walked it forward to meet Arthur in the shadow of the gate. "Valerius," he said. "I command the defences of this place."

"Artorius Magnus, *Dux Bellorum* of the Britons," said

Myrddin, riding out front as usual, to announce his lord.

Valerius looked at Arthur down his long nose. Arthur looked at the walls, the rubbish heaped up in the ditch below, the thistles on the rampart, the half dozen shabby spearmen guarding the gate. He grinned. "We're here to save you from the barbarians," he said.

Valerius just kept on looking at Arthur, and I reckon he was thinking the same I'd thought: that Aquae Sulis might be better off without Arthur's help. But then he gave a smile that seemed to hurt him, and his men stood aside, and Arthur went past him and into the town with the rest of us following.

Inside those walls wasn't much different from outside at first. The buildings near the edge of town were so overgrown they looked like up-croppings of mossy rock in a wood. In the gaps between them market gardens and small fields had been made. Cattle were nibbling at the grass that sprouted up between the stones of the road. In one place a crowd of beehive lime-kilns sent up their fug of smoke. Men with barrows and sledges brought down slabs of marble, pillars and pediments stripped from old Roman buildings, which they were turning into lime for their fields. They stopped and stared at Arthur's band, at the armour and the flags and the sheen of sunlight on the spear-points. Maybe they thought we were the ghosts of some old legion, marching in from victories in the west.

In those leafy, half-countrified parts of the town we stopped to make our camp and set up our horse-lines, and we boys ran about finding water and fodder for the beasts. But Arthur and my master and a half-dozen of the war-band went on with Valerius into the heart of the town.

And the further they go, the finer it gets. There's less ivy on the walls, and more tiles on the roofs, and someone has made an effort to scrape the dung off the pavements. But down near the river, morning mist hangs over what looks like a whole cluster of ruins. "What's happened there?" Arthur asks Valerius, imagining that raiders have already breached the walls.

"There was a temple there in olden times," Valerius replies. "The pagans used to wash themselves in the hot springs and make offerings to their idols. But the bishop of this place prayed a great prayer, and God caused the waters to rise and engulf it. No one goes there now."

The riders cross a place called the forum, which has no weeds at all, just a dried-up fountain and a prosperous-looking market. Hogs squeal and jostle in a pen of hurdles. Pewter-smiths are at work in an open-fronted shop. There's a smell of blood from a pillared building which has been turned into a butcher's shambles; gutted carcasses hanging up in the shade under the portico. Behind the stalls and the haze of blue cooking-smoke from the food-sellers, tall stone walls tower up like sea-cliffs. There are fine buildings here, and some are still in good repair. One is a big old church, but you don't have to look too hard at it to see that it was a temple once, dedicated to the Romans' emperor, who'd been their god too.

Arthur wouldn't be Arthur if he didn't start imagining his own statue perching in the empty alcove where that old emperor used to stand watch. He wants this place. Till now he's thought his little hard-won kingdom in the hills was an achievement. He's felt proud of himself whenever he thinks of all the farmsteads that pay him tribute. But now he sees it's nothing. Wet hills. Ruins. There'll be no happy homecoming for him to his fortress in the west. Not now he's seen Aquae Sulis. He wants it the way a man wants food and shelter after a month on the road. He wants a town. Maybe he'll change its name, like Alexander, once it's his. Arthuropolis.

On the steps of the church the town's council stand waiting. The *ordo*, they call themselves. They're trying to look like Roman gentlemen, but they're just a gaggle of silly old men, togged up in bed sheets. Their bare knees rattle in the autumn chill with a sound like someone knapping flints. The west wind flips their hair about like cobwebs.

"*Salve, Imperator!*" cries the chief magistrate, raising one arm as Arthur swings himself down out of the saddle. "*Salve, Artori, Dux Bellorum et Malleus Saxonici! Macte nova virtute, sic itur ad astra!*"

Arthur straightens his helmet and squints sideways at him. He likes to call himself the heir of Rome, but he's never learned much Roman talk. He grunts, and glances back at Myrddin to make sure the old man's not insulting him.

"We welcome you," the chief magistrate explains. He's eager to please, and this isn't the first time he's run up against blank looks when he's tried out his Latin. He comes flapping down the steps to where Arthur waits. "Christ our Saviour has heard our prayers, and sent you to protect us in our time of greatest need! The Saxons are only two days' march away. . ."

Arthur pushes him aside and stalks up the steps, peering into the church, into the faded glory of old Britannia. The *ordo* draw back and watch expectantly. A group of women hide shyly among the pillars outside the door. They are servants, mostly, clustering around their mistress, the wife of Valerius. Arthur's eyes meet hers for just a second before he turns to take in the view of his new town. He forgets her as soon as his back is turned. She's not his sort. Tall, bony, serious, with a long white neck. She looks like a heron.

Her name, he'll find out later, is Gwenhwyfar.

Big grey clouds marched in from westward. Cold handfuls of rain came down on Aquae Sulis like coins flung at a beggar. We found shelter in the town, ate what food the grudging citizens gave us, and took more when it wasn't enough. The people watched sullenly as we dragged the pigs out of their pens and the hens out of their runs and rummaged through their storerooms for bread and wine and apples, and cleared their granaries of corn.

That evening, when the rest were dozing round the fire in the house we'd taken for ourselves, Bedwyr and I went down to see the old healing springs that gave the town its name. I was curious because I'd heard Myrddin talk about the place, and I made Bedwyr come with me because I didn't care to go alone. The common people resented us, and while they were too scared of Arthur's men to stand up to him, I guessed they might feel braver if they could corner a boy alone in their labyrinth of old stone streets.

Bedwyr, of course, didn't see how much they hated us. Couldn't imagine that anyone could hate a lad as handsome and as brave as him, striding along with his sword at his side, in the hand-me-down red cloak he'd cadged from Medrawt. All that worried him were ghosts. And those towering houses did look like the homes of spirits in that damp grey light, and the drinking songs and shouts and laughter that splurged out of the buildings where Arthur's men were quartered sounded ghostly too, like the shades of Romans celebrating some forgotten victory.

Valerius had been lying when he said no one went to the springs. They'd been a place of power and magic since the hills were young, and however hard the bishop preached against them his flock kept going to the waters to cure their ills as well as praying to his god. A dozen small paths wound shyly through the reeds and grass and alder-saplings, leading towards high stone buildings: bath houses, a half ruined temple. The doorways had been barred, and filled up with stones, but the walls themselves were crumbledown, and full of holes that a boy could easily slip through.

It wasn't long before Bedwyr and I were standing in a great hall, beside a muddy, misty mere that had once been the Romans' sacred bath. Square-cut pillars, tall as trees, rose from the water. Beneath the mud and moss the floor was paved with stone; you could feel the hardness of it when you walked, and see the paleness of it in places, showing through. Most of the roof had crashed down, making reefs of tiles and rubble in the water. The water was green as garlic soup, and it smelled like piss and vinegar. Stone steps went down into it, faint and yellowy under the surface.

"We shouldn't have come here," said Bedwyr, his voice tight-sounding, high with fear.

"Scared?" I asked, as if I wasn't.

"There are ghosts here," he said.

"Myrddin says there's no such thing," I told him. I was afraid as well, but I was too curious to run away. A strange warmth was in the air, and when I reached down and touched the water that was warm, too. How could there be warmth without a fire? I looked for one, but there were no flames anywhere, no smoke, only the steam rising from the water, hanging in veils between the crumbling pillars.

We crept along the pool-side, squelching through mud. Narrow doorways led off into rooms full of shadows and man-high nettles. We passed through one and crossed a narrow, mossy space, and looked through a sort of window into a place where the mist hung thick above another pool, and ferns and small trees grew from the walls, and evening sunlight came down in golden spears through gaps in the high, vaulted roof.

Maybe Myrddin was right, and there were no such things as ghosts. But someone like Myrddin, long years ago, had built and dressed that place to make you think of ghosts, and gods, and the unknowable mysteries of the hot springs. The water stirred and bubbled; the mists swirled; birds sped through leafy holes in walls and roof and swooped above the water. On the far side there was space enough to stand, among the rubble where part of the wall had tumbled down. A statue of a woman in a war-helmet lay toppled off her plinth there, but I could not tell if she'd been knocked down by the falling masonry or by angry Christians. I tipped my head on one side to get a look at her face. She'd been painted once; you could see the flakes of colour clinging to her cheeks and hair. She must have been beautiful when she was new and bright, standing there in all that mist. A better goddess than I'd made.

"This is the heart of it all," I said. "The sacred spring. . ."

We weren't the first to go there, neither. I've never seen so many charms and offerings as hung from the branches of the saplings that had grown out of the walls, and lay glinting like fish-scales on platforms just beneath the water. It looked to me as if some people round about still trusted the springs better than their bishop's god, and I couldn't blame them. There was magic in that place.

Bedwyr threw a coin into the water with a plop that echoed off the old walls. "Now the goddess of the waters will watch over us when we fight the Saxons," he whispered. "She's on Arthur's side. She gave him Caliburn. I was there, that day. I saw the sword rise out of the water, all shining with light. I heard Arthur tell afterwards about her golden hair, drifting on the waters all about her face."

I would have liked to tell him different. I almost did. I felt close to him, standing there, just the two of us in those haunted ruins. I thought he'd keep my secret. But the look on his face was so strange that I hadn't the heart to take his story away from him. He believed it, see. He believed the old gods were on Arthur's side just as he believed that winter would follow autumn and the sun would rise tomorrow. And I thought that maybe that believing would make him strong and brave and lucky when the fighting came, and maybe without it he'd be killed, or turn and run away, which was worse than being killed. So I kept quiet, and the magic waters lapped against the sides of the pool.

"We'll smash the Saxons," Bedwyr said. "And Britain will be one land again, and Arthur will be our emperor."

And then something screeched, away in the ruins behind us, and we squealed and ran pell-mell through that maze of shadows and pillars and young trees, laughing and gasping and scaring each other until we found our way into a street where lights showed in windows, and staggered homeward, mocking ourselves for being scared of an old owl.

XVII

Two days later, in the grey of dawn, and I'm sat by my pony in a dripping wood. Around me, in the gathering light, the other boys of the war-band wait. Sometimes somebody speaks, but we're quiet, mostly. Good Christians among us pray, face down on the wet earth with their arms spread out, like fallen swallows. The rest of us finger lucky charms, and look for omens in the way the dew drips off the twigs above our heads. We all have weapons; not just our own knives and spears but old swords and rusty javelins that Aquae Sulis's cowardly mercenaries forgot to take with them when they quit. We can't stop touching these new toys; rubbing the worn leather bindings on the grips of swords, picking splinters off of spear-hafts, stroking the hide coverings of our clumsy, heavy shields. The horses snort steam and clomp their hooves in the beechmast and nose about vainly for grass to eat among the grey, still trees.

This is how I come to be here. The Saxon raiders,

according to farmers fleeing into Aquae Sulis, are close on a hundred strong. They're heading towards the town, but slow, distracted by all the farmsteads and villas that lie in their path waiting to be looted, and held to walking pace by the wagons of plunder and columns of slaves that they've gathered in their push from the east. They've heard that the citizens of Aquae Sulis have a treasure-house stuffed full of gold.

Arthur, who knew that his men and their horses were tired after their own journey to the town, had been all for waiting a few days and meeting the raiders at a place just a mile from the walls, where the old roads crossed the river. But my master had a better idea. He looked at an old map and saw which way the Saxons would be coming. The best route would bring them to a ford that lies beneath the Hill of Badon. What if Arthur could meet them there, where his father Uthr and Ambrosius Aurelianus won their great fight all those years ago? A new victory at Badon would add far more to Arthur's legend than a skirmish beside some fading town most men have hardly heard of.

Myrddin is not in the battle-line, of course. "My head's too valuable to have some Saxon axe-man use it for a whetstone," he said. He'll be watching from a safe distance, up on the wooded ridge west of the ford. He wanted me to stay there with him. I told him Bedwyr and the other boys would never let me forget it if I did not ride with them into the fight, but he said, "They are fools, and I need you by me. What if you were killed, Gwyn? What if you were wounded? What if someone found you on the battlefield afterwards and peeled your

95

clothes off and found what's underneath, and what's not? No, boy; you stay with me, safe from harm."

But boys will be boys, even the ones who are only girls dressed up: that's one of the rules of the world. And another is that servants are always up before their masters. So in the dark before dawn, while Myrddin was still snoring, I crept away to join the others, a long line of us, riding silent as we could across the ford and up into the hanging woods on Badon's lower slopes. It was a fearful thing, to disobey my master, but not as fearful as facing the jeers of all the others calling me coward.

So here we are, in the wet wood, waiting. The battle-line is drawn up west of the ford, out of sight of us. There aren't many of them, for Arthur's hoping to make the Saxons think it's just a few men from Aquae Sulis come out to try and bar their way. Valerius, in his old Roman gear, has been put in command at the ford. But Arthur is waiting in the trees behind. Once the Saxons start to cross, his horsemen will come thundering down on them. And since the enemy are many, Arthur has decided to throw us boys into the fight as well. We may not be warriors yet, but the Saxons won't realize that when we come charging from behind them out of the trees, and our coming will push them back on to the swords of the real war-band.

The light grows. We stand as the hoof beats of a single horse come drumming uphill. It's Bedwyr; my friend Bedwyr, with a leather helmet on his head and straw stuffed in under the rim to stop it sliding down over his eyes. I feel my heart fill at the sight of him. You never love your friends more than when you fear they might be taken from you in the next few moments. I feel almost as much love for the other boys, for my pony, Dewi, for the trees, for the droplets which fall on my face as Bedwyr reins his horse in close by and spatters me with watery mud.

"They're coming." He's breathless. "Their scouts came at dawn. They saw our men at the ford and heard their challenges, and laughed when they saw how few there were. Now the whole band is moving up, wagons and everything. . ."

Through the trees behind him we catch distant shouts. Insults are bellowing back and forth across the ford. We strain our ears. We cup our hands around them to catch the drips of sound. We can't make out words, and even if we could, the Saxons speak a different tongue from ours. But we all hear the shouting blur into a roar as the attackers surge forward into the ford. It's that battle-noise again, that ugly music woven out of shouting voices and hoof-falls and the clang of swords. I start to wish I'd stayed with my master. Then we hear the high horns ringing, calling Arthur's hidden riders out of the woods.

"Mount up!" shouts Medrawt, who Arthur's put in charge of us. He feels ashamed at being left to lead this rag-tag army of boys, and he cuffs the heads of those who stand closest and bellows loud to make himself feel better. "Ride!"

There's no more time for fear, or prayers, or anything. We struggle into our saddles and dig knees and heels into our mounts' flanks and crash against each other as the animals turn and fret. But at last we're all moving, faster and faster, down through the trees with branches flailing at our heads like clubs, with twigs snatching at our caps and cloaks, with the whole world gone to a whirl of sky and trees and hooves and the hot stink of horses. I reach for my new sword, but Dewi is galloping so hard and the ground's so rough that I slip sideways in the saddle as soon as I take my hand off the reins, so I forget the sword and grab a handful of his mane instead, and a thick branch comes swiping at my face and I duck under it and suddenly there are no more trees and we're rushing out across open land, a water-meadow where the mist hangs in woolly ribbons above the drainage ditches, and the other horses are beside me, foaming, racing, and boys are shouting, and Medrawt ahead of us with a spear upraised, and ahead of *him* is a big crowd of men, white faces flashing under helmets as they turn to see us.

I have just time to think "Saxons!" before our charge carries us into the middle of the battle. Off to one side I see Arthur's red banner flying. The Saxons are bunched up on the road where it slopes downhill to the ford. We gallop past a wagon that has pitched sideways into a ditch and spilled out pots and cloth-wrapped bundles and a shrieking woman. Cows get in our way, white-eyed with terror, blundering across the line of our charge. Dewi rears up, and I lose my grip and slither backwards over his arse and down with a thump in wet bracken.

The battle wraps me in its noise and reek. I get up quick, not wanting to be kicked to death. Where's Dewi? This isn't like the battles Myrddin tells about, where brave warriors fight one against another. It's more like shoving through a packed marketplace. I blunder against friends and enemies. My ears fill with the sound of blades against shield-wood: a cosy thud, like someone chopping logs. My face gets shoved into a Saxon's side; I taste the hairy weave of his tunic, smell his sweat. Lucky for me he's too busy to notice, flailing with his sword at Bedwyr, who's still mounted. The edge of a shield catches me and pulls me sideways. A yellow-haired man is shouting something at me and waving a great big axe, which I suddenly understand he means to hit me with, but the blow never comes; the battle tugs us away from one another. A riderless pony sends me sprawling. I crash into the reeds at the edge of one of those drainage ditches, slither down into the water. The reeds are spear-high, with flags of thin, pale stuff at the top, waving. Between their stalks the water is brown and brackish, covered with a film of dead flies, their spread-out wings like tiny windows, hundreds of them, thousands. Beyond the reeds men are yelling and horses are shrieking.

Were they really Saxons? There weren't many of them; less than a hundred. How could such a small army have struck so deep into the British side of Britain? I think maybe they were no more than a gang of foreign *foederates*, mercenaries hired to protect some town up in Calchvynydd who had grown tired of waiting to be paid and turned to banditry instead. Saxons are hard fighters, I've heard. Saxons would have found high ground and formed a shield-wall, made a fence of wood and steel that Arthur's cavalry could not have broken. This lot just scattered when they saw the horses coming. Ran this way and that, pursued by horsemen. Rallied in small clumps, easily cut down. It was more like a hunt than a battle.

Later, when it's quiet, I part the reeds and scramble out.

I'm frightened that people will ask where I've been. I have worked out a lie to tell them, about being stunned and waking up in the ditch to find the battle over. But no one asks. They're busy in the piles of dead, digging out fallen friends or stripping the Saxons of the things they carried. Crows are circling. Up above, the green hill of Badon rises from its blankets of woods. I see Arthur on his white horse, and Medrawt among the knot of men around him. In the mud near the ford lies Valerius, and I can't help but notice that he's been speared in the back.

"Gwyn!" someone is shouting. "Gwyn!"

It's Bedwyr, leading Dewi, who he found wandering in the meadows eastward, where our men are plundering the Saxons' baggage-train. He runs up and hugs me. "We won," he says, but he doesn't sound triumphant. He says it like a question, as if he can't quite believe that any of us is still alive. "I killed a man. I killed him, Gwyn. We won."

He hugs me hard. He smells of sweat and other people's blood. And when my face presses against his I feel a prickling where his first, thin, boyish beard is starting to grow.

XVIII

Badon fight was a turning point. It was a change in the tide. Arthur and the people round him would talk often of the battle, and the men would swap tales of it whenever there was fighting or drinking to be done. It wasn't long before people who hadn't been there started to get Arthur's little victory over the robber-band confused with that other battle of the Hill of Badon, the big, important one that old Ambrosius had won. Which was exactly what my master was hoping for when he picked out the battlefield.

As for me, all Myrddin said when he saw me alive and whole after the fight was, "So you came through unscathed. Did you enjoy your battle?"

I nodded, of course, but he knew I was lying. "I am never, never, never going into a war again," I promised myself. And I felt sorry for Bedwyr and the other boys. They must have been as scared as me, but they'd be men soon, and would have to keep on plunging into fights like that until they got into one they would never come

101

out of. I pulled out my sword and looked at it, and I wanted to cast it away. I'd not used it, but I knew that someone had, in the days before it was mine, and that there must still be dried traces of blood grained in the grooves of its hilt and the cracked ivory pommel.

Myrddin went stalking off to help tend to the wounded men who had been dragged from the field by their friends. He talked a lot about the great healers of times gone by, men with names like Hippocratus and Galen. He did his best, after the battles, binding wounds and applying poultices of herbs and cobwebs, lashing dead pigeons to the feet of men with blood-souring to draw their fevers out. I don't know if it did much good. It seemed to me that if a man had a wound that was more than a shallow cut, he'd most likely die, and if that was what God wanted for him then there was nothing my master's bandages and ointments and long words could do.

Down by the river Bedwyr and my other friends were wading about among the dead, pulling Saxons' boots and sword-belts off.

We pulled back from the ford and camped on Badon Hill, among the green slopes of an age-old fortress. That night, around the campfires, there was less talk of war than usual, as if the memory of the real thing was too fresh in everybody's minds for the old boasts and poems to work their magic. Even Arthur looked sombre and thoughtful, staring at the sparks as they danced up into the dark. We all kept close to the fires, wary of the ghosts that would be wandering in the dark beyond those circles of light. But when we had eaten, Myrddin took out his harp and spun the day's fight into stories, listing the brave deeds that each man had done, leaving out none of them, not even Bedwyr. He touched his story with humour, telling us how none of the enemy had dared face Owain, because he was so beautiful they thought he was an angel sent to help Arthur, and how they had fled before Cei, who was so ugly they thought he was a devil come to help Arthur. And slowly, as we listened, we started to forget how afraid we'd all been, and began to remember it as he told it: Arthur's shining victory.

And when the stories were done and we were winding ourselves in our blankets and settling down to sleep, Arthur and Cei came and found my master and they went away together into Arthur's tent.

I was a long time finding sleep. I lay on the hard ground and felt the bruises blooming on me where I'd been knocked and jostled in the fight, and all the while I could hear Arthur and Cei and Myrddin talking low. And I remember wondering what they were planning, and where it would take us to next.

XIX

Before dawn, my master's toe prodded me awake. I scrambled up quick and followed him between the turf ramparts to the horse-lines. There was a line of light like a tide-mark along the bottom of the eastern sky. I could see the curve of the river shining below us, and on the dark land beyond it I could dimly make out the heap of dead enemies we had left there for the crows and foxes.

"Where are we going, master?" I asked, as we saddled the horses.

"Back to Aquae Sulis."

"Just us alone?"

"The rest will follow later. Arthur is sending me ahead, with a message for the town."

"What message?"

"Was there ever a servant as impertinent as you? No business of yours, that's what message. Did you never hear of the boy who was turned into a stone because he asked too many foolish questions?"

We rode out of the camp before anyone but the

sentries were stirring. My mind worked all the way to Aquae Sulis, worriedly wondering what Arthur and my master were planning, and what it might mean for me. Was there to be another fight? Did Arthur mean to take Aquae Sulis for himself? I knew fretting about what was going to happen wouldn't stop it happening, but I couldn't help myself.

This was what my time with Myrddin had done to me. In the old days I'd never given a thought to the future, and not much to the past. I'd lived simply in the now. I'd been happy if I had enough to eat, and nobody was hitting me. I'd been miserable when I was cold, and frightened when I was ill, but mostly I gave no more thought than an animal did to what might happen tomorrow, or next week. Just an animal walking about on two legs, that's all I was till Myrddin changed me. It seemed to me sometimes I'd been happier that way.

The town greeted us uncertainly, not sure if we were good news or bad. People always expect news to be one or the other. Usually it's both, as the news we carried was. The *ordo* raised their old lizardy arms in praise of God when Myrddin told them how the battle had gone, and then set to groaning and looking downcast when they heard of Valerius's death. The servant-women who waited on the dead man's wife started to shriek and sob and pull their hair about, but the lady herself just stood there silently, her long face whiter than ever and her grey eyes fixed on my master, until they turned her about, and led her away.

"What is to become of us?" the chief magistrate

wondered as he watched her go. "This victory has come at a high price. With Valerius gone, who will be our defender...?"

"Arthur wishes to bring your town under his protection," said Myrddin helpfully. "In exchange for quite reasonable tributes he would be prepared to make Aquae Sulis his capital. Build up its defences and improve it in every way."

"But we pay our taxes to Maelwas of Dumnonia."

"Maelwas is as weak as a woman. Has he sent you any help in your present need? No. So how can he object if you turn to another lord, one who *can* protect you?"

"A half-heathen savage out of the western hills," grumbled the bishop, not loudly, but loud enough for all the rest to hear.

Myrddin ignored him. "Arthur would like a treaty. A sign of lasting trust between us."

"Gold," muttered another councillor. "He'll want gold."

The chief magistrate closed his eyes and ran his hand over his face like he was counting all the wrinkles. He wanted to be left alone to take in this news of Valerius's death. He didn't want my master standing here, pressing him for an answer that would seal the fate of his whole town.

"Valerius had a wife," said Myrddin lightly.

The magistrate opened a beady eye. "Gwenhwyfar?"

"Arthur is unmarried," said Myrddin. (I wondered about red-headed Cunaide, but Myrddin told me later she wasn't a Christian wife, so didn't count.) "I gather that the lady Gwenhwyfar's father came from the family of Ambrosius himself," he went on. "And that she is related on her mother's side to King Maelwas. That would be an auspicious marriage for our *Dux Bellorum*."

The other old men clicked their tongues and shook their heads, but the chief magistrate was snared. You could see the calculations going on behind his eyes, driving out whatever sorrow he'd felt for Valerius. If what he'd heard was true, Arthur might have all Britain under his command within a few more years. An alliance with a man like that might be most useful, and if all it took was a marriage with Valerius's beanpole widow. . .

He turned to a servant, sniffing delicately. "Call Gwenhwyfar here. We should talk with her, before the *Dux Bellorum* returns."

XX

Arthur's army arrived the next day, and fat black clouds came with them like a baggage train, drenching the town in rain. It ran in rivers down the street-gutters and waterfalled from clogged downpipes. It drummed on the canvas roofs of the plunder-wagons Arthur had taken from the Saxons. It drowned out the bleating of the women who ran to mourn beside Valerius's corpse. The dead man had been carried back in honour from the battlefield, wrapped in a cloak and laid upon a shield, a noble Roman fallen in battle. But the rain soaked him through and through, and by the time they reached the church he looked like he'd drowned in a flooded ditch.

The dead man's widow steps out into the rain to meet him. Gwenhwyfar has a striking face; too long to be pretty, but a face you notice. She has dark eyes, with secrets in them. Her hair is dark, too, ash-streaked with grey. It hangs low over her forehead, as if she would like to hide behind it. Her eyes and nostrils are red like she's been crying, but maybe it's a cold. Her body, what I can see of it under her woollen cloak, is all bony angles. Her name means "white shadow", and there *is* something shadowy about her. She looks as if she can't quite believe in herself.

The boys I run with could talk of nothing but Gwenhwyfar last night. They say she's bad luck. She was promised to Valerius's brother when she was young, but he was killed in a cattle-raid before they could marry. She wed Valerius instead, and gave him a son, but the child died and there have been no others. Now she has no husband either. We boys can't believe Arthur means to make a wife of this grey icicle.

She steps forward to kiss her dead husband's forehead, and the men carrying him lower the shield a little to let her do it, almost spilling the corpse into the mud. She looks at him thoughtfully. Her white fingers rest on his chest.

"There is no wound," she says, looking across the body at my master.

"He was struck from behind," says Myrddin. Her eyes stay on him. The question in them makes him shift awkwardly. I wonder about how Valerius died. Did one of our men drive the spear into his back? Did Arthur order it? Did my master advise that it be done?

"It is not unusual for a blow to come from behind in the turmoil of battle," Myrddin says, answering the lady's question as if she'd spoken it aloud. "Your husband was such a valiant fighter, Gwenhwyfar, that I doubt any Saxon dared meet him face-to-face."

Gwenhwyfar lowers her eyes and steps back into the company of her waiting-women. She can't press my master any further without insulting *his* master, Arthur, whose riders and spearmen pack the streets around. The question of her husband's death blows downwind, unanswered.

Arthur watches her carefully from the far side of the church all through the bishop's funeral prayers. He has the same look that he gets when he is thinking about buying a horse, or taking a new stretch of land.

Outside, in the skinny, driving rain, the men of Aquae Sulis dug a hole in the wet ground and bundled Valerius into it. Before they had finished filling in the grave, Arthur was making himself at home. Working men were ordered to repair the defensive walls and clear the rubbish from the ditches below them. What soldiers the place still had were set to drilling with spears and shields. We thought that when Maelwas learned of the bite Arthur had taken out of his borderlands he would send men north to take it back, and we wanted to be ready for them. We shod horses, and sharpened spears, and dragged felled trees across the places where the walls had tumbled down. We took turns to stand on the walls at night, watching the mist steam off the wet woods, watching the hills keep their secrets.

XXI

We watched and watched, but Maelwas never came. Maybe he'd heard tell of the great victory Arthur had won under the Hill of Badon, and didn't fancy meeting him in battle. He sent heralds instead, all in white on white horses, with green branches held up high to show they came in peace. They passed on to Arthur Maelwas's thanks for preserving Aquae Sulis, and asked that he send gold and cattle as a token of his loyalty. Arthur gave them half the gold they asked for, and none of the cattle, and the heralds went back to Maelwas's strongholds in the Summer Country, leaving the town in the hands of its new lord.

Winter set in soon after. The air grew cold. We lit fires to warm our quarters. Mist hung over the ruined temples at the heart of town. From the hill-tops, I thought, Aquae Sulis must look like a steaming stock-pot.

One morning we woke to find those hills all hoary with first snow. Parties of men went to and fro between the town and Arthur's western strongholds before the roads were buried. They brought back treasures to deck Arthur's new capital, and the women and hangers-on of some of his followers. Cei's wife and daughter rode in, but I noticed Arthur did not send for Cunaide. I felt sad for her, abandoned in that cold fortress, her place taken by Gwenhwyfar.

Arthur had wanted a quick marriage, but Gwenhwyfar made him wait till Easter, when her time of mourning for her husband would be done. Arthur asked the bishop to cut short her mourning-period, but the bishop refused. Arthur thought about killing the bishop, but Cei and my master reminded him it might be bad for his reputation.

To take his mind off killing bishops, Myrddin advised that a new hall be built for the wedding. "What is the difference between us and our forefathers?" he asked one night when the men were lounging around the big fire in Arthur's hall. "They built great palaces, while we are content to live among the ruins! Arthur should build here, to show that in him the spirit and the pride of old Britannia are come again! We'll build a round hall, with tiles upon its floor and painted garlands on its walls. And at the heart of the hall, a round banqueting chamber, where we who have fought at Arthur's side may meet as equals. . ."

"I've never seen you at my side in a fight, Myrddin," shouted Arthur. "You skulk safe out of danger's way with the women and the baggage-train." But you could see the idea at work on him, even as he raised his cup to acknowledge the gusts of laughter from his men. He'd never dreamed of building halls before, but now he was starting to see himself as a man who built; a ruler who left his mark upon the world in the form of splendid halls.

For the next week or so, my master pored over drawings in the smoke-fug of his quarters and took me out in the wincing cold to mark where the post-holes should be dug. "Here. And here. And here!" he ordered, walking a circle in the forum with instruments made out of willow-staffs and twine. The bishop and his priests and their wives looked on and muttered about witchcraft and conjurings.

But Myrddin's efforts conjured up nothing, and the snow kept falling to blot out the marks I made. It quilted the roofs and streets. It froze the water in the horse-troughs so that we had to smash it with stones and spear-butts of a morning before the animals could drink. In the after-Christmas dark Arthur lost interest in hall-building, and Myrddin's schemes withered like a flower in the frost. "It was only the seed of a hall," he said, rolling up the skins he'd drawn his sketches on. "We'll let it lie hidden till spring, then see what grows."

Arthur was tired of waiting for his wedding, and for fighting-season to come round again. He left Cei in charge and took his favourite companions off into the hills, hunting deer and wild pig down the same combes they'd hunted Saxons through that autumn. They took Bedwyr with them – he was almost one of them, since Badon-fight.

Myrddin whiled away the time by teaching me to write. So if you are following my story, you have

Myrddin to thank for it, and if it bores you, you have him to blame, for these crabbed black inky words that you're reading are built from letters that he showed me how to make, scratching them with a stick in the ash before a winter fire in Aquae Sulis.

One day, while the hunters were still away, I went down by myself to the waters, where I'd gone with Bedwyr when we first came to the town. The weather was warming, and the snow was gone from the streets, though the hill-tops were still speckled white. I was itchy and flea-bitten inside my clothes. I'd not had a chance to wash since Christmas, and even then I'd only splashed my face, too scared to even take my tunic off in front of the other boys. In the silent town the warm waters of Minerva seemed to call to me.

A couple of serving-girls from Gwenhwyfar's household were lingering near the pillared front entrance to the baths, the entrance the bishop had boarded up. I ducked along the building's side before they saw me. Bedwyr and the other boys were forever seeking out those girls, swapping stories about them and wrangling over which one was prettiest or friendliest, but they scared me. I thought they might not be as blind as Bedwyr and his friends to my smooth chin.

I crept into the baths through the same hole in the wall I'd found with Bedwyr, pushing my way through the twigs and the dangling charms. The big pool lay shadowed by its mossy, sagging roof, like a pool in a cave. I reached my hand down through the wreaths of mist and touched the water and it felt hot. It still smelled bad, but not as bad as me. I pulled off my leggings, unwrapped my breech-cloth, bared my whole white body to the shivery air. The water clopped gently against the old steps, and I walked down into it, grateful for its warmth.

Have you bathed in warm water ever? I never had. It was like a miracle, to be warm again after those months of cold. Not warmed by a fire that roasts one side of you and leaves the other cold, but wrapped and coddled in warmness. My skin tingled with pleasure as I ducked under, smoothing my fingers through the greasy louse-nest of my hair, imagining the winter dirt coming off me in a cloud. Old coins and tin charms slithered beneath my toes, and drowned holly leaves pricked my soles. Opening my eyes in the soft green dark I saw something glimmer on the mulchy floor, and reached for it. My fingertips closed on a moon-shaped slip of metal that some old Roman had thrown there as an offering to the sacred waters.

When I surfaced again, someone was watching me.

How had I not seen her before? It was dark in there, I suppose, and my eyes were not used to it. Gwenhwyfar was in the shadows, just her head and shoulders showing above the lapping water, watching me with her grey eyes. I didn't even recognize her at first. Her hair hung straight and wet around her face. I took her for the goddess of the place, and went under in a panic, snorting and gurgling.

She came through the water to me and pulled me up, looking intently at my face as I choked and spat. "I know you," she said. "The magician's boy."

115

She smiled. I'd not seen her smile before. Had she seen me naked on the pool-side? Or had she only turned at the splashings I'd made? I shrank down in the water till it hid everything except my hedge-pig hair and flat brown face. Wavelets lapped at my nose and made me sneeze.

Gwenhwyfar said, "Bishop Bedwin would be filled with righteous anger if he knew I came here. He says it is a wicked place, and full of pagan spirits. But I would rather risk meeting a spirit or two than smell as bad as Bedwin does."

I hugged myself under the water. My fists were clenched so tight that the moon-shaped charm I'd dredged up dug its points into my palm. "I won't tell," I promised.

Gwenhwyfar backed away from me in a swirl of water. "Turn your back, magician's boy."

So she still thought I was a boy! Or did she? I thought I saw an odd light in her eyes. Maybe I imagined it. I turned and bowed my head and shut my eyes, and heard the water shift and slosh as she waded to the far side of the pool to climb out. I stole one glance, and had a glimpse of her long body before she wrapped a square of woollen-stuff around her. White, she was, like a stripped twig.

XXII

She hadn't always lived in a town. When she was a girl
Gwenhwyfar lived in a villa on a green hill beside a
steep green cleave. The cleave was tangled with trees,
feathery with ferns, a secret stream slinking black and
gold through the oak-shadows. Gwenhwyfar went
riding there on her pony, or hunted along the wood-
shores with a little bow one of the servants made her.
She was as wild as a fawn.

At least, that's how I see her, when I make pictures in
my head of the life she led before.

But fate had laid a snare for Gwenhwyfar; set to trap
her when she reached the age of marriage. Her father
was a half-brother of Ambrosius Aurelianus. The old
general's blood ran well diluted in her, but still it ran.
You could see it beneath the skin at her temples, and on
the long, pale column of her throat. Those winding
veins, bluish under her white flesh, with maybe a hint of
imperial purple. She was a bridge between our time and
the happier times of Ambrosius, and the man who

117

married her would link himself and his sons with the great name of the Aureliani.

Valerius's brother was the first. He'd been chosen for her by her family and by her father's allies among the *ordo* of Aquae Sulis. Gwenhwyfar didn't mind. Marcus was handsome, light-hearted, kind; everything a girl could want. He brought her gifts. The seed of his son was already growing in her when the word came of his death in a cattle-raid.

After that, it was Valerius's turn. It's not uncommon for a dead man's brother to marry the girl he'd been promised to. Why spoil a neat arrangement just because the bridegroom had run himself upon some rustler's pike? But Valerius was a poor substitute. He was cold and stern. He'd grown used to being overlooked in favour of his older brother, and it had soured him. Now Marcus was gone, Valerius took the things that had been his with a sort of bitter triumph. It didn't please him to find that the baby in his new bride's belly was one of them.

It was a hard birth. The child was sickly, and soon dead. But in the few short days he lived, Gwenhwyfar loved him. Holding him made her happy. His little blue hands clutched fistfuls of her hair. She sang to him. When he died, the happiness went out of her for good. The cold old town they made her live in felt like a tomb. She dreamed her son was crying out for her, down under the cold ground, and she could not go to him. Her husband hated her. There were no more babies.

And now a new husband had come for her. However hard she tried to slow the approach of her wedding to

Arthur, the days kept slipping through her fingers. Her women made jokes about him. His strength. His manliness. All she could think of was the name his men gave him. The Bear. Sometimes it seemed to her that he really was a bear, poorly disguised as a man. His short, black bristling hair, his watchful eyes. The way he tore at his meat in the feast-hall. His snarls and roars when things displeased him. In the growing warmth of spring she shivered as she stitched her marriage-gown and imagined her wedding night.

I felt sorry for her. Poor old heron.

XXIII

We went travelling that springtime, my master and me, with Arthur and Gwenhwyfar's wedding-hymns still ringing around inside our skulls. "We'll let the Bear have some time alone with his new bride," said Myrddin. "He's a Christian lord now, with a Christian wife, and he doesn't need an old heathen like me about him." So we went south and west, into the Summer Country, and I found out why they called it that. There would be good grazing there in summer, the people said, pastures of lush green grass where their red cows grew fat and sweet. But when I was there with Myrddin it was barely land at all. Water covered acre after acre, leaving nothing dry except the hedge-banks and the causeways.

We'd come there with a purpose. King Maelwas of Dumnonia spent his year on a long round of travels from one of his holdings to the next. He was feasting that spring at Ynys Wydryn, the apple-isle which rises steep and green out of those wet levels, with a monastery balanced on its top. Maelwas was a Christian king. The monastery on Ynys Wydryn was his doing, and there was a fine hall there beside the wooden church where he and his sons and servants and his shield-companions could stay when he came to pray.

The monks who kept the place were wary of Myrddin, even though he took care to hide away his old charms and amulets before we crossed the causeway to their gate. They knew his reputation as a magic worker, and I think they would have turned him away, but someone went to tell Maelwas who it was who had come seeking him, and Maelwas sent a messenger to the abbot and told him to let us in.

Maelwas surprised me. I thought the king of so much country would be a man like Arthur, hard and scarred, forever sniffing the wind for fresh fights. But Maelwas was old, and spoke soft, and seemed gentle-mannered. I suppose he had been wilder in his youth, when he rode with Ambrosius. He greeted Myrddin, and asked after Gwenhwyfar, who was a kinswoman of his – his half-sister's daughter's daughter. "I remember her as a girl," he said. "A pretty thing. Your Arthur is a lucky man. I trust he'll treat her well."

That night in his hall Myrddin told his tales of Arthur. No enchanted swords or green men there. Just Arthur the soldier of Christ; how he'd driven back the Saxon army that tried to seize Aquae Sulis, and beaten the Devil in a rock-throwing contest out in the west somewhere.

Maelwas listened with a little smile about him always, as if to show us that he knew these tales weren't true, however pleasant it might be to hear them by the hearth.

We stayed a few days at Ynys Wydryn. On the

121

morning we left, when a booming wind was combing the grass flat and making cats'-paws on the flooded fens, Maelwas spoke alone to Myrddin. I heard them as I brought the horses close.

"I've had no tribute this year from your master in Aquae Sulis. Perhaps his wedding to my pretty kinswoman drove it from his mind."

"Arthur would like to pay you all he owes," Myrddin promised. "But he has an army of cavalry to feed. His warriors aren't untrained levies who can go home to their farms between fights and grow their own food. They are soldiers, who live for war. He must put their needs first if he is to keep them together, and strong enough to defeat the Saxon threat."

"But the Saxons have not troubled us since Ambrosius's time," Maelwas pointed out. "A few raids. More of a nuisance than a threat."

"They will come again," said Myrddin fiercely. "All the time we British fight among ourselves, the Saxons in the east grow stronger. They will drive west again one day, unless we smash them utterly."

"And is Arthur truly strong enough to do that?" Maelwas asked. "To drive them back across the sea? Can he really finish the work Ambrosius began? End the dismal partition of Britain and win back the lost east for Christ?"

"Not alone," my master said. "But if you would make him leader of your war-band in battle, and command all the lesser kings who pay you tribute to do likewise, he could be the new Ambrosius."

"Except that Ambrosius fought for Britain and the

Christian faith," said Maelwas mildly, "and I do not think Arthur fights for anything but Arthur. More robber than soldier, I've heard. A wild, roving man, like Uthr before him. A looter of churches. A cattle-thief. Only last summer he came plundering our westward lands, making men pay him tribute that was not his to take."

Myrddin shrugged. "A mistake. When a man is as strong as Arthur, he over-reaches himself sometimes. But your kinswoman Gwenhwyfar has tamed that wildness out of him. Her love of Christ has set him a good example. Arthur is God's strong man. Henceforward, he'll fight only Saxons. He would lead your war-band with honour and victory."

Maelwas was silent a moment, his eyes on Myrddin's, considering. The watching monks and warriors shuffled and stirred. Cloaks flapped in the breeze and a man coughed. I don't think they liked to see their master dealing so friendly-like with mine. There were men there who hoped to lead Maelwas's war-band themselves one day.

Suddenly Maelwas chuckled, and slapped Myrddin's shoulder. "Thank you for your stories," he said. "I shall consider what you say, and if it seems to me that Arthur is really all you claim, you will hear from me." Then, walking with Myrddin towards the place where I was waiting with the horses, he nodded at me, and said, "Why do you dress her as a boy?"

Myrddin must have been taken by surprise. Knowing him, I could see that he was startled. But he plucked a story from the air as calmly as another man might swat a fly. "She is my daughter," he said gravely. "But this travelling life leads us often among wild places and fighting men. For her own protection I dress her as a boy."

Maelwas smiled, looking me up and down. "It is a good disguise," he said. "But I don't think it will work much longer."

My master did not speak to me as we rode back across the causeway. I could feel anger coming off him like warmth off a fire. It had been bad for him, being found out in a trick at the last moment like that. I felt ashamed of myself for letting old Maelwas see the truth. Had it been my fault? Had I not been boyish enough? I'd let my hair get longer, following the same fashion as Bedwyr and the other boys. It hung below my ears, and maybe it showed up something girlish in my face.

I felt in the pouch on my belt and gripped the old moon-charm I'd taken from the baths that day Gwenhwyfar saw me there. When I found it I'd been thinking to give it to my master, so he could string it round his neck with all the rest, or hang it up outside his door to keep thieves out. But he would have wanted to know where I had found it, and I knew if I'd told him he'd have made me spill out the whole story, somehow: how I'd met Gwenhwyfar, and how she'd nearly found my secret out. Rather than face his anger, I had kept it hid. And now he was going to be angry anyway.

He didn't speak until we reached the old troop road. Then he said, "He's a cunning old fox, that Maelwas. He sees things other men don't." He looked at me a long while. Nodded, as if something had been decided. "The weather is set fair. We won't go back to Aquae Sulis yet."

"But you must tell Arthur what King Maelwas said. . ."

"I'll send him word. Arthur can cope without me for a season, I think."

And he turned his horse west instead of east, and what was there for me to do but follow him? He'd not been angry with me, but I couldn't help thinking, as I urged Dewi after him, that this was some sort of punishment.

Summer rolled us along like stones in a stream. Moridunum to Isca, Isca to Tamaris, and in between them all the little places, Caer this and Din that, which the Romans had never given names to, and had left with their old names and their old ways. And after Tamarisford there were barely any Roman names at all, just the long land of Kernyw under its wide sky. But wherever we went, people had heard of Arthur, and were glad to hear more. Myrddin scattered stories like sparks, and the brush-fire of Arthur's fame spread.

"One day Arthur will set up his standard, and the kings of Britain will flock to him like starlings," Myrddin said. "King Maelwas of the Dumnonii has as good as promised that Arthur will command his warband come the fighting season. With all those warriors behind him, he'll be the new Ambrosius. He'll win the lost lands back, and the Saxons will throw themselves into the sea to escape him."

He was so sure that it would happen that I didn't think to doubt him. But it frightened me, the thought of all that war to come. Why did Myrddin want it so bad? Why did he seem so fierce, when he spoke about the Saxons? Sometimes I thought, why not let Arthur hold his territory and all the other kings hold theirs and leave the Saxons quiet in the lands they'd settled? But I didn't speak that thought, in case it sounded womanish.

At Din Tagyll, from the heights above the sea, I watched the ships go out on the evening tide. In winter Din Tagyll is too storm-threshed for any but a few mad monks to live there, but in summer King Cunomorus makes it his capital, and the steep headland's sides bloom bright with flags and awnings, and in the cove below the ships drop anchor. I watched their sails fill with the wind as they slipped clear of the cliff's lee, and they went out like swans over the wide ocean. Some of the men who sailed them had skin as black as coal. They were bound for shores I couldn't even imagine; lands of leopards and unicorns; harbours whose names burst sweetly in my mouth like ripe grapes. Alexandria. Antioch. Constantinople.

After midsummer we turned back. I'd hoped we'd go along the south coast, and maybe to Peredur Long-Knife's place. I would have liked to see what had become of Peri. But we stayed north, keeping to the shore of the Severn-sea, then striking inland towards the country I'd been born in; to Ban's hall, which was held for Arthur by the Irishman.

It was around then that I started to realize my master had plans to work a fresh enchantment on me. After so long on the road, my hair hung almost to my shoulders. One morning, as we were saddling the horses in a dell where we'd spent the night, I spoke of finding some shears to cut it.

He shook his head. "You'll not pass as a lad much longer," he said. "That old fox Maelwas was right."

I got frightened. I thought maybe he meant to leave me behind in those same soggy hills he'd got me from. I thought he meant to marry me to some shepherd, or one of the rough chieftains whose halls we'd been passing nights in. I went down on the earth and hugged his knees and said, "Please, master, let me come back to Sulis with you. I've been a good servant, haven't I?"

Myrddin smoothed my too-long hair. I wasn't looking at his face, so I don't know if he was smiling, but I like to think there was a smile about him as he said, "You've been a good boy, Gwyn. But you'll be a better girl. It'll be Gwyna who rides back with me at fall-of-leaf."

His words kicked the breath out of me. I suppose I'd always known it would have to come, but not yet, surely? "I don't want to be a girl!" I cried. "I'll never be able to go home. People will recognize me!"

"Of course they won't," said Myrddin. "Half a year will have gone by. Do you think they have statues of your head standing around Aquae Sulis as if you were some old emperor? You will go back in a woman's dress, with your long hair loose. You will walk like a girl and talk like a girl, and they will think, 'That maiden looks a little like Gwyn,' if they think anything at all. And I shall tell them you are Gwyn's kin, and they will think of you no more."

"But I don't know how to be a girl!" I told him. "I'll have to do the things that women do. . ." I gaped like a fish, groping about for examples. I barely *knew* the things that women did. "Sewing and stitching and spinning and brewing barley-beer. . . What will they think when I don't know how to do those things?"

"Then you must learn."

"I'll be no good at them. Slow and clumsy."

"Gwyna," he said. (His firmest voice, the one that brooked no replies.) "You will be a young woman soon. You'll look more out of place in Arthur's war-band then than you will fumbling your weaving-work in his wife's house."

"His wife?"

"Of course. Do you think *I* want a woman servant? You'll join Gwenhwyfar's household. Be one of her waiting-women."

I thought of Gwenhwyfar's house, which was a little small building, half hidden behind Arthur's big hall. I thought of the graceful, perfect girls she kept about her there, slender as withies. "She'll not take *me*."

"She will. To please Arthur."

"But I don't want to," I said, like a little child. I could feel the tears tickling my cheeks and creeping in salty at the corners of my mouth. "I don't want to leave you."

"Since when did it begin to matter what you *want*?" said Myrddin angrily, and turned away from me, stalked off with his shoulders hunched up like an old hoodie crow. Hid his face with one brown, bony hand like he was trying to rub the image of me off his eyeballs. Then turned and came back, kinder. "I have another purpose in this, Gwyna. When you are part of Gwenhwyfar's household you will keep your eyes open, and whatever you see you will bring to me."

"You want me to spy on her?"

"It would be wise for me know what goes on in her mind. She is the wife of the *Dux Bellorum* after all. I should know what goes on in her heart, and who could tell me that better than one of her own waiting-women?"

I wiped my tears, and hiccupped, feeling glad that he did not want to cast me off entirely.

"Now come," he said, "I want to sleep at your old lord's home on the hill tonight. We have miles to go yet."

He kicked his horse's flanks and it trotted ahead, leaving me to follow. I didn't try telling him the other thing I disliked about becoming a girl again – that it would mean the end of my friendship with Bedwyr.

But riding on, I started to see that my friendship with Bedwyr was almost ended anyway. Those last few months in Sulis there'd seemed a barrier between us, like the horn pane of a lantern. He was almost a man, with a scruffy stubble of beard that he was vastly proud of, and a host of boastful tales about his skill at hunting. He'd ride as a warrior with the war-band when the next fight came. I remembered the way that he and the other boys talked about girls. They hadn't the courage yet to talk *to* girls, but they talked *about* them endlessly. They watched them at the marketplace. Their heads turned like the heads of watchful birds when Gwenhwyfar's handmaidens passed them in the street. They laughed, and scoffed, and compared one with another, and I couldn't join in that talk. It uneased me to hear the way they spoke. How hard they thought of girls' bodies, and how little of their feelings. Like women were just creatures to be used and traded. They respected horses better.

I was sure Bedwyr never guessed the truth about me, but I knew I unsettled him. My smooth cheeks, and my voice that had never cracked and deepened as his had. Perhaps he thought my master had put me under an enchantment, so that I would never grow.

We skirted the borders of the Irishman's country, and turned towards my old home up the river-road. In the afternoon, when the flies hung in lazy clouds above the water, we came to the pool with the waterfall where it had all begun for me.

My skull was filled up with a moil of thoughts. While the horses drank from the shallows I knelt down and stared at my reflection in the water, and tried to see something girlish in my sunburned face. "Gwyna," I tried saying. And it was like I was calling her back from the dead.

XXIV

The old farmstead where I'd grown up had been rebuilt, and roofed with thick, fresh thatch. There were red cattle lowing in a pound, and children playing in the river when we came riding past at set of sun. They followed us a little way, naked and shrieking with laughter, calling out to Myrddin to tell them a story, for they'd seen the harp among his saddlebags and guessed his trade. They didn't look at me, and if any of them were my friends from the old times, I didn't recognize them. A lot of water had flowed downstream since then.

The Irishman was summering at Ban's old holding. It was better than his own damp hall in the hills, I dare say. He had got an Irish wife from Demetia with red cheeks and a quick smile, and their children squabbled like puppies beside his hearth. He seemed a happy Irishman, though when Myrddin raised the matter of the yearly tribute he owed Arthur he was quick to say how hard his life was; how half his cows had died last

131

winter, and Cunomorus of Kernyw kept sending raiding-bands to rob his tinners on the moors.

In return, Myrddin told him news from the east; Arthur's latest victories; the battle at Badon and the wedding to Gwenhwyfar. And when he had done he drew me forward out of the shadows where I'd been standing, and said, "This is Gwyna."

It was strange to hear my name made whole again after so long being Gwyn. "Yes," said my master, "I know she looks boyish, but she is a girl. Look closely. You see?"

They looked closely. They saw. My smooth face and slender fingers and the beginnings of my small breasts under my tunic. The Irishman gave a grunt of surprise.

"I brought her with me out of the mountains beyond Bannawg," Myrddin explained. "There is a dragon in those parts, and the people of the place make a sacrifice to it every year of three maidens."

The Irishman and his wife leaned forward, hooked. The cup bearers and the guards at the door pricked up their ears to listen, and even the children on the floor stopped pinching each other. I wondered what life my master was inventing for me, and did my best to look like I came from dragon-country.

"Well," Myrddin went on, "Gwyna's father swore he'd not let his little girl be breakfast for some worm. So when she was born he let it be known that his wife had given birth to a boy, and he dressed the child as a boy, and let her run with the boys of his place, and it is as a boy that she has lived ever since. But now that she is almost a woman, the ruse is wearing thin, and so I agreed to take her back to Aquae Sulis with me, there to enter the service of the lady Gwenhwyfar."

The Irishman nodded, as if this was the only reasonable thing to do, where dragons were involved.

"Trouble is," Myrddin went on, looking into the guest cup and finding it empty, holding it out for a slave to refill, "the trouble is, she knows nothing of the ways of women. She knows about horses, and the hunt. She has fought against the heathen Scots who plague her country whenever the dragon rests. But of being a maiden among other maidens she knows nothing at all."

The Irishman frowned slowly, realizing that something was being asked of him. "Then let her stay here a while!" he said suddenly. It was Myrddin who had put the idea in his mind, of course, but he thought it was his own, and seized on it, and flourished it proudly as a sign of his loyalty to Arthur and to Arthur's friend. "Yes! Let her stay here with Nonnita! Nonnita will teach her everything! Weaving and . . . and . . . the rest of it. Yes! Anything to help Myrddin!"

And so I stayed there through the summer's golden end, with Nonnita and her ladies, while Myrddin went travelling off alone, carrying new tales of Arthur down into Kernyw.

At first I lived in fear of running into someone I'd known when the hall was Lord Ban's place, but all Ban's followers were dead, or fled, or scattered off as slaves across the world, and I was never challenged. I doubt they would have known me anyway, for I'd been an urchin then, and now I was a maiden, with a dress of wool dyed kingfisher blue and a russet cloak that did up at the shoulder with a tin brooch. The clothes were faded, and had belonged to a girl who'd died of fever in the spring, but they fitted me. I was still enough of a boy not to care much about clothes.

The girls and women of the household didn't like me. They thought I was strange and clumsy and spoke too loud. But slowly I learned from them the things women do. They don't speak to the menfolk unless they're spoke to first, that's one. They don't tuck up their skirts and run. They sit for hours stitching and mending, which is slow torture, and embroidering, which is worse. They spin wool and linen. They weave cloth, singing in time to the clack of the clay weights which swing against the loom's frame. They steep meat in brine-barrels, and grind flour. They knead soft dough into loaves, getting flour on their arms and their cheeks and the tips of their noses. They make cheese, and butter, and cream, and buttermilk. They brew beer. They giggle. They whisper. They gossip.

It wasn't for me, that life. I missed Dewi and I missed my master. I promised myself I'd talk to him when he came back; plead with him, beg him, make him understand. "I tried being girlish," I'd tell him, "and it didn't work. I've been too long a boy. My voice isn't right. I don't move like the rest of them. My stitches don't hold. My yarn gets tangled. My loaves are soft as wet wool, or hard like river stones." And I told myself that Myrddin would see. He'd see his mistake. He'd find some other way, and I'd be a boy again.

"What was that dragon like?" they asked, every day or

so, until I cursed Myrddin for thinking up such a story.
"Did you see it at all? Did you ever hear it roar?"

"I heard it once," I told them. "I couldn't not. It was
loud enough to shiver rocks down off the mountainside.
And I saw it fly over. Big as three horses it was, with
bat's wings and bear's claws and a snake's tail."

"Was it red or green?"

I thought quick. "It was every colour. Red, green, all
the colours of the rainbow. It *rippled* with colours. And
in its jaws it carried a poor maiden from the village, as
big as Rhiannedd." And I pointed at the plumpest of the
lady Nonnita's girls, who turned pastry-coloured and
began to twitter. The rest stared wide-eyed at me, like
girls who would have nightmares later.

That night, like punishment for my lies, I woke with
griping in my belly, and a sudden marshiness about the
mattress under me. When I touched that damp and
lifted up my hand into the moon-glow from the window
my fingers were wet and dark with blood.

I thought I was dying. I'd not seen that much blood
since Badon, and then it had been other people's, not
spilling out of my own secret insides. My cries woke up
the other girls, and they thought I was as big a joke as
I'd thought them when I was scaring them with dragon-
stories. It was only my monthlies, said Nonnita. It was
the same for every woman in the world. We had tides,
like the sea. The moon called forth our blood. Did I not
know that?

Well, I'd heard something of it. But I'd thought myself
too boyish to suffer it. I lay and snivelled while the others

settled back into sleep. It seemed to me my own body had betrayed me, and sided with Myrddin. There'd be no way back into boyhood for me now. What would the warband make of me washing bloody rags once monthly?

But later, when I'd learned to cope with it, as we have to cope with all things we have no hope of changing, later I thought, Myrddin must have known. The same craft that let him know when rain was coming, or a mist would rise, had warned him what would soon be happening inside me. If we'd turned east instead of west after Ynys Wydryn, if we'd gone back to Sulis in the normal way, it might have been Bedwyr and the other boys I'd woken in my panic when it started.

Halfway through apple-harvest Myrddin returned, and said it had come time to leave. I was surprised by how sorry I felt, to be saying farewell to Nonnita and fat Rhiannedd and the rest. But I packed up my few belongings, and the things I had learned, and set off behind him again, riding eastward through the first of the autumn's rain. Now I was a girl I rode sideways on Dewi, which felt awkward and unnatural. The colour seeped out of my blue dress and sprinkled off my toes in sky-blue drips. My shoes shrank and pinched my feet, and my newly long hair hung down in rain-dark rat's tails round my face. The west wind blew up my skirts and chilled my damp legs through. I hunched inside my cloak and consoled myself with daydreams where I was a boy again, and running after my brother Bedwyr towards adventures. There were no adventures in my future now, I thought, glaring bitterly at Myrddin's back.

Women don't have them. They just suffer when their men's adventures go wrong.

We went slower and slower as we drew near Sulis. Myrddin kept thinking of reasons why we should turn off the road and call in at scruffy settlements where he could exchange his songs and stories for a meal and a place to sleep and a few cups of watered wine. I think he was afraid of learning what Arthur had been up to in his absence. Like a father who leaves his children alone for the first time. But when we reached the crown of the hills that stand behind the town, and looked down, it all seemed much as I remembered. It was a day of sunlight and sudden, shining showers, and the red roofs of the old Roman buildings were as bright as the autumn woods.

A few miles from the walls stood a place that must have been a rich man's house in the olden times, with outbuildings and slaves' quarters and a smithy of its own. It was all fallen into ruins, but a part of the main house was still roofed over and Myrddin turned in at the gateway. A man and woman were waiting there, country people from a nearby steading. They fell down bowing at the sight of us. "Welcome, Lord Myrddin," the man called out. "It has all been made as your messenger commanded."

"This is my new home," he told me, leaving them to quarter our horses and taking me inside, into a long room smelling of fresh lime-wash. He'd sent word from the Irishman's place, and hired the man and woman to make the house ready, and bring his few possessions there from his old place in Aquae Sulis. He said, "If

Arthur is to lead the armies of Britain he must be seen to be a Christian lord, and keep magic and wizards at arm's length. The old ways still speak to his soldiers and the common people, and they will know I am close. But when he talks to Maelwas's envoys he must be able to deny me. He must be able to say, 'Myrddin? That old trickster? No, he has no place in my town. . .'"

I went through a pantry to a window at the back of the place. It had had glass in it once. Through the rusty frames I looked out on a garden, a few bean-rows fluttering with leaves and curved green pods, a cabbage-patch, a huge old oak rising among the scrubby younger growth along the wood-shore. It was a giant of a tree, but ivy had wrapped it round, and rot had hollowed out its trunk, and it held up only a few last golden leaves to the afternoon sun.

The servants brought wine and food and then went home to their own place, over the hill; Myrddin didn't want them living there with him. When he had eaten he rode on to Sulis, leaving me alone. He told me later what he found there, and so I'll tell you, for I did nothing that evening except pace about between the bean-plots trying to get used to the strange, flappy freedom of my new skirts.

Myrddin rode up to the gates of Sulis and announced himself and entered into the town. The walls had been repaired as he'd suggested, and the men who guarded them looked better trained. The town was as shabby and prosperous as ever, and old friends greeted him, and took his horse for him when he drew near the forum.

There, inside a cage of wooden scaffolding, the feasting-hall he'd planned with Arthur in the winter-time was rising, and he felt proud and then disappointed as he looked at it. For it was a great thing that it had been built at all, and yet it was not as he'd imagined. Its round walls bulged out-of-true. The big, glazed windows he had planned were crooked holes. Instead of baked clay tiles, it squatted under a hat of thatch. Myrddin knew without even looking inside that it would be dark, and stuffy, and earthen-floored, and that the smoke of Arthur's feast-fires would gather in a fog under the leaking roof.

He felt suddenly uneasy. He had been away too long.

Arthur was in the old amphitheatre, watching a white colt run circles on a rein. There was a knot of men around him. As Myrddin walked towards them he heard a familiar, silvery laugh, and there was Cunaide, Arthur's woman from the old days, standing at Arthur's side.

"I thought you had put her away," said Myrddin, when the greetings were done and he could talk quietly to Arthur. "What has become of your new wife?"

"The heron?" Arthur kept glancing at the colt, admiring its glossy flanks and the sharp tilt of its lifted hooves. "A cold nature she has. Why couldn't you find me a wife like Cunaide, with a bit of fire in her?"

"You need Gwenhwyfar. She's Maelwas's kin. Her sons will be descendants of Ambrosius."

"What sons? She's barren ground. Six months now, and no sign of a child."

That might not be Gwenhwyfar's fault. After all, Cunaide's never fallen with child in all *her* years with

139

Arthur. But Myrddin didn't voice that thought, of course. Instead he watched the colt go past, head up, mane flying, hoof-falls echoing from the raked stone seats all around.

"A beauty, isn't he?" asked Arthur, glad to turn their talk from wives to horses. "I took him in a raid last week."

"You have been raiding against your neighbours? Arthur, Maelwas will never give you command over his war-bands if he thinks you are a brigand!"

"Maybe I don't need Maelwas's war-bands," said Arthur, eyes on the colt. "This is good country. A man could live well here, without going fighting into Saxon lands." He glanced at Myrddin quickly, sensing his disapproval. "Anyway, it wasn't Maelwas's lands I hit. We rode north and east, into Calchvynydd."

Myrddin was too angry to answer. He'd worked hard to convince Maelwas that Arthur was the one, and now he would have to begin his work again. He'd hoped for an alliance with the lords of Calchvynydd, too, but they wouldn't want it now. He watched the stolen colt go round, running and running and getting nowhere.

"I brought a young kinswoman of mine back from the west," he said at last. "My boy Gwyn has returned to his family, but his half-sister came home with me. She's a good girl. I thought she might make a handmaiden for Gwenhwyfar. . ."

Arthur didn't even trouble to pretend to be interested. "Yes. Why not," he said. He turned away, shouting at his horse-handlers, "Give him more rein! Let's see him run!"

XXV

And so my transformation back into a girl was completed, and I entered the world of women, and the household of the lady Gwenhwyfar. I swapped my knife for a bone needle, and my shield for a sewing-frame, and my dreams of hunts and battles for . . . well, for nothing, for I did not yet know what maidens dreamed about. Husbands, mostly, if the chatter of Nonnita's girls had been anything to go by. But I didn't want a husband. I sat and listened in the winter evenings around Gwenhwyfar's hearth while Gwenhwyfar and the older of her women told stories about love, and men who did high deeds for their beloved. But I'd lived among boys, and I knew how men really thought of women, and I knew love hadn't much to do with it.

That hidden, bidden life was as big a shock to me as when I'd first become a boy. My time in Nonnita's place had given me a taste of it, but at least Nonnita's women had work to do. It wouldn't have been fitting for Arthur's wife to churn butter, or go laughing to the orchards with the harvesters. Arthur had slaves to do those jobs. For Gwenhwyfar and her women there was only a little sewing – new dresses for ourselves, an altar-cloth for Bishop Bedwin's church – and a lot of gossip. I was no good at gossip. I was so afraid that if I opened my mouth some rough, rude phrase from the horse-lines would slip out of it I kept it shut most of the time, and the other girls, hearing me say nothing but mumblings in my hilly accent and seeing how I was not pretty, nor well born, nor clever with a needle, decided I was simple, and left me alone. Some of them were a little scared of me at first. They knew I had something to do with Myrddin, and someone started a rumour running that he'd made me by his magic, out of flowers. But Gwenhwyfar came to my rescue, and gathered them together, and told them I was just a poor waif from over the sea who they must treat with Christian kindness. They weren't kind to me after that, but at least they stopped waiting for me to turn into a hoodie crow and fly off with their souls. After a while they didn't even bother making the sign against evil when I came near.

Arthur didn't often trouble himself to come looking for his lady Gwenhwyfar. It was enough for him to know that she was there, safe in her part of the house with her women around her, like a proper wife. Unless there were guests he wanted to impress, it was Cunaide who sat beside him in his hall at each day's end. He hadn't much time anyway for women's company. They none of them did. The worlds of men and women were as different as night and day, air and water.

And what was I? I'd lived in both those worlds. I didn't fit in either.

I missed Dewi. Myrddin had said my pony would be happy in the long paddock behind his new place where there was good green grazing. But I missed him still, and I thought he'd miss me. Who'd comb the knots out of his forelock now, and stroke and cuddle him, and bring him treats? I couldn't see Myrddin doing that. Couldn't see Myrddin keeping him long at all. What use would a pony be, with no boy to ride it?

I missed Myrddin too. Sometimes, when Gwenhwyfar sent me off on an errand, I thought I would keep walking, out of the town and along the track that wound beneath the green downs to his house. But I was not supposed to go anywhere alone, and none of the other girls would have gone with me. They were afraid of Myrddin, and convinced they would be cursed if they ventured through the fence of charms and skulls and knotted strings which he had hung across the entrance to his place. A spell woven into every knot. And what would Myrddin say if I showed up at his door? He'd done with me, and cast me off. He'd not be missing me the way I missed him.

That first winter I lived for the times when I saw Myrddin. When we were all together at a feast in the great hall, and he would get out his harp and tell us a story and his eyes while he was speaking would find me, singling my face out of all the watching faces round the fire. Or when I went to the marketplace with other girls and he passed by. Then the others would cross themselves and back away, but since I was supposed to be his kinswoman they could not stop me speaking with him, and him asking me how I did, and me telling him. I always expected him to ask me what was going on in Gwenhwyfar's heart, too. After all, that was the reason he had given for sending me to live in her household. He seemed to have forgotten that I was his spy. Or decided that Gwenhwyfar was not worth spying on.

I was glad. I'd grown to like my new mistress, and I didn't want to go passing on rumours about her loveless marriage, not even to Myrddin. Cold and shadowy she might be, but Gwenhwyfar was kind, in her vague, distant way.

It was like living with someone who was already halfway to being a ghost, but a pleasant ghost. Sometimes, when the right mood was on her, she would tell us stories. An old slave of her family, her father's tutor, had told her these stories when she was a girl. Tales of Odysseus and Aeneas and Queen Cleopatra. A better class of stories than we grow in our wet island. And when some of the girls were sick with the marsh-fever that first winter she gave up all her comforts and tended them herself, sat up beside their pallets at night and bathed their hot faces with cool water and sang to them although she was half dead herself with tiredness. They grew better, too, although the doctors said they'd die. My mistress might not have Myrddin's knowledge of the uses of herbs and the writings of men with old Greek names, but she was a better healer than he'd ever been.

Of course, I didn't tell Myrddin that, either.

Bedwyr was off with Arthur's war-band when I first became one of Gwenhwyfar's flock, so I had a week or so to fret about him, and to wonder how he could fail to recognize me. But when he came riding home I barely recognized *him*. He was a warrior now, with a warrior's windy vanity, and five notches cut in the edge of his shield to show the men he'd killed. He'd put his life as a boy far behind him, stuffed it away as if it shamed him, and the memory of his friend Gwyn along with it. He eyed up all the girls as he rode past, but he only saw the pretty ones. I heard them giggling about him, how handsome he was and what a fine husband he'd make, and wondered how they'd feel if they knew I'd beaten him in running-races, and picked prickles out of his arse the time he'd fallen in that gorse bush.

Only once, around Christmas, at the dark hinge of the year, he stopped half drunk in the marketplace while I was passing with two other girls. "I know you," he said, staring into my face, which was veiled by wind-blown strands of hair. "I know you. You look like Myrddin's servant, Gwyn, who rode with me at Badon-fight."

"Gwyn's my half-brother, lord," I said, shy as a cat, with my eyes on his boots.

"I can see him in your face. You're as ugly as him!"

I looked at the cobbles in front of him, speckled with small rain. The girls beside me, who'd gone taut with envy when he singled me out, relaxed when they heard him call me ugly.

"I heard he went home to his people," said Bedwyr.

"To Armorica, lord," I mumbled.

"He thought they'd all been killed. But I suppose they escaped? And sent for him?" There was a crack in his voice. I wondered if he was about to start weeping, the way soldiers do about old comrades sometimes when they've emptied one too many wineskins. But a couple of his friends came up laughing, calling out things that made my companions shriek, and they carried him off towards some wineshop by the walls.

I watched him go, stumbling away from me into winter twilight, his friends holding him up when he threatened to fall over. When there was no fighting to be done the days of the men were as dull as the days of women, but instead of needlework and gossip they killed their time with drink.

I would have given anything to be a boy again, and running races with him in the water-meadows.

Arthur's wars went on. Sometimes he rode way east into the borders of Saxon country, but most of his raids were closer to home, against soft settlements in the marches of Calchvynydd and up into Gwent. It was harder than ever to know the truth of it, now that I was penned up in Gwenhwyfar's house. All I know is that Myrddin's Arthur-stories grew and grew, painting him as the red dragon of the prophecies who would drive the Saxons back across the sea. Sometimes, when the war-band rode home, there were empty saddles, and I heard that men I'd known as boys had fallen in this fight or that. Sometimes one of the girls I lived with would be given in marriage to one of Arthur's companions and another girl would come to take her place in Gwenhwyfar's household.

So two years ran away like rain down a culvert. They were good years, mostly. Maelwas was slow about making Arthur *Dux Bellorum* over all his war-bands, but he seemed content to let him hold Aquae Sulis and the other lands he'd taken further west. And on the northern border scraps of country which had been loyal to Calchvynydd were coming under Arthur's rule one by one, and the store-houses of Sulis were filling with tribute that should have been sent to Calchvynydd's king.

For me, in Aquae Sulis, nothing changed. Except that one spring night, after weeks of rain, I was woken by a rushing, crashing, slithering sound and went out of doors to see that Myrddin's great round feast-hall had fallen down.

XXVI

The small lives of women don't make for good stories. That's why there were no girls in the stories Myrddin told, unless they were there as a prize for the hero to win at the end of his adventures. So I'll take you south from Aquae Sulis and tell you about something else. I'll tell you what had happened at that hall on the seastrand, Peredur Long-Knife's place. I thought of it sometimes, wishing I was as graceful and girlish as young Peri, and dreaming back to the day when he and I had fooled that old drunkard saint into thinking he'd met an angel. But I never guessed the change that had come upon the place after I left it.

They called it Saint Porroc's miracle. Ever since Arthur's war-band came to claim a feast from Long-Knife's widow, the old saint had been on fire with the Holy Spirit. His monks processed about the ramparts, keeping everyone awake as they proclaimed the wondrous sign that God had sent them. For Porroc had been visited by the Angel Gabriel, who had commanded that he throw himself into the stormy sea. And Porroc had obeyed, trusting in the hand of God to buoy him up and keep him safe. No man could have lived in such a sea, they said. The great tempest of the world had been blowing, tearing the white tops off the breakers and driving fishing-smacks a mile inland. But the blessed saint had braved it and survived. Hadn't they seen with their own eyes his holy head bob on the long slope of the waves like a fisherman's float, hollering joyful prayers as each torrent of foam came curling down on him?

(What he'd actually been shouting was, "Oh, God! Help! Arrgh! Glug!" But I suppose that counts as praying.)

Saint Porroc grew more pious than ever. Crouched in that dazzling, sudden sunlight, in the gritty wind from the blown-open door, with the winged after-image of the angel seared on his squeezed-shut eyes, he had felt his soul reforged. His wallow in the icy sea had tempered it hard and true. The theft of the treasures of his church by the tyrant Arthur had only sharpened its edge. He was become a sword in the right hand of God.

He upended his wine-jars and let the sandy soil drink up his wine. He set free his pigs from their pens, and said a prayer over them before they went snuffling off into the woods behind the dunes, asking the Lord to grant them long lives. From now on he and his monks would live on water and cabbages. They would go each morning to the sea and cleanse themselves in the cold waves. If they were lucky the vicious undertow would carry them to Glory.

The monks weren't much pleased by the way things were going. Without meat and wine to warm them they shivered in their huts, which were no better than upturned baskets with the sea-wind blowing through them. The saint sent them into the hungry sea by day and by night. Their cabbagy diet caused great blatting farts to issue from beneath their robes like the trumpet-blasts of tuneless angels. One by one they slunk away, bound for places where God was served in less uncomfortable ways.

The saint's community took on a dwindling look, the empty huts rotting. But Saint Porroc never gave in to the sin of despair. He gave up his hermitage and went to and fro along the wind-scoured coast, preaching his miracle in the villages. The people set down their nets and listened. Their lives were hard. It gave them a strange sort of pleasure to hear that their troubles were their own fault. If only they'd been truer to the true God, and given up the old ways! The saint's words spurred them to a frenzy of smashing and breaking. Small shrines were battered into pieces. Decorations were torn off sacred wells. A wizened old sea-widow was found out to be a witch, and washed clean in the surf till she drowned.

And by way of reward God sent them bacon. The woods inland, which had never yielded anything more nourishing than a bramble, were suddenly home to pigs so tame it was simple to lure them close and stick a spear in them. A second miracle! Sick of fish, the villagers filled their bellies with roast pork and gnawed on the crackling, and agreed that the Kingdom of Heaven must be at hand.

From the walls of old Long-Knife's hall the girl called Peredur looked out, and saw the cook-fires burning. Sometimes the gusting wind brought snatches of distant, feverish prayers whirling through the gaps in the palisade.

The hall itself was falling into ruin. It had been a ruin really ever since Peredur's father died, but Saint Porroc and his monks had given it a semblance of life, like wasps rattling inside a rotten apple. Now that he had gone, and the monks' cells were coming apart like dried-out cowpats, the place felt empty. Spent.

Peredur's mother believed it was her own fault. Saint Porroc had told her before he left that she was a wicked woman for welcoming Arthur, that tyrant, that black she-wolf's whelp. She had fallen on her face and begged his forgiveness, but he'd not been in a forgiving temper, and stalked off, shouting curses over his shoulder. After that, she had retreated further into her own small world, whose walls were prayers. She spent whole days mumbling in her chamber. Her women lost patience with her. They grew tired of going hungry in that starveling hall, where the wind blew through the smoke-holes till the whole building hooted like a shawm. In ones and twos they went away. Some married fishermen. Some went to follow Saint Porroc. That girl who'd slept with Arthur on the night he visited ran off with one of the former monks. Only the old ones stayed.

Washed-out, ancient women with nowhere else to go. They rustled in the shadows of the hall like moonwort seeds.

Peri was changing, too. She'd grown even taller, and however often she altered her dresses they always looked wrong, stretched over her broad chest and strong arms. Her voice deepened. Flecks of beard began to show on her chin and upper lip and throat.

Her mother showed her how to shave, using the sharpened edge of a seashell. Peri noticed that none of the other women had beards. Did they shave in secret? "Hairiness is a blessing God sends only to a few maidens," said her mother wistfully. "It means that men will find you ugly, and you will never marry. You will stay here at my side always and always."

Peri wasn't sure how she felt about that. After the war-band left, that girl who'd slept with Arthur and would run off with the monk had teased her, saying she'd fallen in love with one or other of Arthur's bright shiny riders. But Peri had known even then that wasn't how it was. The visitors enchanted her, and filled her eyes for weeks, long after the last glitter of their helms and harnesses had vanished into the haze of sea-spray on the road. But she didn't want to marry any of them. She wanted to be *like* them. She wanted to have a horse, and go riding far away into the wide world on it, and leave the lonely hall behind.

In secret, among the empty monks' huts, she sharpened a hurdle-stake into a spear and practised throwing it. Soon, from twenty paces, she could drive it through the heart of the drawing of Saint Porroc she chalked on the chapel wall.

Using her maidenly skills – her weaving and her needlecraft – she made herself a pair of breeks, and a man's tunic. She ventured into Saint Porroc's chapel and stole down the old curtain from behind the altar, which she turned into a cloak. Needing a helmet, she crept into the kitchen and took a cooking-pot. She took a kitchen knife to be her sword. The cook didn't miss them. The cook was so old that she barely remembered her own name.

Dressed in her makeshift man's clothes, Peri ran through the woods, chasing birds, hunting pigs with her wooden spears, fighting desperate duels against the purple-plumed thistles that stood guard in clearings. She used the kitchen knife to cut her beautiful brown hair short, thinking that under her head-scarf no one would ever notice.

One day, she came home and changed back into her maiden's clothes in the shadow of the rampart and went inside the hall and found that her mother was dead. The old moonwort women rattled and rustled, laying out the body on a table. Peredur wondered what to do. Sea-water tears ran down her face, and she licked them absent-mindedly when they reached her mouth. It had never occurred to her that her mother would die.

It was spring. Still a windy, salt-scratched time on that cold coast, but at least there were some flowers out in the burying-place below the hall. She fetched a spade and dug a hole and buried her mother, and the women stood round and mumbled prayers while she shovelled the earth back.

She was propping up a flat rock for a headstone when Saint Porroc arrived. Somehow, word of the widow's death had reached him. He brought a great rabble of his followers behind him. Peri saw them from the rampart-top, running along the sea-shore like an army of beggars. Some stretched their skinny white arms up, as if they were hoping to snatch a few angel-feathers from the underside of Heaven. Others waded and wallowed through the sea, heads bobbing on the steep swell like a flock of mews. At the front of the procession, on an old cob horse, rode the saint himself. What hair he had left stood out around his fierce, holy face like a white-hot halo.

Up the plank-road to the hall they came, dripping and sneezing and praising Christ. The women scattered. Saint Porroc climbed down off his nag and stood blinking at Peri, who waited beside her mother's grave.

"The Lord has delivered this place from the rule of that sinful woman!" he bellowed, pointing at the fresh grave with a quivering hand. Too much preaching on windy beaches had left him with a voice like a bull. Peri covered her ears. "Death has taken her," the saint boomed. "This house which was hers will be the house of God now!" (For he had grown tired of sleeping on nets and fish-scales, see, and had taken the news of the widow's death as a sign that his wanderings were over and he should settle down in her hall.)

"But she is my mother!" said Peri. "I thought you had come to say the burial-words over her. . ."

"And who are you?" The saint had not been blessed

154

with good eyesight. He squinted at Peri, alarmed at hearing a man's voice in this place of women.

"I am her daughter."

"Daughter?" The saint stepped nearer. "Daughter?"

The hard work of grave-digging had streaked Peri's face with dirt and sweat. She had pushed the sleeves of her dress up, baring her lean, strong arms with their hatching of dark hair. In the confusion of her mother's death, she had not thought to shave. There in the sharp, raking sunlight of the burial-place there was no mistaking her for anything but what she was.

Saint Porroc's wiry eyebrows waggled. He'd shouted his throat raw telling the fisher-folk about the ways of the sinful, but he'd never seen anything quite so steeped in sin as Peri. He grabbed the brocade bodice of Peri's dress and dragged her past him, displaying her to his ragged flock.

"Behold!" he bellowed. "See what wickedness lurks in this house! What unnatural things this roof has sheltered! Look at this youth, this boy so wrapped up in iniquity that he dresses himself in women's raiment! Can we plumb the depths of such wickedness?"

Boy? What boy? thinks Peri, looking round, surprised. A roar bursts over her like a great wave of the sea, and with the noise comes understanding. She – he – looks round at the ring of shouting faces. Righteous anger, mostly, but with a bit of hard laughter mixed in, for what could look more ridiculous than this tall, gormless young man dressed in an embroidered gown?

Saint Porroc rips off Peri's head-scarf, baring the

clumsily shorn hair. "Be gone!" shouts the saint. "Leave this place! Run, if you can run, weighed down with such masses of sin!"

Peri's fist catches him in the middle of his holy face. The crunch of his nose breaking is louder than the laughter. There's a gasp. Silence, in which the saint totters backwards and sits down hard. One hand to his nose. Blood squirting between his fingers. Everyone draws back, expecting fire from Heaven, or the opening of a burning Pit. They pull each other aside to let Peri pass. He glances back once at his mother's grave, then strides towards the gate with all the dignity a young man in a dress can muster. One of the saint's men lunges at him, but others tug him back. Maybe they're afraid of facing this angry, hurt youth. Maybe they feel sorry for him.

Peri ran into the shelter of the woods and, safe in a cage of young birch, watched the saint's army taking possession of his home. He felt no anger towards them. They'd done him a favour, in a way. Told him what he was. A boy. A young man. His man's name made him proud now. Peredur, son of Peredur.

He'd known it always, really. A long time, at least. He thought back to the angel-day, and the strange thing that boy Gwyn had asked of him, "*Why do you dress like that?*" He'd wondered sometimes what Gwyn had meant by that. Now he understood.

And thinking of Gwyn made him think of Arthur.

That night he crept back secretly to his mother's hall by the sea. Inside the hall he could hear the saint's followers at their prayers. From his hiding place beneath the ramparts he fetched out his breeks and shirt and travelling cloak, his kitchen-weapons and his cook-pot helm. He knelt beside the fresh grave and said a prayer for his mother, wishing that she had lived long enough to give him the answer to Gwyn's question. Then he stole Saint Porroc's horse and set off to look for Arthur.

XXVII

A spring day stands in my memory, clear as a white stone. Blossom on the trees and a hundred hundred flowers in the long grass of the water-meadows. I'm about fifteen. My life as a boy lies far behind me, vague and half-forgotten. My hopeless hair reaches right down my back now, tied in two fat plaits. I wear a dress which was given me by my lady Gwenhwyfar, one of her own cast-offs.

I'm quite a young lady, you see. I gossip with the other girls my own age, and look after the young ones, and serve my mistress, and at the moment I am trying to catch the eye of the young man who has been sent out with us as an escort. His horse paces along beside us as we walk; its yeasty smell mixes with the scent of flowers, and the girls vie with each other to see who can walk closest to him. Unfortunately he has eyes only for Celemon. Celemon is Cei's daughter, but she has turned out nothing like her ugly father or her fat mother. She looks the way the rest of us look in our dreams. She has corn-gold hair, and grey eyes with flecks of gold and copper in them. She is wearing a wide hat, like a wheel of woven straw, because the sunshine brings her out in freckles, which she hates, but I think they suit her. And specks of sun come through the hat's weave and dapple her face with tiny patterns of light, so she is twice-freckled, dark and bright.

The little girls laugh, the bigger ones chatter. Even my lady Gwenhwyfar, going ahead of us, is smiling. We are going to picnic by the riverside.

Halfway there, someone spies a horseman coming down a hillside not far off. The girls clump together nervously. There have been rumours that the king of Calchvynydd has been boasting he'll take back the lands Arthur has scrumped from him. Is this the out-rider of a raiding-band?

Sunlight shines on metal as his distant horse brings him down through the trees. Our bodyguard kicks his pony in front of us and draws his sword, glad of a chance to show it off.

"He's alone," says Gwenhwyfar, in a warning voice, not wanting him to go and skewer some harmless traveller.

Through the wild flowers, glittering with light, the lone rider draws closer. His horse is the colour of sour milk. His cloak is a moth-eaten curtain. His helmet is a kitchen pot. One of the girls laughs, and the others lose their fear and join in as he swings his nag to a stop in front of us. His leather jerkin is too small, his boots are too big. An old carving knife is stuck through his belt, and the javelins bound to his saddle are just willow withies, sharpened to points and blackened in a fire. Under the shadow of the pot's brim his face is sun-browned, and his smile is big and brilliant.

"I'm looking for Arthur's place. Is that it there?"

It's Peredur. I'm so ashamed of him that I have barely time to feel astonished at seeing him here. I'm pleased to see that he's learned he's not a girl, but I wish he'd left that cooking-pot in the kitchen. He doesn't seem to know how dim-witted he looks. In fact, he sits there beaming at us as if he thinks he's the finest warrior in the whole island of Britain. I burn red, blushing for both of us.

Gwenhwyfar is well enough brought up not to join in her maidens' tittering. But even she can't quite keep a smile from her face as she goes forward to greet this newcomer. "Aquae Sulis is in Arthur's charge, and I am Arthur's wife," she says kindly. "And you – you have ridden far, sir?"

"Days and days!" Peredur can't stop grinning. He has *no idea* how to speak to a high-born lady! The girl's hiss with shock, hearing him address their mistress as if she were a goose-girl. His pot slips over his eyes so that he has to tilt his head back to look at us. Is he a madman? Dangerous?

"A saint took my home, so I've come to join Arthur's war-band," he explains. "I'm Peredur, son of Peredur Long-Knife."

He looks from face to face, as if it surprises him that we haven't all heard of him, or at least of his father. His eyes go past me without a pause. Of course, he'd hardly be expecting to find his old friend Gwyn among the maidens, and as a girl I'm not worth looking at, specially not when I'm standing next to lovely Celemon.

He reaches up to hold his pot in place with a soft, womanish gesture, which makes the girls about me titter louder.

"Arthur does want warriors, doesn't he? They told me that's what he came looking for when he came to my mother's house once. And there were lots on the big road, riding towards that town. I saw them from the hilltop."

Warriors on the road? Riding to Sulis? What can he mean?

I still remember how the laughter stopped, and the sunlight seemed to dim. We turned to look towards the town, and there, like blood in water, we saw the reddish smoke lofting from kindled thatch.

XXVIII

Those stories we'd been hearing that spring were not just stories. A war-band from Calchvynydd had threaded itself through the eye of the woods and into the vale where Sulis stood, and taken us all by surprise. Later, I wondered why no one had ridden in from the settlements they'd looted on their way to warn Arthur they were coming. But maybe the country people there were so sick of Arthur that they were pleased to see someone squaring up to him at last. Or maybe they didn't see any difference between these rival war-bands. They might as well let the raiders take their stuff as give it up in taxes to Arthur.

Whatever the reason, the raid came unexpected. The Calchvynydd men didn't breach the walls of Sulis, and twelve of them were cut down in the fighting round the gate, but they set fire to the great huddle of buildings in the wall's lee, and drove off a lot of cattle from the farms about. And as Arthur and his riders woke and buckled on their swords and spilled out to meet them, the

162

raiders broke this way and that, and two of them came thundering out across the water-meadows to where we girls stood watching.

"What is happening?" Peredur kept asking, innocent as a child. "What's that smoke? Is someone's house a-fire? We should warn them! Look, here comes somebody!"

Here came somebody all right. A stranger on a great tall roan horse, scarlet his cloak and his tunic, scarlet his helmet and shield. Behind him, shouting vengeance, rode Bedwyr.

Gwenhwyfar stood watching as the riders closed with us, pounding across the meadows through a storm of flung-up turf and hurtling flowers. We girls hurried this way and that, half wanting to run to the river and hide among the willows there, half thinking that it would be safest to break back to the town and hope we met no more raiders on the way. And the red man veered towards us, scenting plunder.

The boy who'd come to guard us kicked his pony to a run and went out to meet the raider, swishing his sword about. He was brave, I suppose. The raider's horse crashed sideways against his pony, like two ships colliding in a surf of flowers, and the raider's sword went through his throat. A splurt of blood fell down the sky, poppy red. The riderless pony cantered off. The raider glanced back, and saw Bedwyr driving towards him. He sheathed his sword and drew a short stabbing-spear, turning his snorting horse to meet the charge. "Bedwyr!" I squealed, with all the other girls. I saw Bedwyr's red hair flap like a flag in the wind. He'd

163

not bothered to put his helmet on. I thought of the hardness of blades and the thinness of skulls. "Bedwyr!"

Bedwyr raised his shield as the spear came at him. The blade glanced from the shield rim and drove down, through Bedwyr's leg, nailing him to his own horse. He screamed. The horse screamed. They went down together, Bedwyr underneath. The raider dragged his own horse round and his hard eyes slid across our faces. Far away, more riders were speeding across the meadows. The raider's comrades, off to some safe place to count their loot and stolen cattle. I saw that he was scared. Scared to rejoin his friends without some stolen treasure to brag about.

I ran to Gwenhwyfar. I don't think she'd moved since all this began. She had one hand up to Peredur's saddle, as if to stop him spurring his old horse forward and trying to fight the raider with his kitchen-knife. I shoved her sideways as the raider's red horse cantered towards her. But he wasn't after Gwenhwyfar. He didn't know who she was. He'd seen a brighter treasure; pretty Celemon. I heard her screech as he leaned out of his saddle and swept her up. I saw her legs kicking as he dumped her across his saddle-bow and urged his horse towards the river. Her hat bowled down-wind.

I called her name. The other girls were scattering. "Celemon!" I shouted.

"I'll stop him!" called Peredur. "I'll save her!" He dug his heels into the flanks of his horse and was away, holding his pot on his head with one hand, clinging to the bridle with the other, a scared girl diving out of his path.

The red raider was pushing his horse hard, but it had been hurt by its collision with the pony, maybe lamed. I was afraid that Peredur would catch him up, and challenge him. I started to run. I stopped and bunched up my skirt and stuffed it into my belt, and then ran on. Thistles slashed at my bare legs. I slithered through a cowpat, startling up a storm of brown dung-flies. I ran till the back of my throat was one cold gasp, and I'd lost sight of the horses. Then I saw sunlit metal flash, away among the willows. The red man had reached the river, and was casting to and fro along the steep bank, looking for a place to cross. Peredur was galloping to cut him off.

I ran again, and reached them as they met. Peredur was lucky. The red man was encumbered by the squiggling girl across his horse's shoulders. He hadn't a chance to draw his sword. Instead, as Peredur came riding at him with one of those toy spears upraised, he caught it by the shaft and wrenched it sideways, tugging Peredur out of the saddle. I heard the yelp of surprise as he fell.

The sour-milk nag, indignant at being made to run so far, trotted off a little way along the riverside and started cropping the grass.

The red raider swung himself down off his horse and tramped back to where Peredur had fallen, pulling out his sword as he went. The boy lay face up. The pot had come off his head and rolled down the river bank, which was steep just there. I could see spreading ripples in the water where it had sunk. The red man lifted up his sword.

I wanted to shout out and tell him no. I wanted to beg him to take pity. But they don't have pity, those armoured, riding men. Even if he left Peredur alive, he'd still make off with Celemon.

So instead of words, I threw myself at him. Down the slope between the willows, across a few yards of short green grass. I can't have weighed half what he did, but he didn't know I was there, and didn't see me until I was almost upon him. He was turning towards me when we hit. I reckon I caught him off balance. He went backwards with me on top of him, and the river took us both.

I was all right. I felt safer in water. I swim like a fish, remember? But the raider had a helmet, and a belt with big bronze fittings, and a scabbard with more bronze on it, and a fat gold ring around his neck, and all those wanted suddenly and very much to be down in the soft mulch of the river bottom. A big bubble came out of his mouth as he sank. Squarish it was, and silvery, like a pillow of light. It wobbled past me to the surface, and I kicked free of him and went after it. Hauled myself out and sat shivering, watching the ripples spread.

When the water was still again I climbed back up the bank. The dead man's sword stood in the nettles, point down, still quivering, where he had dropped it as he fell. There was shouting from the water-meadows. More of Arthur's riders had come to save Gwenhwyfar and her ladies. Celemon was snivelling quietly, hung head down across the raider's horse. I left her to it, and went to

Peredur. He lay where he had fallen, looking dead, but when I touched his face and the water from my wet hair dripped on his eyelids he frowned and sat up, trying to look fierce.

"Where is he?"

"Don't you remember?" I said. "You fought him, and he's dead."

Peredur looked about for the body. He put up one hand to his head and ruffled his tangled brown hair. "My helm. . ."

"It went in the river," I said. "It smelled of soup, anyway. We'll find you a better one."

"And the red man?"

"He went in the river, too."

"He was Arthur's enemy?"

I nodded.

"And I defeated him?"

"Oh yes," I said, and nodded so hard that even I started to believe that it was true. And I turned and grasped the hilt of the sword and tugged it out of the earth, and gave it to Peredur.

XXIX

I was steeped in river water, but no one thought to ask me why as we tramped back across the fields to Sulis. I doubt they even looked at me. They were all too taken up with Bedwyr, who had been dragged out from under that wreck of horsemeat by two of his comrades and carried back to the town on a plank, trying hard all the way not to weep at the pain of his gashed and shattered leg. The girls praised his courage in a wistful way, knowing that he'd end up dead or crippled, and less handsome either way. They cooed and sighed about him, and saved their smiles for Peredur, who rode ahead on the dead raider's roan mare, clutching the dead man's sword and looking confused but happy to find himself so suddenly a man. Celemon, who was unhurt, was busy telling everyone how brave he had been; how he had challenged the man who'd taken her, and stuck one of those silly willow-spears clean through him.

A part of me was sorry that I'd given Peredur my triumph, and angry at him for accepting it so easily. But

Peredur wasn't someone you could be angry at for long. He was too open and smiling, and he looked too good. I stole glances at him through my wet hair all the way. Filled my eyes with him, and felt sorry, knowing that he'd be swallowed into the warrior-life, and learn to hide all his sweetness under bluster and ironmongery.

Arthur was red and shouting when we found him. Striding through the forum, past the rubble-heaps where the banqueting hall had been, demanding to know how the raiders had been allowed to come and shame him at the gates of his own place. Knocking down any man who tried to give him an answer. It was useless to tell him, as Cei was trying to, that only a few farmers and slaves had been killed, and a few huts set ablaze. The insult hurt Arthur more than the raid itself. The thought of men telling how he'd been outwitted.

But even he looked twice at Peredur. His anger faltered. "Who's this?"

Gwenhwyfar, kneeling before him, told him quickly what Peredur had done. Arthur looked at him, and put his anger aside, and smiled. "Peredur Long-Knife's son, is it? That mother of yours told me there were no men left in her fish-stinking hall. But you look like him, all right, and you fight like him too. You'll ride with us now, eh?"

In the ground behind the marketplace horsemen were mounting up, getting ready to ride out and cut off the raiders' retreat and win back the cattle they had stolen. Arthur heaved himself into his saddle and drew Caliburn and swished it about in the sunlight,

169

bellowing some bloodthirsty oath. I saw Peredur clambering on to a fresh mount, and then lost sight of him as the riders clattered away.

I tried not to care. I thought if I didn't care, he might come back all right. It's the people you let yourself care about, they're the ones fate takes away from you. Look at poor Bedwyr.

They had carried him to the dingy, damp-smelling place which he shared with Medrawt and with Medrawt's wife and babies. Gwenhwyfar sent her girls home, and asked me to come with her, and went inside to see how he was being cared for. I thought she had asked me to go with her because I was the oldest, but perhaps she already knew we would find Myrddin there. He was stooping over the pallet where Bedwyr lay, his fingers parting the lips of a wound so deep that it made me feel sick and scared to look at it. It was like a red mouth.

"He'll not walk again," I heard Myrddin say.

Medrawt was there, at the head of the bed, cradling his brother, who was asleep, or unconscious. "Better to die than live a cripple," he said grimly. "Don't say it! God will heal him."

The wound in Bedwyr's leg filled with blood and dribbled it down on to the coarse sheets, which were already sodden. Medrawt's dogs nosed close, and Myrddin cursed them and kicked them away. I looked at Bedwyr's white face, and felt glad I'd drowned that raider.

"Bring him to my house," said Gwenhwyfar.

The men hadn't noticed her till then. She stood near

170

the bed with a corner of her mantle raised to her face, as if to shield herself from the smell and sight of blood. She looked pale, but she always looked pale. She said, "He won't heal in this place. He needs quiet, and air, and cleanliness."

"He needs splints and bandages more," snorted Myrddin.

"Then splint and bandage him, and bring him to my house," said Gwenhwyfar. "I shall tell my women to make ready for him."

Medrawt said, "Do it!"

My master glared past Gwenhwyfar at me, like he was wondering if I was part of this challenge to his doctoring. Then he nodded, and snapped at me to find a straight ash-stick and tear some linen for bandages, as if I was his servant still. But while we were working together, wrapping the wrecked leg in white cloth that kept soaking through red, he asked me softly if I was all right, and if I had been harmed or frightened by the raiders. As if it meant something to him. As if I meant something to him.

At last the bleeding slowed. Myrddin lifted Bedwyr's head and made him drink a cup of wine with stinking herbs in it. Then he was carried in the twilight across to Gwenhwyfar's hall, and I went with him, and looked back and saw Myrddin watching from the rushlight-glow in the doorway of Medrawt's place.

That was a summer of small wars. Arthur meant to teach Calchvynydd he was a man they should respect. Stories are all well and good, he told Myrddin, but if you want men to respect you, you have to show them strength. They burn one of your holdings, you burn two of theirs. Most days that summer, if you stood on the hill-tops above Sulis and looked northward, you'd see the smoke of torched thatch on the sky.

The cattle driven off in that first raid came home again, along with Arthur and his riders, flushed with revenge and carrying the heads of three dead raiders on spears. I saw Peredur ride in with them, still looking bewildered by it all. I think the world of men was not turning out to be quite as he'd expected. He was not quite what they'd expected, either. He didn't speak the language of men. He didn't know the rules I'd learned in my time among the boys. Cei and Medrawt and the rest treated him now as a simpleton; a sort of mascot. Medrawt made him the butt of the same half-friendly jokes he'd had flung at himself when he was younger. Peredur didn't ride with them again that summer, but stayed with the garrison in Sulis.

It wasn't that he was cracked, I tried telling Celemon and the rest. Just he'd been raised different, and come to things by his own road. He'd not grown up around fighting men, the way we had. That was why he stared so much at them, and took such a delight in polishing the fittings of the old shield they gave him till it shone, and thought it looked splendid to fit jays' feathers in his helmet and strut around the town like a dunghill cock. But the girls just teased him more, and laughed at the way he followed Celemon with his eyes, as if she was a lady out of one of Myrddin's tales that he listened to in the fire-hall of a night.

Peredur didn't seem to feel their cruelty. He forgave them everything. He was God's fool. He liked everyone. Well, almost.

When he'd first come my heart jumped up inside me. I remembered how glad I'd been of him when I first found him, just the gladness of knowing there was someone else in the world like me. I thought he'd be a friend to me, and one day soon I'd tell him (if he didn't guess) that that boy he'd met at his mother's hall that time was me.

I'd never told anyone my old secret, see. Even Celemon, who was my friend, would have been sure to think it strange or wicked that I'd been a boy, and she'd have told the other girls, and it would have spread all round Aquae Sulis, how Myrddin had disguised me. But telling Peredur would be different. We'd keep each other's secrets, and laugh about our strange pasts, my boyhood and his gowns. It would lead to deeper friendship and – who knows? I was so alone in my life. For a while I woke up every morning vowing that today would be the day I'd go to him. "Don't you remember how we scared old Saint Porroc?" I'd say. "Didn't you look a treasure, in your shift?" In my mind, I could already see his brown eyes widening, and his slow smile.

But it turned out Peredur, who liked everybody, didn't like me. I frightened him, maybe, or the sight of my face reminded him of his first and only fight; how scared and startled he'd been, and how doubtful his victory was. When he saw me his hand always went to the hilt of the red man's sword, which he wore on his belt, as if he thought I might take it away from him. When he saw me coming towards him in the town he'd go some other way.

Well Gwyna, you fool, I thought, what did you expect? And after a while I stopped trying to find excuses to talk to him. And sometimes, when the other girls were laughing about him, I'd join in.

Life in Sulis was good with Arthur off about his wars. The old buildings gave sighs of relief and let their shoulders sag, basking in the summer sun. Outside the walls, riders patrolled the margins of the ripening wheat. Cei, who ruled in Arthur's absence, made an easy lord. Nights in the feast-hall were full of laughter and stories of the old days, and sometimes he'd come to pay his respects to Gwenhwyfar, which was more than Arthur ever did.

He was a good man, Cei. In the stories Myrddin told

he was quick-tempered, violent and clumsy, but in truth he was none of those things. I think Myrddin made him that way in the stories because he was afraid that men might prefer him to Arthur if they knew what he was really like. Cei laughed off the slanders. "They're only stories," he would say. "What do stories matter?" But he wasn't stupid. He knew as well as Myrddin that in the end stories are *all* that matter. I think Myrddin's stories hurt him, and had led to a dying away of the friendship between them. At any rate, I never heard of him going to visit Myrddin at his new place outside the town. He visited Gwenhwyfar instead, and Gwenhwyfar liked him, and kept him talking often late into the evening, while we girls sat round yawning and dozing and wondering how they found so much to talk about, our fine lady and this rough old soldier.

Cei must have known who I was. He can't have forgotten the night he'd helped Myrddin turn me into a boy. But he never spoke of it, nor gave any sign that he knew, nor treated me different from the other girls. He was a good man.

Meanwhile, Bedwyr mended slowly. His sickroom was one of Gwenhwyfar's own chambers, which had doors that folded open to reveal a terrace and a tangled summer garden. A trickle of water fell endlessly into a cistern. There were foxgloves.

Bedwyr's fever left him pale and bony as his brother. The pain and shame of his bust leg left him bitter. He didn't think he'd ride again, or fight, and what good was a man who couldn't ride or fight? He snapped at the girls Gwenhwyfar sent to tend to him, until we hated going. He had a girl of his own he'd got in some raid the year before and grown fond of and given gifts and good clothes to, and she came into the house to be near him when he was first hurt, but he sent her away, as if it made the shame worse to have her there weeping for him. He cast her off, and after a while another of Arthur's men took her. After that it was just Medrawt, who would call in when he was not riding with Arthur.

We'd got off to a wrong start, me and Medrawt. You'll remember that business in the burning wood, how he waved his sword at me and sent me to seek shelter in the river. I'd never liked him since. But the way he was with Bedwyr changed my mind about him. He was a prideful man, and cold, and hard to like, but he wasn't all cruel, not by miles. He sat by his brother's bed, talking about old times with him and telling him he'd be up and running by fall-of-leaf, while I stood waiting, forgotten, clutching fresh sheets or the jug of watered wine they'd asked for, and saw a different Medrawt, a loving brother, a man who talked fondly about his wife and his children. I wondered if they were all like that, when you stripped the armour and the pride off them.

By summer's height, in the bright, bee-buzzing, flower-full days, Bedwyr was trying to walk. Gwenhwyfar went one afternoon to see how he was faring, and she took me with her. She had to take someone, I suppose, for Arthur's wife couldn't ever be alone with another man, even a poor cripple young enough nearly to be her own son, and I was about the only girl who would go near his room by then, he'd been so fearsome to the others.

176

While I spread fresh sheets on the bed, and smoothed the pillows, Bedwyr went leaning on a staff across the terrace, into the bobbing pinkness of the foxglove-filled garden. Each step tore a grunt of pain from him as he set his weight on his twisted leg. Watching him go, it was all I could do not to run and give him my arm to lean on. But I wasn't his friend Gwyn any more, and he was a man now. It would shame him if a girl offered him help.

"That's good!" said Gwenhwyfar kindly, from the terrace-edge. "That's good!" But she was lying. Bedwyr was as wobbly as a baby and as slow as an old, old man. Halfway to the cistern he fell, and knelt there, sobbing.

And Gwenhwyfar went to him without a word, and put her arms around him, and rested his head against her shoulder, and stroked his hair. And I stood in the shadows behind the folded-back doors, and watched, and didn't move or speak, because Bedwyr would hate it if he knew someone had seen him crying like a child. But I felt different about Gwenhwyfar ever after. I don't remember my mother, but the way she held him, the way she cuddled him close, that was the way I'd have wanted my mother to hold me if I'd had one and I was sad about something.

And after a little time Bedwyr's sobs stopped and he went still. And Gwenhwyfar kept her white hand moving on the red-gold of his hair. And there was something strange and new in her face when she looked up at me. And she said, "Gwyna – fetch us a little sweet wine, and some of those barley-cakes."

*

177

When Arthur came home for a few days, my mistress grew pale and thoughtful, and called Celemon and me to her chambers. We spent a long time dressing her in different gowns and mantles, and folding them away again when she thought something about them was wrong. When she was finally ready, she went alone to Arthur's hall.

I can see how it must have gone, that meeting, although I wasn't there.

Arthur is sprawled on a chair in his bedchamber, soaking his feet in a basin of water. He's just back from a fight. The cheek-pieces of his helmet have bruised the corners of his face.

He sends his slaves and servants scurrying away when Gwenhwyfar lifts the door-curtain. He would never admit it, but she unsettles him, his tall, quiet wife. She has a grace that speaks to him of old ways that he will never have, no matter how much land and treasure he can grab. In the first months of their marriage, when she was so cold towards him, he used to hit her. He would make the blood of the Aureliani bloom under her skin in purple bruises. She is his wife, after all, so he's a right to bend her to his will. But the more he hit her, the worse he felt. That's why he keeps his distance. Let her have her own life, her own household, her own women, so long as she's there to be displayed when allies and rivals come visiting. She's just one of the things that a powerful man needs.

She kneels before him. Bows low, and hopes he's well. Praises God for sending him safely home. He signals with his hand for her to rise.

"I have something to ask of you, husband."

"What's that?"

"The boy Bedwyr. . ."

Arthur twists his mouth sideways. Young men maimed make for bitter thoughts. Bedwyr had been a favourite of his once. He'd had high hopes. "It's evil luck. My own sister's son. He would have been one of my captains. But now. . ." He shrugs. "Myrddin says he'll die."

"He'll not die."

"Live crippled then, and what's the difference? But you needn't fear for him. He'll be looked after. His brother Medrawt will take him in. And I'll make sure he's got no need to beg. I don't forget my companions."

"He's a proud boy," says Gwenhwyfar. "He won't want to sit by his brother's hearth all his life, watching the women work."

Arthur's face darkens. He doesn't like to talk of things like this. Wishes Bedwyr had been killed outright. What's God playing at, sparing the boy's life but not his leg? Better a dead hero than a living cripple. "What else can he do?" he demands.

"He can guard me," says Gwenhwyfar, treading careful now. She knows how thin her husband's patience is. She feels like she's walking out across ice, with cold deeps of drowning-water under her. "He can guard me. Let him keep his sword and his place in the feast-hall, but instead of riding with you he can stay here to protect me and my ladies. It will give him a meaning. That's all he needs."

Arthur is surprised. Who'd have thought she'd understand so well what goes on in men's hearts? He looks at her, there in the rush-light dusk, and she's not unbeautiful. For a moment he wishes he loved her. Good, it would be, to ride home from battle to a wife like that. A woman his own age, instead of some chit like Cunaide who's just vanity and giggles and nothing but air between her pretty ears. He grins at Gwenhwyfar, suddenly shy and wanting to please her.

"All right, you can have Bedwyr for your bodyguard. Get a couple of those girls of yours to help him stand up if there's a fight."

"Thank you, my lord." Gwenhwyfar bows, showing him the top of her head, her neat white parting. She stands and turns to go.

"Gwenhwyfar. . ."

Looks back at him, a hand already on the door-curtain. Wary as a doe. "What, my lord?"

Nothing. He waves her away. Doesn't know what he was thinking of. What would his men say of him if he went soft over the old heron? "Go, go," he says, and takes his feet out of the basin, and starts shouting for his slaves and Cunaide.

Well, it must have been something like that. Because next day, she went to Bedwyr and told him he was to be her bodyguard – "Captain of my guards," was how she put it, though I don't know who those guards he was to captain were, unless it was us girls or the spearmen on the town wall. But it was as good as medicine to Bedwyr. He set about learning to walk again, and this time he would not give up. It wasn't long before you'd see him in the town, striding along stiff-legged, his face stone-white with pain and determination, using an old spear-handle for a crutch.

When I next met Myrddin he said, "Your friend has mended well. I didn't think he'd walk again on that leg. Your mistress has done good for him."

"They have done good for each other," I said. Gwenhwyfar was happier that summer than I'd ever seen her. Saving Bedwyr had made her feel useful, I thought. When she was with him, she was in a state of grace.

My old master scratched his nose thoughtfully. "It may be," he said. "Sometimes, on our way through the world, we meet someone who touches our heart in a way others don't."

He looked at me like he was going to say something more, but then he shook his head, and turned, and went away. He'd got a curly-headed boy of eight or nine who carried his bags and belongings for him. I think the boy was the son of that couple who'd made his house ready for him the year I came back to Sulis as a girl. For a moment, as I watched him follow Myrddin away, I felt envious. Gwenhwyfar's hall felt empty now with Bedwyr gone, and the emptiness reminded me again how thin the lives of women were beside the lives of boys and men.

XXXI

The Irishman rode in, bringing bad news from Arthur's lands out west. King Cunomorus of Kernyw had sent his warriors raiding across the Tamar again. They'd taken tin and cattle from the Irishman, and the Irishman wanted Arthur's help to get revenge. "Otherwise," he said, "how can I afford to pay Arthur the tribute I owe him? How can I pay him those three ingots of tin, those three loaves as broad as the distance from my elbow to my wrist, that tub of butter and the sow?"

His hill-country was so remote he hadn't heard of Arthur's quarrel with Calchvynydd. When he was told, his face fell. He knew he'd little hope of Arthur's help. Truth was, Arthur had all but forgotten him. And anyway, it was years since he'd sent Arthur tribute.

But Cei wanted to be polite, so there was a feast for the Irishman and his men. After, in the hot half-light around the hall-fire, Myrddin told us a tale of a young man who came to Arthur's court asking for help to win the hand of Olwen, daughter of Ysbaddaden, chief of the giants. He wove it full of quests and hunts, and the boar Twrch Trwyth was in there, and plenty of battles, to remind the Irishman's followers that Arthur was still a great battle-leader, who would deal with Cunomorus just as soon as he finished trampling the bones of the warriors of Calchvynydd into their own chalk hills. But what I mostly remember about that night was the way he spoke of the love of this young man for Olwen, and of Olwen's beauty, and how her hair was yellower than the flowers of the broom and her flesh whiter than the foam of the wave and her cheeks redder than the reddest foxglove. She was so lovely that four white flowers sprang up where she trod. And during these parts of the story most of the boys and the young men yawned, or laughed among themselves, or called out for their cups to be filled again by the lads who waited with the pitchers.

But Bedwyr, sitting with his bad leg stretched out stiff in front of him, stared into the embers of the big hearth with a look I couldn't read, a sort of shining look, as if there was wild happiness walled up inside him. And sometimes he seemed to be looking across the fireplace to where we maidens sat, in a neat cluster about Gwenhwyfar. I wondered if he had let himself fall in love with one of us now that he was on the way to being a man again, and if he would come back to our hall soon to woo Celemon. I even wondered if it was me he was looking at, and let myself think how it would be to be Bedwyr's woman. I would never have imagined such a thing in daylight, little dun-haired, brown-faced me, but in the kind shadows of the hall and the light of

Myrddin's story even I felt beautiful. As if four white flowers might spring up where I trod.

And the logs crumpled into ashes in the hearth, and the sparks went up out of the smoke-holes in the roof, and Myrddin's words went with them, out into the summer night.

Summer grew old and golden, each barley-plot a yellow-white sea. Season of tick-bites and fly-stings. Of salt-white sweat stains under the arms of my linen summer kirtle. Of walls and pavements hot as new-baked bread.

Gwenhwyfar decided to go bathing again, which I think she had forgot while she had Bedwyr to doctor. And since the girls she'd trusted to go with her in earlier years had husbands and children now, she looked about her for someone else to attend her on her evening visits to the baths, and she settled upon me.

"Me, lady?" I said, when she told me.

"You." We were alone in a quiet part of her house, the others busy somewhere. She said, "Bishop Bedwin would be angry at me if he knew I went near those old temples. So I must not have it spoken of. It will be our secret, Gwyna. And I know that you can keep secrets."

"I have no secrets from you, lady."

She laughed at that. "No? But you used to be Myrddin's boy."

I'd not expected that. Years it was, since that time I stumbled on her in the old pool. She'd never spoken of it, or given any hint that she knew it was me she'd seen that day. She'd stored it up, that little nugget of knowledge, till she needed it to buy my silence with. "You are fond of your old master, aren't you?" she said. "It might go badly with him if men ever found out about his trick."

"Trick?" I felt hot and cornered. There seemed no point lying, but I tried anyway. "I don't know what you mean. . ."

"Oh, Gwyna," said my mistress. "When Arthur has too much wine, he often tells that tale of his, how the lake-woman came up out of the depths and gave him Caliburn. But you and I know that there's no lake-woman. She's only a pagan superstition. The shadow of some old water-goddess, fading away in the light of the new God. So Myrddin must have had someone to help him when the sword was given to Arthur. Someone who could swim like a fish."

She'd worked it all out, see. She'd probably worked it all out that long-ago evening when we faced each other in the pool.

"Imagine how foolish Arthur would look if it became known that Myrddin had a girl to help him," she said. "And Arthur has no love for those who make him look foolish. So I shall keep your secret, Gwyna. And you will keep mine."

In the lavender-coloured, lavender-scented dusk I went down between the ivied houses with her, down to where the old baths waited, more crumbledown and overgrown than ever. I expected her to go into the building where I had seen her that other time, but instead she went round to the temple. A winding, secret

185

path wound through the furze-bushes that had grown around the gateway, leading to a gap in the planks that Bedwin's priests had nailed up there, and into the nettled courtyard itself. Gwenhwyfar threaded her way purposefully through the scrub, past old stone altars. I trailed behind her, wary, feeling suddenly afraid, and sure some danger waited for us in those ancient buildings.

"Lady, this is a haunted place!"

She looked back at me. "God will watch over us, Gwyna. I am not afraid of ghosts. But if you are, wait here. Make sure nobody comes."

She didn't go up the stairs into the pillared, roofless temple, but turned left to where an old grey building stood. Massive buttresses strengthened its walls. Stone nymphs with their faces knocked off still guarded an arched doorway. From the darkness inside I caught the sound of seething water, the hot mineral smell of the sacred spring.

"That water is too hot to bathe in!" I called. My mistress didn't look back. She climbed the three worn steps and went inside.

I waited. Birds hopped and fluttered in the bushes all about me. The white flowers of bindweed that had twined over the altars glowed soft, ghostly white in the twilight. The sounds of the town seemed muffled and far-off. A terrible stone face stared at me out of a tangle of vetch, round as the sun, with long hair and beard twirling out into stony flames and serpents. I kept telling myself what Myrddin had always taught me. There are no gods, no ghosts, no spirits. Nothing but our own fears. But my fears were enough for me. A blackbird started chittering in a clump of brambles and set me running like a deer, after my mistress, up the steps and into the soft, steamy dusk of the old shrine.

It was the chamber I'd looked into once with Bedwyr. Up there were the three windows we'd peered down through, opening into the caverny ruins of the big bath. The rest was greenish dark. I could hear the ferns stirring on the walls, the water simmering in its basin. I blinked, moving forward noiselessly, letting my eyes grow used to the shadows. I was about to call out "Lady," when I saw her in the shadows by the fallen statue of the goddess. There was someone with her, and he clung to her and she to him so tight, like if they let go of each other for even an instant they'd fall. I stared and stared, not understanding. I saw her lift up her face to his in that green twilight. Rapt, she looked. Her teeth showed pale as she whispered some smiling thing, drawing his face to hers, his mouth to her mouth, and her hands in his red-gold hair.

And then I knew it hadn't been me that Bedwyr had been gazing at across the feast-hall fire, nor Celemon neither.

Mouse-quiet, I backed out of that place. The ghosts in the courtyard didn't scare me now. I stood shaking, watching the nettles sway, feeling hot and stupid and ashamed.

That day in the garden, when Bedwyr tried to walk, and failed, and wept in Gwenhwyfar's arms. Had that been the start of it? "Gwyna – " she'd said. "Fetch us a little sweet wine, and some of those barley-cakes."

So off I'd gone to the storeroom. And I imagine her standing there, with Bedwyr in her arms. And he raises his head from her shoulder, and they look at each other, and they don't move, but still something has changed in the way that they are holding each other. And she knows that he is wanting to kiss her, this handsome young man. And he knows that she wants him to. And still they don't move, or speak, or breathe till they hear me coming back with the wine and cakes. Then, guiltily, they pull apart, each staring at the other's face. . .

I felt as huge a fool as Peredur. For not seeing what was in front of me. For not understanding what I had seen. And I felt frightened, because this fire they'd lit in each other would burn them both up one day, and burn me too if I wasn't lucky. Arthur had no love for those who made him look foolish.

XXXII

What is Bedwyr thinking? Why can't he see the danger? I want to grab him in the street, push him into a doorway and say, "Bedwyr, it's me, look, your old friend Gwyn." Say, "She can't be worth it. Don't you understand what will happen when Arthur finds out?"

But he does understand. He *likes* the danger. He's been trained for danger; lived for danger all his life, been taught to go and seek it out on battlefields and in the hunt. And this summer past it's all been taken from him. The best future he can hope for is to be a half-man, riding patrol along the field-banks, watching over Arthur's cows and barley. The pain in his bad leg always, souring him. Gwenhwyfar makes him feel like a man again. Arthur has no use for a broken warrior, but Arthur's wife has.

Each morning when he goes out to see the horses in their stable behind his brother's house he looks across the smoky slope of the town to her roof, and thinks of her asleep beneath it. The hope of meeting her is what pulls him through each day. Sometimes, if she is going

189

out into the meadows, or to visit some friend who lives outside the walls, she sends for him. And he puts on his red cloak and rides out as her bodyguard, and there is something thrilling about being so near her and not being able to touch her or say more than the idle pleasantries that are expected between a young warrior and the wife of his lord. He can't even catch her eye, for fear her maidens will notice some glance, some glint. He does his duty in a daze, like a sleepwalker, knowing that when the twilight comes he'll slip away to meet her at the baths, and they'll say all the things they couldn't say by day.

Let's face it, he's in love. Like a hero out of one of those stories Myrddin tells in the feast-hall. He is in love with her hands; with her slender fingers and the creases of her knuckles. He is in love with the faint hair on her upper lip, which he can feel but barely see. He is in love with the downy hollow of the small of her back; with the hard jut of her shoulder blades, like the stubs of wings. He is in love with her eyelids. He is in love with her voice. He is in love with her kindness. He is in love with the soft sound of her breath when she lies drowsy in his arms. He is in love with the nape of her neck. He is in love with the girl she was before he was even born. He is in love with her because she's *not* some girl, some silly maid no older than himself who giggles and wants presents. Gwenhwyfar wants only him. She's *chosen* him. She watches him so intently when they are together. She takes him so seriously.

And isn't that what all boys want, and all men too? Just to be taken seriously?

XXXIII

Almost every night, while Arthur was away, Gwenhwyfar went to meet her lover. The year ripened into a golden autumn, the fruit heavy on hedge and tree. Apple harvest came and went, yet the weather held, and the war-band stayed gone. Day after day of blue sky and yellow sun and the fat white clouds sailing over Sulis from the west like ships, till it started to seem unnatural, and we grew edgy, waiting for the weather to break and Arthur to return.

And still, most every night, Gwenhwyfar went to meet her lover at the spring. And always I went with her. She knew I knew her secret. I think it pleased her, knowing someone knew. Sometimes she'd look at me with a proud, sly look that said, "I'm not quite as old or as cold as you thought, am I, Gwyna?" But she never spoke of it, except to say, "Wait outside for me," as she went into those warm shadows.

I never did wait, of course. I followed her. Crouched in the gloom just inside the doorway, tickled by ferns,

I strained my ears to sieve soft-murmured words out of the chuckling, bubbling, echoing sounds of the spring.

"What will we do when Arthur comes home?"

"He may never come home, Bedwyr. He may be killed. He may be cut down in battle, or murdered by his own men, the way he had Valerius murdered."

"Not Arthur. He's a great warrior. He can't be killed."

"No warrior is that great, except in stories."

"While he wields Caliburn he cannot be defeated."

"Because it came from the gods? You don't believe that, do you, Bedwyr? Do you?"

An awkward silence. Movements in the silence. The water laughing, and someone turning over on a crumpled red cloak.

"He cannot live for ever, Bedwyr. He might be dead already. He might be dying now, at this moment, while we lie here together. He may never come home. Then Cei would be lord of Aquae Sulis instead."

"Cei does not want to be lord of anywhere."

"That is what would make him a good lord. These men who want power, they're the ones who shouldn't be allowed to get it. They say they'll use it for good, but they only use it to make themselves more powerful still. Let Arthur die, and Cei rule us."

"But if Arthur *does* come home. . ." Bedwyr insisted.

"Then he'll kill me."

"I won't let him! I'll kill him first! I'll kill him and marry you!"

"And what will men say when they see you with your aged wife?"

"You're not aged. Men have older wives. I'll treasure you. He never did. I'll kill him."

Was that what she wanted? A strong young lover who would rid her of her husband? But why Bedwyr? Bedwyr wasn't strong. Bedwyr could barely walk. That wasn't it.

So was she in love with him?

Well of course she was. He had said he'd treasure her. Who doesn't want to be treasured? He'd gone to her head like honeyed mead.

It wasn't just me who saw the change in her. She smiled more, laughed more, was kinder to her girls. Or grew suddenly sad; wept for no cause, snapped at us, went walking by herself in the garden in the drizzling rain. The others gossiped about her, wondering what the reason was.

"She's in love," Celemon told me one morning while we knelt behind Gwenhwyfar in the church. "She has conceived a passion for Medrawt."

"That's nonsense," I whispered back.

"Well what would you know about it, Gwyna? What would you know about love? Medrawt is a better Christian than Arthur. I saw her speak to Bedwyr in the forum yesterday. And Bedwyr's Medrawt's kinsman. Don't you see? He was passing on a message. . ."

"Bedwyr's Arthur's kinsman, too," I reminded her. "Bedwyr has more sense than to betray Arthur."

Above my lady Gwenhwyfar's bowed head Bishop Bedwin waved his hands about, in that way God seems to like. I suppose God must have known her secret, but did the bishop? Bedwin had known her since she was a little girl. Maybe he was happy to see her happy. Maybe he couldn't bring himself to condemn her. Maybe he, too, was hoping Bedwyr might rid us of Arthur.

XXXIV

A secret's a weighty thing to carry. I wondered often if I should hunt Myrddin out and tell him about Gwenhwyfar and Bedwyr. After all, I was meant to be his spy, wasn't I? I couldn't decide. Sometimes I thought no, my mistress was kind to me, I shouldn't betray her, and I didn't want any harm to come to Bedwyr. But sometimes, when I heard him with Gwenhwyfar, I could have killed him myself for wasting all his love and gentleness on the old heron.

One morning, Myrddin surprised me while I was out buying saffron. His hand on my shoulder felt like a bird's talon. I hadn't noticed till then how thin he'd grown. He'd got a threadbare, abandoned look. He'd been travelling all summer, telling his stories of Arthur, helping people to imagine the day when Arthur would lead all Britain against the Saxons. Trouble was, now that Arthur had Aquae Sulis and his other little patches of land, he hadn't much interest in forging great alliances. He was happier raiding, and filling his hall with other men's treasure. Myrddin was wearing himself out for nothing.

Still, he had a smile for me. "It's been a while since I saw you, girl."

I asked him how he did. Well, he said, but he didn't look it. That curly-haired boy didn't look after him the way I used to. His clothes were dirty, and his hair long. A white stubble of beard showed on his cheeks, like mould on a cheese. He scratched his chin and looked sideways at me and said, "What news from the women's hall?"

I wondered, from the way he said it, if he knew something. He was clever, wasn't he? I remembered that thing he'd told me weeks back – how sometimes on our way through the world we meet someone who touches our heart. Had he guessed what was happening between Bedwyr and Gwenhwyfar, even then?

"Well?" he asked. "Does the old heron still spend as much time by her pond? Has she caught any fish yet?" He studied me while I tried to think of my reply, watching my face the way a cat watches a mouse-hole. "Something is troubling you, Gwyna. Tell me. Let me help." He smiled. His kindness was bait to tempt my secret out. He could see I needed a friend to help me bear the weight of it. He smiled, and I couldn't resist him.

"She has caught Bedwyr," I said, and looked round to make sure no one but he had heard me. I hadn't meant to tell him, but I was suddenly glad that I had. It all spilled out of me. "And she knows about me, master, and the sword from the water. She'll tell everyone about it if she finds out I've betrayed her. . ."

Myrddin looked angry. Quiet angry. He said, "When Arthur finds out what she is doing he will strike her dead before she can tell anything. Does she not know that? What is wrong with her?"

"It's love, master."

"Love?" He looked at me despairing, like he expected better from me. "She's not a girl." Then, softer, "Gwyna, you're not betraying her. This would have come out anyway. There are already rumours. Better that I know, so that I can decide what to do. Arthur will be back soon. . ." He groaned and pinched the bridge of his nose between finger and thumb, as if thinking on it all gave him a headache. As if I'd laid one burden too many on his shoulders.

"It's Gwenhwyfar who's the betraying one," he said. "She's betrayed Arthur. She's betrayed you. What right has she to make you part of her lies?"

"Will you tell Arthur?"

"I don't know. I must think what would be best. . ."

When I told him the secret I was hoping he'd say, "It's not so bad. It doesn't matter. It's nothing to fret about." Instead, he'd grown more distracted and grave-looking than I'd ever seen him.

"But Arthur doesn't care about Gwenhwyfar," I said.

"He cares about appearances, Gwyna. If he thinks his wife is false, a man like that, there will be blood. Arthur has this peculiarity: he cannot bear to be thought a fool. Tell your mistress that. Tell her he is only a day's ride away, and will soon be back. Tell her she must put an end to this."

Well, how could I? It wasn't my place to tell

Gwenhwyfar what she should do. But when I reached home with the saffron I went to her and told her that I'd met with my lord Myrddin and that he'd said Arthur might soon be back.

She blushed when I told her. I can see her now, standing in the garden in her robe of flame-coloured linen, turning her face away so that I wouldn't see the colour burning there. "And how does Myrddin know?" she asked. "Did some spirit tell him? Did he summon up his father, the Devil?"

I shrugged. It seemed to me that Myrddin was wiser than she reckoned, and that there were many ways he might know Arthur's movements. Messengers came in sometimes from the war-band, and not all the messages they carried were shared with her. But I had already said all I dared.

I imagine Arthur, next morning, sitting on his horse, somewhere where the round chalk downs are plump as cushions and the smoke of burned farmsteads makes shadows on the grass.

A messenger has come to find the war-band, bringing word from Myrddin. As he waits for the man to draw close, Arthur thinks of home. It'll be good to get back, this time. He's not as young as he once was. Too many nights on his camp-bed, and too many days in the saddle. There's an old wound in his side that aches dull and steady. He thinks, for some reason, of Gwenhwyfar. When he gets home, he'll be a better husband to her. If he can make her happier, maybe she'll give him a son.

Perhaps this messenger brings good news, he thinks. Perhaps Gwenhwyfar is already carrying his child.

(And perhaps I'm being kind to him. Perhaps I don't quite want to believe that what he did next was just out of hurt pride.)

But the man, pale, purse-lipped with worry, won't meet Arthur's eye. Men who carry good news don't wear that look.

"What is it?" Arthur says, and the messenger swallows hard and says, "I've word from Myrddin."

XXXV

I remember the sound her robe made, whispering as she wove her way between the thistles that had grown up around the baths. It was evening, the day after my meeting with Myrddin. Away in the redness of the west great clouds were massing, dark and sky-tall, as if some enchanter had cast spells upon the hills there and they were swelling into mountains. The autumn air was heavy with heat.

As we came into the courtyard I glimpsed Bedwyr waiting for us by the entrance to the spring. He vanished inside with a stiff-legged movement. It was careless of him, letting himself be seen like that. It felt like a bad omen.

"My lady. . ."

"One of the ghosts of the place, Gwyna," she said, trying to sound light.

"We should go home," I warned her.

But how could she? Arthur was coming. She did not know when she would be alone with Bedwyr again.

Maybe tonight was her goodbye to him. Oh, she saw the sense in what I said. It made her pause and look at me. A gust of breeze lifted the edges of her head-cloth. A smell of rain on the wind, and two dark blotches of colour high on Gwenhwyfar's cheeks. Then she turned and went into the shrine, and the first thunder grumbled in the west.

I waited outside this time. Since my talk with Myrddin I'd been edgy as a spooked horse. I was fearful we'd been followed.

The sky didn't help. It was lead colour, curdling, filled with wicked spirits. It wasn't a sky to be out under. A tree of lightning stood suddenly upon a hill-top westward. The temple precinct filled with a brownish, ghostly light, and the flowers of the bindweed showed white, white on the crumbled altars.

I heard shouting from the sentries on the wall, down by the gate. Then thunder again.

No, not thunder. That long rumble was the sound of Aquae Sulis's gates being dragged open, and hooves thrumming on the cross-hatch of logs which covered the muddy place between them.

I ran to the door of the shrine and looked into the darkness. A flash of lightning made all the dangling charms and wet ferns jink with blue light. I called, "Lady?" as loud as I dared.

Thunder. Horses in the streets, torches moving. Was it raiders? No, I'd heard the gates open. A shouted word whirled about like a leaf on the gusting wind.

"Arthur!"

I ducked inside. Storm light flickered off the water in

the pool. Lightning flamed on the white bodies of Bedwyr and my mistress. They looked like Adam and Eve, surprised in their garden by God.

"He's here." I said stupidly. "Arthur. He's back."

They were scrambling up, untying themselves from each other. I shielded my eyes from them. I said, "He'll go up to the hall first. He'll want food and stabling and clean clothes before he sends for you, lady. You've time to get you home. And if you don't want to see him we'll tell him you're sick. We'll say the thunder has given you a headache. . ."

Why did *I* have to make their plans for them? Bedwyr was a warrior. Gwenhwyfar was my mistress. Why couldn't *they* tell *me* what to do? But they just stared at me, numb, holding on to each other.

And Arthur wasn't going to the hall. I remembered Myrddin, and how he had watched me when we spoke in the marketplace. He knew everything. He'd known that if I warned Gwenhwyfar about her husband's homecoming she would be certain to meet with Bedwyr that night. He must have sent a messenger to find Arthur on the road somewhere, and told him to come home quick, and where to look for his wife.

I heard hooves on the old pavement outside the baths. I heard something batter against the planks that screened the entry-way. I heard Gwenhwyfar say "Jesu," as she struggled into her shift.

I ran out into the courtyard as the planks at the entrance gave way. Beyond them, rain, and tossing furze-bushes and men and firelight. Arthur and a party of his warriors, dismounted, some with torches, boys

202

behind them holding the heads of their scared horses as the lightning flickered. The men looked confused. Maybe they were wondering why Arthur had ridden so hard to Sulis just to lay siege to this old temple. Arthur shoved past them into the courtyard, a black shape against another flare of lightning, hairy in his wolf-skin cloak. I'd forgot how big and broad he was. How tall. How like a bear.

Lightning flashed on Caliburn's blade. Rain was starting, hissing on the flagstones.

He bellowed, "Gwenhwyfar!"

"She is at the spring, lord," I squeaked, running at him, like a mouse running out of the wainscot. "She only comes here to bathe. Give her time to dress, lord, and—"

A hard blow of his fist sent me sideways, spraddled me in a nettle-clump. I was lucky I was on his left side, or he'd have used the sword on me. What was I, to Arthur in his wrath? A mouse, that's all. I saw his face. The anger in it. Blood dark in his cheeks and the spittle blown white from his hollering mouth.

"Gwenhwyfar!"

He went past me, and I scrambled up to keep from being trod on by the men that followed him. Hands caught me from behind, twisting me round. Myrddin's black robes flapped at my face. I heard him say, "Come, Gwyna. This is no place for you. . ."

"You told him!" I screamed, trying to break away from him. I twisted my head and I saw Arthur climb the three steps and go inside, swiping down handfuls of the dangling charms. I heard Bedwyr in there shouting something. Later people said it was a challenge, but it didn't sound like a challenge to me. Arthur shouted back, no words, just a roar. There came scuffling sounds, a clatter of kicked stones, a noise like a hurt dog whining.

Myrddin's grip was weak. I broke free of him and ran. "Gwyna!" I heard Myrddin shout. Inside the shrine Gwenhwyfar was screaming. Arthur's men were bunched in the doorway, staring into the dark. One said, "Jesu, Christos. . ." as I squirrelled my way between them. Inside, rain spewed through the rotting roof, spattering into the spring. The torches lit up Gwenhwyfar, over by the felled statue of the goddess, half crouched, cowering, her hands up shivering in front of her. I thought she'd wrapped herself in Bedwyr's red cloak, but it was just her own white shift, splashed red. On the floor lay a red and white thing that jerked like a killed pig. Arthur stood over it. He raised Caliburn high and grunted as he hacked down.

"Bedwyr!" screamed Gwenhwyfar.

Arthur turned to face us, Caliburn red in his red hand, his whole arm red to the elbow. He held up some gaping thing for us to see.

"Jesu, Christos. . ."

"Gwyna!" my master shouted from behind me somewhere, angry sounding.

Hailstones hissed furiously on the roof. I ran past Arthur and round the pool's side to my mistress. "Bedwy-y-y-y-r," she was grizzling.

I picked up Bedwyr's cloak. I don't know why. Who knows why they do anything, at times like that? I wrapped it round her. It slapped wetly against her bare legs. Arthur was bellowing again, shouting at his men to look at what became of traitors. When he's finished, I thought, he'll come for Gwenhwyfar. For me too. Rage like his strikes anything it sees. I dragged her with me to a crack in the wall. "Bedwy-y-yr!" she sobbed, hiccuping.

"He's dead!" I said. And he was. I'd not believed it till I said it.

I shoved her in front of me like a bundle, through that crack and away along black nettly passages between the bath-houses, out into the pouring streets. While Arthur's men stood at the pool's edge and watched as Arthur swung Bedwyr's head by its hair and flung it from him – that tumbling, woeful, boyish, lightning-lit face, that red-gold hair like the fires of a falling star – and the waters took it with a feathery splash.

XXXVI

Where was I going? Just away. The animal fear that had set me running the night I first saw Arthur had hold of me again. Just get us away, me and my mistress, before he kills us too.

I steered Gwenhwyfar through the rain, making for the gate. Men barged past us, hurrying to the baths to see what the commotion was. The sky tipped water on us. Peredur came by, a straggle of wet feathers plastered over that helmet he always wore. I caught him as he passed. I yowled into his wide-eyed face. "Find Medrawt! Tell Medrawt that Arthur's killed his brother!"

I don't know why I did that either. I think I remembered the love Medrawt had shown Bedwyr when Bedwyr was sick, and thought he should know what had happened. Maybe I hoped he'd take his sword and come like an avenging angel and kill Arthur. Blood must have blood. Bedwyr's other kin might take Arthur's side when they heard what Bedwyr had done, but not Medrawt. You kill a man's brother, he's got to kill you, it's only natural. But as Peredur ran off with my message I realized that Arthur would know that as well as I did. He'd be expecting Medrawt's vengeance, and he'd likely have sent men to kill him too.

Then we were out of the town somehow. We were scrambling through wet fields. We were blundering through scratchy woods. Gwenhwyfar was so slow and stumbly I almost left her, for fear Arthur and his men were coming after her and would catch us both. Three times I ran on ahead. And three times I went back for her, because I couldn't bear to leave her lone and helpless. She was making a hurt, raw-throated noise that I could hear above the hiss of rain and hoo of wind-whipped trees. It was like she was a child, and I her mother. I held her hand and tugged her after me.

Where were we going? Just away. I think I had an idea of getting to the Summer Country, where Gwenhwyfar might beg her kinsman Maelwas to shelter us. But I didn't know how to find Maelwas, beyond just going south, and I couldn't tell which way south was, with no moon, no stars, and the wind coming from every way at once.

At last we came to a place where the track we were following sloped down into a flood. A swollen river filled the world ahead, glinting scaly under the lightning-flashes like a huge serpent winding its way between the hills. We turned back, shoving through alder and tussock-grass to a line of trees on a rise above a little lake, and we huddled on the wet grass in their shelter.

I'd been right to fear for Medrawt. When Arthur rode back into Sulis he sent his old companion Greidawl Widowmaker with a couple of men straight to Medrawt's house to kill him. But fate had better ideas. As Greidawl rode up through the streets that first great crash of thunder booming over the rooftops scared his mare so much she reared up and threw him backwards and he broke his head on a lead trough by the wayside. And since he'd not told his men where they were going or what they were to do there, they busied themselves getting him indoors and fetching doctors to him, and while they were about it Peredur went past them with my message.

"Arthur has killed your brother."

Anyone else, hearing those words from a bedraggled clown like Peredur, might have thought it was all some sort of joke. But maybe Medrawt suspected the truth about Bedwyr and Gwenhwyfar. Maybe he knew. For all I know Bedwyr had told him everything. At any rate, it took him only a moment to understand that this was real, and what it meant. He called for his sword, ready to go and get his vengeance, but while he was waiting for his man to bring it he thought again. He couldn't fight all Arthur's band. And he had his wife to think of. He could hear her voice in the next room, comforting their daughters, who'd been woken by the storm. More thunder broke over the house, so loud that it left no space in his head for his thoughts and he had to clutch his hands over his ears. His man came back, the sword-hilt flaring as lightning spiked in through the shutter-cracks. Medrawt ignored him, ran to the room where his wife was.

"Dress," was all he said. "Bring the girls and your women. We're leaving."

*

The storm tore eastward. It went away to throw its spears of light at Saxon men, and left us quiet upon our lakeside, my mistress and me. The moon came out, like a startled eye. She rolled dazedly through the wrecks of cloud. Stars showed. The wind grew gentle again.

All this time, and all this way, my lady Gwenhwyfar had said nothing. I began to think she'd left her wits behind. But in the grey before dawn, when the black shapes of the stooping trees were starting to show against the sky, she started talking. The creel of her ribs heaved and she retched out words. I wasn't in a mood to answer, but she didn't care. She was that wrapped up in herself she could hold a whole conversation without any need for me to say a thing.

She said, "It wasn't my fault."

She said, "Why did God let it happen?"

She said, "But I loved him so badly."

She said, "He needed me. I never thought anyone would need me."

She said, "Love made us mad." (Like it was something to be proud of.)

She said, "I will go to Hell."

She said, "I don't care. He was my man. Not Arthur."

She said, "He was so young! He was still a boy!"

She said, "Oh, what am I to do?"

She said, "Where am I to go?"

She said, "I cannot live in this world."

Myself, I thought she should maybe say "Thank you, Gwyna," or "You did well, Gwyna," or "God bless and protect you, sweet Gwyna, for saving my scrawny

209

neck." But she didn't. Didn't even know I was there, I reckon. Didn't think I was grieving over Bedwyr too. Didn't think people like me felt things as hard as a lady like her. Selfish, she was. What else had it been but selfishness that made her take Bedwyr as her lover? She must have known how it would end.

After a while I got so tired of her talk that I went off into a kind of sleep, cold and footsore and scared as I was.

When I woke I found Bedwyr's cloak laid over me. The cloak was as wet as me, and as wet as the turf beneath me, but I was glad of the thought. I looked sleepy-eyed at the tree I was lying under, and saw how the moss on its trunk had been combed all one way by the wind and the rain. But the rain was gone now. The sun was coming up, a brightness behind the early-morning mist. Down on the edge of the mere we'd settled by a heron stood in the shallows. It heard me stirring and took off, flapping away on its big grey wings, neck curled like a snake, legs trailing like winter sticks. I watched it go.

"We'll head south, lady," I said. "Maelwas ought to show you kindness, being your kin and all."

No answer. I sat up, and saw I'd been talking to nobody. Gwenhwyfar was gone, and not even a footprint in the soggy earth to show me where. All I could hear was the water drip-drip-dripping off the trees. "Not even a goodbye," I thought.

A hand rose from the mere, white, sequined with water-droplets. Pale fingers uncurled from their own reflections and seemed to beckon me.

*

At Aquae Sulis, rainwater and rumours gurgled in the streets. All round the town and for as far about as anyone had ridden trees were down, roofs gone, houses fallen, bridges washed away.

In Arthur's hall, in the dim, stunned dawn, Arthur and his captains meet. He looks at their faces, ringed round him in half-light, and sees doubt in them. For the first time they aren't sure where he's leading them, nor whether they want to follow. Even his own half-brother. Even Cei.

He spreads his big hands. "You saw how it was. You think I wanted to kill the boy? My own kinsman? My sister's son? But he betrayed me. When a man steals your own wife, what are you to do?"

The others shift uneasily, and won't meet his eye.

"What are you to do? Bedwyr and Gwenhwyfar. They were together. You saw them, Gwri. . ." He thumps the arm of the man beside him, urging him to tell the others, the ones who reached the spring too late to see more than the spilled blood and the boy's butchered body.

Myrddin, behind him, says, "I saw her. She was there. They were together."

Cei says miserably, "He was my kinsman too, Arthur. He brought death on himself, I know that. There's not a man in the world who'd blame you for killing him, after what he did. But it was the manner of it. You threw Bedwyr's head in the spring. Think how it looks. . ."

"I was angry!" shouts Arthur, growing angry again. "He betrayed me! My own kinsman! Do you stop to think when a red rage is upon you?"

Cei keeps talking, head down, like a man walking into a gale. "Think how it looks. As if you're some old heathen hill-chieftain who throws the heads of his enemies in a sacred well."

Owain says, "Bishop Bedwin and his priests are putting it about that you promised the old gods sacrifice in return for your victories in the north. They say Bedwyr was your gift to them, and the storm was the true God's tempest, sent to show us his displeasure."

Arthur curses. "Who holds this town? Me or Bedwin? And the storm had started already by the time I killed the boy."

"God's tempest makes a better story," says Cei. "That's what God-fearing men will believe."

Arthur strikes him across his doleful face with the back of his right hand. "Do you mean to stand here all morning moaning and drizzling like a woman? Get after Medrawt. Find him and finish him, before I have a blood-feud on my hands."

Cei's face is very pale in the smudgy shadows. One of Arthur's rings has gashed his cheek, and beads of blood show there. Arthur breathes hard, watchful. Some of the men who stand beside Cei, men who were Arthur's when he left them in Sulis at the summer's start, reached for their swords when that blow was struck. Just quick movements, quickly stilled when they saw that Cei was not going to fight. But they'd have been ready to back him, if he'd chosen different.

"I'll not go after Medrawt," Cei says carefully. "We don't know which road he took. And whichever it was, the bridges are gone, the rivers have broken their

212

banks. My men are needed here, in Sulis."

Arthur's nostrils flare. He's not used to disobed... What Cei says has truth in it, but is it his only reason? Can it be that he's on Medrawt's side now, not Arthur's?

Myrddin says, "What of Gwenhwyfar?"

Arthur looks round. "What?"

"What of Gwenhwyfar?" asks Myrddin again. "What has become of her?"

"I don't know," says Arthur impatiently. "How could I know? That girl of hers spirited her away. Lucky for her, or I'd've had her head too."

"She is Maelwas's kin."

"Would Maelwas blame me for punishing an unfaithful wife?"

"Of course not," says Myrddin. "But it must be done properly, a high-born woman like her, your ally's kin. You cannot simply kill her. Maybe you should send her to Maelwas, and ask him to do with her as he sees fit. Show him you are merciful, and you respect his judgement. But first you must find her. Her and that girl of hers."

And I sat on the wet grass and watched that hand beckon to me from the shining middle of the mere. White as a stripped twig.

I was already wet as I could be, so I went down to the shallows and waded in. My torn skirts flowered out round me. The water was clear. There was grass on the bottom, neat and green and standing up on end, like it was startled to find itself under water.

…rowned grass. She had torn
…k and used it to knot an old
waist, to weight her down. She
…ne arm had drifted upward, lazily,
…ne bright surface. Her stained shift
…ff of hair under her arm tiny bubbles

… …was, I didn't feel anything. I just stood
there loo… …g at her, and I couldn't find a feeling
anywhere in me.

I sloshed back to the shore. What now? I asked
myself. If I went back to Sulis, Arthur would likely kill
me. He'd say I'd helped her betray him. I *had* helped her.
There was no life for me any more with Arthur's band.
So maybe I'd try for Maelwas's country myself, I
decided. My feet felt as if I'd come twenty miles through
the rain and the tempest the night before. I reckoned I
must be already halfway to Ynys Wydryn.

I clambered up a hill that chuckled and shone with
little streams. I looked out from the top, where the gorse
grew thick. And I saw Aquae Sulis, not two miles away.
Smoke was going up from the cooking fires as if nothing
had happened. Closer, where the woods crowded down
to the floody pasture-land, the roofs of Myrddin's house
shone in the sunlight.

I was too tired to think. Too tired for sure to start out
again for the Summer Country. So I went instead down
the steep, slippery sheep-tracks to beg the mercy of my
old master.

XXXVII

Myrddin wasn't there. The curly-headed boy – his name was Cadwy – was alone in the place. He was looking for eggs out where the chickens scratched. When he saw me squelching towards him he knew who I was, and let me inside. Said his master was still in Aquae Sulis. I asked for dry clothes, and he found me some to wear while he washed my soiled, soaked dress. I sat by the fire in his own spare tunic and a pair of old trews, eating bread which I smeared with sooty white fat from a skillet that stood on the hearth. The boy watched me like I was a spirit sprung out of the flames. Even with my hair grown I looked boyish in those clothes. Whatever I'd learned of grace and girlishness, the night had wrung it out of me. Cadwy couldn't tell what I was.

Later, he showed me a bed to lie down on. And I slept there till that day was near gone.

Myrddin was back when I woke. I heard his voice outside, talking to Cadwy, and went out to find him

215

climbing down off his old black horse. My own pony Dewi came across the paddock to nuzzle me, and I hugged him and laid my face against his and wished there was a human being in the world who loved me as well as he did.

Myrddin looked strange when he saw me standing there. I'd have said he felt shy, if I'd not known him better. He came towards me cautiously, watching my face.

"You told Arthur," I said.

Myrddin reached out towards me, but didn't touch. He said, "Stories were going about, that Gwenhwyfar had a lover. I had to put an end to it. It would have been bad for Arthur's reputation."

"You knew she'd go to Bedwyr last night," I said. "You sent word and told Arthur to ride home quick, and where to find them."

"Something had to be done," said Myrddin. "The kings of Britain will never let Arthur lead them against the Saxons if they are laughing behind his back about his wife." He looked old, I thought, and ill. Kept kneading at his arm, as if it had gone numb. He said, "You should have come with me last night."

"My mistress needed me," I said, to make him understand I wasn't his any more. I don't know if he did. The mention of my mistress distracted him. "You know where Gwenhwyfar is?" he asked.

"Dead," I said.

That made him curse. Not because he cared about Gwenhwyfar, of course. "I told Arthur he must spare her," he said.

"Wasn't Arthur's doing," I said. "She drowned herself."

Myrddin's eyes went past me to the hills, the steaming woods, looking for ways to make a story of it. "That might work. She tempted Bedwyr, betrayed Arthur, and then, in guilt and remorse – but that makes Arthur seem weak. And will Maelwas believe it?"

Cadwy was leading the horse away, with Dewi following. I went after Myrddin into the house.

By Myrddin's fire I heard the news from Sulis. How Medrawt had fled in the storm's confusion, and how the slaves he left behind said he'd been making for Ynys Wydryn, to lay his sword at Maelwas's feet. The story was spreading of how Arthur had made sacrifice of Bedwyr and given his head to the old gods at their sacred spring. Bishop Bedwin had preached to a crowd in the forum, saying the tempest had been punishment for Arthur's sins, and warning the people to throw down their tyrant before God sent worse punishments. Arthur had him beaten, and let his warriors help themselves to the treasures in his church.

"And that has made those who hate him hate him more," said Myrddin, not talking to me really, just letting his thoughts pour out in words. "And there is Cei. The trust that was between them has soured. Cei may be Arthur's half-brother, but he's uncle to Bedwyr and Medrawt too, and a friend to Bishop Bedwin, and he had a liking for Gwenhwyfar. He's still loyal, but it's a grudging loyalty now. Arthur's afraid that there are men in the war-band who will try to throw him down and set Cei up in his place."

"Cei would never betray Arthur," I said.

217

Myrddin glowered, ignoring me. "And Cei knows about every trick I've pulled. What if he tells people the truth about Caliburn, or the other tales I've built Arthur's power upon? What if he tells them about you?"

"Why not help Cei throw him down?" I said. "Cei'd be a better lord. Or do you love Arthur so bad you can't see that?"

"Oh, Cei'd be a good lord," said Myrddin sourly. "He'd keep Aquae Sulis fat and calm and prosperous, right up until the day the Saxon hordes come west and burn it. Cei means nothing. Arthur's the one. He has to be. All those stories that I've sent out into the world – do you think I can just whistle and they'll come running home to me like hounds? Arthur is our hope. He is the hope of all Britain. One day the other kings will rally to him and he'll lead them in a war that will. . ."

". . .drive the Saxons out of this island for ever," I said wearily. I'd heard that tune before. Believed it once. Now it sounded staler every time.

Myrddin wasn't listening to me. He said, "Cei's a problem. Can't be trusted. I was a fool to let him in upon my secrets. The one thing worse than an enemy is a friend turned false." He set down the cup he'd been drinking from and rubbed his arm. "I must find a way to be rid of him, before more blood is spilled. Send him away so there is time for all this to blow over. Yes. But how? What reason could there be?"

And he looked at me as if he was expecting me to tell him, but he wasn't. He'd have looked at the wall for an answer if I'd not been in the way.

*

Next day when I woke he'd gone again. It was just me and Cadwy, and Cadwy was so nervous of me that he left me well alone, and I had time to think. I wondered if Medrawt and his family had made it to Ynys Wydryn, and what sort of welcome he would get from old Maelwas. The storm had washed away many things, and made others clearer. I saw now that Maelwas had never honestly meant to give Arthur command over his warbands. He'd just been playing for time, afraid of this arrogant bandit who'd set up camp in his borderlands. He would be glad of the news Medrawt would bring, of strife in Arthur's gang, and God's displeasure. He would maybe think the time was right to move against Arthur, and give the holding of Aquae Sulis to a better man.

Myrddin came home in the late afternoon, while I was tending to Dewi in the paddock. If he had been thinking about Maelwas it did not show in his face. As he let Cadwy help him down from his horse he was smiling the old, sly smile that I'd first seen when he showed me Caliburn all those years before. A smile of simple delight at his own cleverness. "Well, Myrddin has mended it, as Myrddin always does," he said. "I had Arthur gather all his men on the steps outside the church. Had him remind them how the Irishman who is our ally has been insulted by Cunomorus. Now we've humbled Calchvynydd we must ride to the Irishman's aid and help him punish Cunomorus before he grows still more ambitious and land-hungry."

I blinked. So much had happened those past few days that it seemed an age since the Irishman had ridden in to ask for Arthur's help. "I'd forgotten Cunomorus. . ."

Myrddin chuckled. "So had they. So had Arthur. But I remember. A leader should always keep a few spare enemies to hand. You never know when you might need a good, far-away war to take men's minds off troubles close to home. If we let Cunomorus get away with the Irishman's cattle today, what will he try tomorrow? He must be humbled before he grows any bolder. That's what I had Arthur tell them. Some of our warriors must ride west at once, to join with the Irishman's band. Of course, Arthur can't lead them. He and his riders are war-weary, travel-sore. Cei and his followers will go in their place. By the time they return all this trouble will be behind us. And some may not return at all."

"What if they won't go?"

Myrddin scowled at me. "Have you forgotten all you learned about the lives of men? Of course they'll go. They would look like cowards, else. Anyway, Arthur promised them a good fight, and a share of the booty. Said he wished he could go in their place, but he must stay and guard their homes for them against the traitor Medrawt. And I told them about all the treasures they will take from Cunomorus's hall. A herd of red cattle. A golden shield. A miraculous cauldron, which is never empty – a drink from it can heal all wounds. . ."

"And does Cunomorus really have those things?"

Myrddin shrugged. "Who knows? Maybe. I made it up. But the promise of plunder will cheer Cei's men on their way west. They leave at dawn."

I could see why Myrddin was so pleased with himself. Cei's men were those who'd been left in Aquae Sulis while Arthur was off fighting that summer. For the most part they were men that Arthur couldn't quite trust; Valerius's former comrades, the sons of the old *ordo*, men not linked to him by blood or long companionship. The very men who might rather have his brother as their leader. Now, thanks to Myrddin's cunning, they were all to be sent out of the way for a month or more. They'd return weighed down with plunder, with coin and cattle and magic cauldrons maybe. Plenty of reasons to like Arthur better.

Later, when we'd eaten, and the boy was outside cleaning the plates, and I was thinking about my bed again, another thought came to me.

"Peredur. He's not going?"

"Long-Knife's boy? Of course. Didn't I say? Cei's taking every man who didn't ride with Arthur this summer past."

"But you can't send Peredur to a war! He's too. . ."

"Stupid? Can't help that, Gwyna. He's not Arthur's man. I heard it was he who went to warn Medrawt. Maybe he's not as foolish as he looks."

"But he is! I know it's hard to believe, but he is!"

"So you say. All I know is, I can't leave him in Aquae Sulis, to plot against Arthur."

I wondered if I should confess that it had been me who sent Peredur to warn Medrawt. But it wouldn't have made a difference.

I went to bed, but I couldn't sleep. I watched the light of the dying-down fire lap on the roof-beams, saffron-colour. I'd been thinking about Bedwyr and Gwenhwyfar so hard I'd half forgotten Peredur, and how his open, silly face once made my heart catch, and how he'd been when I first met him, dressed up as a maid. My mirror-boy. I couldn't bear the thought of him riding off to that war. Not even a real war, but one made up to serve Arthur's purposes, a needless, reasonless war, spun out of lies. Either he'd not come back at all, or he'd come back changed. He'd change the same way Bedwyr had. The last of his girlishness would be gone from him, and he'd be just a man like all the rest.

I slept, and dreamed of Gwenhwyfar walking into the lake. She cradled her wooden anchor like a child, vanishing into her own reflection.

When I woke, I knew very clear what I must do. It scared me, but not enough to turn me back.

Myrddin was snoring in his bed-place. The boy Cadwy was curled up by the hearth. He stirred a bit as I crept round him, but I said, "Sshh, sshhh," and he settled like a sleepy dog.

I still had Bedwyr's cloak. It had faded in the rain to a tired brown, and the strip Gwenhwyfar had torn off the bottom made it about the right length for me. I had Cadwy's tunic and breeks, and in Myrddin's oak chest I found my own old belt from when I was a boy. There was a white bloom of mildew on the leather, which came off like chalk-dust when I rubbed it with my thumb. I had no shoes except my ruined buskins, so I stole Myrddin's boots. And I stole a knife, and a leather bag.

Outside, in the dark, old Dewi was sleeping, head down, one hind hoof tilted against the turf. He woke with a soft whinny when I threw the saddle-cloth across him. Turned his head and nibbled up the hunk of bread I gave him, and seemed glad that we were off again upon our travels, he and I.

XXXVIII

In dripping woods close by the Sulis road, I stopped and waited for the dawn. As the light gathered, pools of flood-water showed like glass among the trees. I crouched by one and looked down at my reflection and cut my long hair with the knife. Not too short. I left it shoulder-length, the way Bedwyr had worn his, and tied it back with a string I found in my pocket. I washed my face in muddy water to darken my skin till the sun could darken it properly. Then I stuck the knife through my belt and got me up on Dewi's back again.

Myrddin had told me they'd be setting out at dawn, but I didn't wait to meet the war-band on the road. I remembered too well all the snags and delays that beset armies setting off to war: lame horses and snapped saddle-girths, things left behind that had to be hunted for. Men waking late, stupid from too much mead or wine the night before. The lingering goodbyes. Anyway, I wanted to meet them further on, where they would not just have to take my word that I was a young man.

I rode west through the woods, crossed the swollen river at Camlann-ford and came late that afternoon to a place called Din Branoc. I remembered it from my journey with Myrddin two summers before. We'd stopped a night there on our way to the Summer Country, but passed it by when we were coming home. People there might remember a boy who had gone west with Arthur's wizard, but not the girl he had brought back.

It had suffered in the storms. The hall slumped on its low rise amid the flooded fields like Noe's Ark wrecked upside-down on Ararat. Men of the household were sculling across the fields in wicker boats, rescuing stranded sheep from knolls and hummocks where they'd fled to escape the deluge. As I urged Dewi through the knee-deep water on the track I felt a knot of fright grow in my gut. These people wouldn't be in any mood to offer shelter to a stranger.

But they were glad of me. It did them good to have someone to tell about the terrors that had overtaken them. They pointed at their landslip-scarred hills and torn-down trees like men who had seen wonders, and watched my face while they told me of the storm, making sure I was astonished.

I did my best. My time with Myrddin had made a good actor of me. I pretended awe, and never let on that the disasters they were so proud of had happened just as bad or worse at Aquae Sulis, and every other place, probably. For all I know they're still talking of their great storm in Din Branoc.

And when they asked me who I was I said, "Gwyn.

Servant to Myrddin. Don't you remember me?" And they nodded and welcomed me again, and said how I'd grown, and never thought to notice that I'd grown into a girl.

"What news from Sulis?" they asked.

I wasn't sure, at first, what I should say. And then I was. That night, sitting with them on the dais-planks in their mud-floored hall, while wet clothes and bedding sent up a fog of steam about me in the fire's heat, I told them the story of Bedwyr and Gwenhwyfar.

It didn't come out quite as I'd expected. I set out with good intentions, and I meant to stay on the road of truth, but somewhere along the way I strayed. Maybe I'd learned too well from Myrddin. I made Bedwyr older and finer than he really was, and told all the usual tales about his feats in battle, glutting the ravens and killing nine hundred enemies and such stuff. And I made Gwenhwyfar younger, and more beautiful, and less selfish. What harm could that do? These people had never seen her. She'd been kind to me at the end. She tucked me up in Bedwyr's cloak before she went into the mere. It was the least thanks I could show, to make her young again.

I couldn't tell their story's ending, neither. The Arthur my listeners knew was Myrddin's Arthur: noble, wise, and brave. So when I came to the part where Arthur found the lovers out, I made him sorrowful instead of savage. And I let them get safe away. Safe down the storm-lit roads to Ynys Wydryn they went, my Bedwyr and my Gwenhwyfar.

After that, I could never quite believe I'd seen them

both dead. It seemed so much more likely that they were safe together in the Summer Country.

Morning brought Cei's war-band. Twenty riders with shields on their backs and swords at their waists, and twenty more reflected in the wet fields as they passed along the road. Not many, even if you counted the reflections, but the Irishman would be grateful for them, and when they combined with his band they'd be enough to give Cunomorus some trouble.

The headman of Din Branoc came out with me to meet them. "My lords!" he called, as he waded ahead of Dewi through the flood. "You are welcome! Welcome!" I thought he was going to tell them all about the storm, but instead he pointed to me and said, "Here's Myrddin's boy, come to meet you on the way."

Cei, reining in his horse, looked at me hard.

"Gwyn," I said. "I'm kinsman to Myrddin."

Cei nodded. There was a smile hidden somewhere down behind his eyes. "I remember you. I'd not thought to see you again. Any news of your sister, who was in Gwenhwyfar's household?"

"Gwyna. My half-sister."

Another nod. "She came safe out of all this?"

"I left her yesterday, at Myrddin's place. Myrddin sent me to ride with you. I know that country west of Isca, see. I can guide you."

"You're welcome then, boy, and I'm grateful to your master. I've not been near those hills since we took old Ban's hall. The time the sword rose from the water." The faintest trace of a wink. Then his face set hard, as if thinking on the old times pained him. He looked past me, taking in the sodden buildings and the drowned fields. "We'll press on. These people don't need us adding to their troubles. Besides, the sooner we reach the Irishman's hills the sooner we can finish this."

The column of men started to move again. Someone was singing a song. The swaying tails of the horses gave off a sweetish smell of old dung. I rode Dewi up on to the track and joined them, and looked for Peredur.

XXXIX

We rode west through the wreck of autumn. These things I remember of that journey. The ringing of metal cooking pots as they swung from the packs of the baggage-mules. The slither-splash of red mud in the deep lanes. Rubbing the horses down at day's end, blanketing them against the cold, seeing to their fodder before we saw to our own, the chores of the horse-lines coming back to me fresh as if I'd never stopped being a boy. The soft munching sounds of hooves on wet hill-tracks. Ambling, tuneless songs. Apples and bramble-berries. The hard, ashy-tasting rounds of bread we baked over our fires. The long detours around flooded valleys, flooded roads, washed-out bridges.

The men grumbling. Why couldn't Arthur have left Cunomorus in peace till spring? Arthur had lost his luck. He couldn't even rule his own wife. They wished they had a better man to follow. They looked hopefully at Cei. His sandy head was bare in the sunshine, hooded in rain, and he kept his thoughts inside it.

I hung behind the others. My old pony Dewi was sturdy enough, but slow. Anyway, I didn't want them questioning me too much. Most of them were lads I didn't know, men from Sulis, relatives of the *ordo* and the big local land-owners. But there were a few who might remember Gwyn, and wonder what he'd been doing in the years since he'd ridden with Arthur's boys.

Riding alone, listening to snatches of their banter blowing back to me on the breeze, I got to missing my life among the girls. I never thought I would, and never a day went by I didn't feel glad to be up on a horse and going somewhere instead of trapped indoors, but I wished I'd had Celemon there to tell some of my inward thoughts to. Girls tell each other things, in honest whispers, when the night is drawing on. Boys just brag.

Peredur was the only one I truly wanted to talk to, and he kept clear of me. He remembered me, I could tell, but he looked as if he hoped I didn't know him. He'd had sense enough to keep quiet about his girlish upbringing, and I suppose he was afraid I'd tell the others of it.

By night, around the campfires, or in the little shabby halls we stopped at, I would tell stories. Cei asked me to. "You're Myrddin's boy," he said. "Tell us some of your master's tales to make us forget our troubles and our poor cold toes."

Truth be told, it *was* cold, and I was as much in need of comfort as the rest. So I pitched my voice as deep as I could and paced my words to the tramp of the sentries patrolling at the edges of the firelight, and told them stories. I gave them old tales at first: the Green Man, and

230

the Chief of the Giants. But slowly I got bolder. They all knew what had become of Bedwyr, but they'd not heard anything of Gwenhwyfar since the storm began. So I told them how she'd got away to Ynys Wydryn, with Medrawt. And though I couldn't tell them she'd been young, the way I had with folk who'd never known her, I made her kind and wronged enough that they started to think she had been beautiful, and not so old as they had thought. Sometimes, in the firelight, on one face or another, I'd see tears running down.

Peredur was one of the tearful ones. He never tried to hide what he was feeling, the way the others had all learned to. Once he came to me after a story and hugged me and thanked me for telling it. Looked at me strange when he'd said it, and said shyly, "You came to my home once, I think."

"That was me. We tricked old Porroc, you and I. You made a fair angel."

The smile lit up his face. "I thought it was you! I wasn't sure. . . You look so like that girl Gwyna. . ."

"My half-sister," I said quickly. The old lie came so natural to me now it felt like truth. "She told me she'd met you."

"She was there in the water-meadow the day I came to Aquae Sulis. It was she who gave me this sword, after I killed the red man. . ." His smile grew worried. "You didn't tell her about how I used to be before?"

"The dress? The hair?"

"I'd never live it down."

"It's safe with me," I said

He laughed. "I've never forgot that day! That was the

231

first time I'd seen men, real men. I was so jealous of you, riding off with Arthur. . ."

"And the look on Porroc's face when we. . ."

"I'd always known there was something not right about him, but till you came I couldn't see what a liar and a leech he was. . ."

And he sat by the dying fire with me while the others slept, and told me all the things that had happened to him since, which I've already told to you. It made me feel shamed, as you'll have guessed, to learn all the things my game with the angel led to. And as I sat listening, I could not help thinking what it would be like to hold Peredur's narrow face between my two hands, and say the sort of things to him that I'd heard Gwenhwyfar tell Bedwyr. To treasure him. I reckoned it was my bad luck that I could only come close to him by turning myself back into a boy.

We kept to the old road till we were near Isca, then veered north. Isca was loyal to Maelwas, and Maelwas might not look friendly on Arthur's gang any more.

"King Maelwas will want a new man to hold Aquae Sulis for him," said one of Cei's captains, Dunocatus. We were resting on a hillside-road, the smoke of Isca filling its wet valley a few miles south, the big river silver beyond. The horses cropped the grass with steady tearing sounds. Cei stared off westward at the Irishman's stony moors and said nothing.

"If a good Christian man was to challenge Arthur, and throw him down, and take his place, Maelwas might be glad of it," Dunocatus insisted. Other men, who felt the same but hadn't had the courage to say it, watched hungrily for Cei's reaction.

"Why are we fighting for the Irishman against Cunomorus?" Dunocatus asked loudly. "Why do we not ride back to Sulis and fight for Cei against Arthur?"

Cei turned and knocked him down into the grass and kicked him hard a few times and strode off, leaving him groaning there. "Arthur is my brother!" he yelled over his shoulder as he climbed back on to his horse. "We have promised to help the Irishman. Do you want your sons and your sons' sons to hear how you hadn't the stomach for that fight?"

We rode on, through steep-walled, thick-wooded valleys. Up the long shoulder of the moor we went, the road dwindling to a peat-track, climbing through knotted woods. Mossy boulders lay crowded between the trees, like sleeping beasts with thick, green fur. When we came up out of the trees at last there was nothing to see but the hills, folded one behind the next, all wrapped in fog and dragons'-smoke.

Cei had me ride with him up on to a hill-top where a great mass of stones stood, hooting and wuthering as the wind ripped round them. "You know this country," he said.

I knew a few of the high hills westward, or thought I did. I did my best. "The Irishman's place is over that way, where the moor slopes down towards Kernyw. Just north of here is Ban's hall. The river. . ."

"Your water-home, lake-lady," said Cei. He looked at

me wryly. "I've thought of that day often. What Myrddin had you do. It's a strange life he's led you."

I stared at the wind stirring Dewi's mane. I'd always known Cei knew my secret, but it still made me feel naked to be talking of it. I said, "I wish he'd let me be sometimes. Why didn't he? Why did he come back for me, that day at the waterfall?"

"He loves you," said Cei. "He never had children of his own. He had you instead."

"No! He sent me away. Made me be a girl again and gave me to Gwenhwyfar."

"He found you a comfortable living-place, one that might put you in the path of a good husband, just as I did for Celemon. The old man loves you, girl. Surely you can see that."

He wheeled his horse and rode back to the waiting column, shouting, "We'll camp here this night. Tomorrow we feast with the Irishman!" I was left on the hill-top with my thoughts. Cei had been Myrddin's friend, and should know what Myrddin thought. But I couldn't believe Myrddin loved me as a daughter. I couldn't believe Myrddin loved anyone, except maybe himself.

The naked feeling stayed with me as I went back down the hill. I began to feel that someone was watching me, out among the rocks and tussock-grass. But we had no enemies here. Cunomorus's lands were two days' ride away. This was the Irishman's country, and tomorrow we would reach his hall, and make ready for our raid into Kernyw. I shook myself to try to get rid of the feeling, and I told myself that men must always feel like that when they knew there was a fight coming.

That night around the fire the others wanted tales of battles won, and enemies cast down. They wanted to hear again about the treasure that would be waiting for them in Cunomorus's stronghold.

I wasn't sure what to tell them. If I promised them gold drinking cups or a jewelled throne, what would they say when they looted Cunomorus's hall and didn't find such things? Then the stories I'd spun might twist around like snakes to bite me.

"What about his magic cauldron?" said one, a man called Bodfan. "Myrddin told us once about a cauldron that was never empty, and in this cauldron every man could find the food he most wanted to eat, and the drink he most wanted to drink."

I nodded warily. If Bodfan hoped to find a thing like that anywhere outside a story, he was in for a disappointment. But Myrddin had promised us a cauldron, hadn't he? I said, "Cunomorus's cauldron's not like that."

"Like what, then?" someone asked.

"Shall I tell you the story of it?"

"Yes, yes," they said.

I hesitated, as if I was gathering my memories of the tale. Really I was stitching something new together out of scraps of other tales I'd heard.

"Back in the long-ago years," I said, "Cunomorus's grandfather was the finest of the warriors of the island of Britain. Tewdric was his name. And he came raiding with his war-band into these very hills."

(My listeners nod and mutter approval at this Tewdric's courage. A couple look round, as if they expect to see the ghosts of his war-band still sweeping across the moor. They'll be lucky. I just made him up.)

"Now in these hills are many lakes, and many rivers, and many pools of still, clear water, and the lady of the waters, the lake-woman herself, she looked out of one of them one day and saw Tewdric riding by and thought how handsome he looked, and how fine, and young, and strong, and a great admiration was in her heart for him.

"And one day, while Tewdric's men were hard pressed by their enemies, Tewdric was wounded, and parted from his band. Lost and alone, he wandered in the mazes of the woods, until hope deserted him, and he lay him down to die among the roots of a great thick oak which grew upon a lake-shore. But the blood of Tewdric's wounds fell into the lake, and the redness of it stained the clear waters until the lake-lady herself saw it, from the windows of her hall down in the depths, and she came up and found Tewdric laid there.

"Now the lake-lady thought it a very pitiful thing that such a fine young man should be left to die, so young and all alone, still in the flower of his beauty. So from her hall beneath the waters she brought this cauldron. . ."

(I spread my hands and curve them, like I'm holding the curved sides of a vessel.)

"A fine thing it was, made of beaten gold, with knots and swirls and fish and men and serpents wrought upon it. And the lake-lady knelt beside Tewdric where he lay, and told him to drink from it, and he would be healed. And he drank, and the pain of his wounds went from him, and his torn flesh grew whole again, and his eyes were made bright, and up he sprang. But the lake-lady had returned already to the waters, and whether she took the cauldron with her, or whether she left it and Tewdric took it home to his hall, I do not know."

My listeners nodded wisely. All of them were afraid of the wounds that might be waiting for them in the days to come. Now they had the hope of the healing cauldron to hold on to. "The lady of the waters has her favourites," I heard a man say. "Bedwyr was one. He saw her at the old springs once. He made a gift to her. That's why our luck turned sour when Arthur killed him."

They tugged their cloaks around themselves and settled on the grass to sleep. The sentries paced beyond the fringes of the firelight. A mule whickered, down in the horse-lines. I lay down too, pleased with the story I'd invented, and thinking already of ways I might better it when I told it next.

In the dark around our camp, all the gorse-clumps looked like armed men crouching.

I come awake at first light surrounded by raw-throated shouts. "Attack!" "It's Cunomorus!" Scramble up, and fall again, still tangled in my cloak. Fall just in time, because arrows are winging out of the gorse on the hillside, whistling like curlews as they cut the air above me. Dunocatus catches one in his throat and curls round it, gargling. He topples into the embers of the fire, throwing up sparks and wood-ash. Other men are on their feet, running to and fro. In this dimsey-light I can't tell who are my friends and who're not. They are all shouting, and the arrows chirr among them, and sometimes someone falls. "The horses! The horses!" someone yells. There is a smell of burning hair. I get up again, groping for the knife in my belt. I run past our dead sentries, towards the horse-lines. Dark shapes spill like ghosts between the frightened, stamping beasts, cutting their tethers. Some horses are free already, running. Cei's bare-headed, bellowing at us to form a shield-wall round him. Then he's down on his knees, dropping forwards, a spear-shaft between his shoulders, and the man who'd stuck it there wrenching it free and pounding it down again and again, as if he's churning butter.

I know that spearman. I know his black spade of a beard, even in this light. The Irishman.

Groggy with betrayal, I blunder on. "Peredur! Peredur!" I'm shouting, and I trip over someone, and it's him.

He's down on his side, curled up, whimpering with fright and pain. One of those arrows is stuck through his shoulder. He turns a white face to me, eyes filled up with fear. "It hurts," is all he says.

Round us, the battle is falling apart into a dozen furious little fights. Screams, and smithy sounds. The Irishman's men yelling their wild, shrill war-shouts. Freed horses flick past us, trembling the ground, raining clods of earth on us. I can't think. I can't even breathe. Then I remember the thing I do best at times like this. I grab Peredur under his arms, and start to pull him downhill.

Not far from the campsite the gorse humps up thick. Peredur's heavy but the slope of the hill helps, and he struggles with his legs, half walking. The gorse drags sharp combs through my hair. The sounds of battle dim, but not enough. I go down on all fours. Gorse is thick in the crown, but underneath it's all woody stems, and bare ground brown with fallen needles. I shove and tug Peredur into a basket of twisty trunks. The wind hisses through the needles above us. A man is screaming smashed-bone screams away up the hill. Below us in the dark I hear the clatter of water.

I lie on top of Peredur. His heart hammers at my breastbone. His every breath comes out as a little sob of hurt. I cram my hand across his mouth and listen hard. Something rackets through dry bracken a few yards off across the steep curve of the hill. A loose horse, or a friend, or a foe-man who saw me creep away and has come hunting me? I lie quiet. My hip bones press against Peredur's. His blood is soaking through my tunic. I drop my head next to his and say into his ear, "Shhhh. Shhhhh."

Nothing moves. All is quiet. Whoever it was in the bracken has gone. We are alive.

We lay there a long time, till the sky above the gorse turned cheerless grey. Then, half walking, half sliding, we made our way down to the stream, and a pool under some alders where I struggled him out of his filthy tunic. I broke off the arrow's flight-feathers and pinched the smeared, shiny point which poked out of his back. He fainted when I pulled it through him. It had made a bruised hole under his collarbone, a red gash behind his shoulder blade. I washed the wounds with stream water. I pressed pads of moss over them, and ripped strips from my shirt to bind the moss in place.

I didn't want to have to look after him. It wasn't so long since I'd been forced to look after Gwenhwyfar, and I remembered how happily *that* had ended.

"I was afraid," Peredur kept saying, when he woke.

He was white and shaky. Too ashamed to meet my eye. "We ran away, Gwyn. We shouldn't have run. It was womanish."

"It's natural," I tried telling him. "You couldn't have fought them. They were too many. They caught us by surprise."

Of course he didn't believe me. He'd bathed too long in stories of heroes and battles. In the stories, running away is the worst disgrace. If ever anyone told the story of that morning's fight, Peredur and Gwyn would be remembered as cowards, who'd run like women. And being a coward is worse than being dead.

"Who were they?" he asked. "Cunomorus's war-band?"

"It was the Irishman. We were betrayed. He was waiting for us."

"But why?"

I hadn't an answer. I couldn't imagine. How could it profit the Irishman to murder Cei? "Maybe he means to oust Arthur, and his tale about strife with Cunomorus was just a trap to bring us here. Maybe he's gone over to Cunomorus's side himself. Or maybe Maelwas set him on us, to weaken Arthur."

"And what of the others? Are we all that's left?"

"We can't be. The others will be somewhere around. We'll find them. . ."

"I don't want to. They'll know we were cowards. We ran away."

I tied his bandages tight, but not too tight, the way Myrddin had taught me when we were tending to the war-band's wounds back in my boyhood. I thought there was enough blood left inside of him to keep him alive. But I kept thinking of something Myrddin had told me. When someone no longer wants to live, it's beyond any earthly doctoring to save them.

Downstream I found an old building. Just a heap of stones really. Two low walls standing, a wedge of sheltered grass between them, roofed with holly-trees. It was not a good hiding place, for close by it the stream fell whitely into a narrow black pool, and the noise of the water would drown out the sounds of enemies creeping close. But I found nothing better, so that evening I moved Peredur into it. At least it was out of earshot of the crows at the battle-place.

Peredur was weak and feverish, inclined to sleep. Bad dreams kept waking him, and he would jerk his eyes open and say, "I was so afraid. I should have stayed a girl."

So should I, I thought. I hushed him, and soaked my neck-cloth in stream-water and bathed his face with it. By morning he was worse. Some ailment was working in him, and I was afraid he hadn't the strength to fight it. It was the shock, I think, as much as the wound itself. Since that day Myrddin had come to his hall Peredur had lived in stories. He'd expected war to be the way it was in stories: banners and glory and brave deeds. He'd not expected defeat, or pain, or fear.

I sat with him all through that day. I tried telling him that there might be other endings for his story. Maybe this was just a setback. Something to make the listeners gasp and draw closer to the storyteller and think, "It cannot end like this!" before the hero gathered himself up and went on to triumph after all. "You'll get well soon. Then we'll go and fight Cunomorus, just the two of us, if we must. Or creep into his hall by stealth, like Odysseus at Troy, and steal some plunder from him that you can take back as tribute to Arthur."

Peredur smiled. "The lake-lady's cauldron," he said. "That will heal me."

"Of course it will," I said.

And then I thought, why shouldn't it? He'd *have* to find the strength to live if he had something like that to carry home to Arthur. Something wonderful. A new gift from the otherworld.

"Sleep, and be strong," I told him. "Tonight I'll go and find where the others are. Where *we* are, come to that."

The day was cold. I risked a little fire, praying that its smoke wouldn't show among the moor mists. There were speckled brown fish in the pool of the stream and I leaned over the water until one came near enough and I snatched it out. I slit its belly with my knife and cooked it in hot ashes at the fire's edge. I fed Peredur on baked fish and brambles under the pinkish smears of the evening sky. Afterwards, he slept, and I piled bracken over him to keep him warm and then scattered wet earth on the fire.

Then I left him there and climbed back up the hill, not knowing if he'd be alive or dead when I came back.

I climbed past the battle-place. The heap of our dead was so high it made me think Peredur had been right, and none of the others had escaped alive. I told myself to stay calm, but the thought of ghosts got inside my head, and set me running, fearful that dead men were running behind me, angry at me for being still alive. I imagined cold hands reaching out to snatch me by the hair. That's the trouble with this story-telling life. Stories start creeping into your head unbidden, and not all of them are good.

By the time I stopped myself, a lopsided moon had come out from behind the clouds. It showed me the road we had been riding on the day before. Hills whose shapes I knew stood black against moonlit clouds. I followed the road, down through trees, off the moor's edge. An eye of fire winked at me. Ban's hall. The woods, bare-branched, making the hillside below it bristle like a hog's back. Beneath it, out of sight among the riverside trees, my old home. I left the road and pushed through cages of young birch towards the smell of the river.

Halfway there, a noise in the underbrush brought me up short. A rippling shiver, a scraping metal sound like a dragon unwinding itself, ready to strike.

I drop down in the moon-shadows. The wood-floor between the birches is made of rocks and water. Big tumbled boulders, and little pools between. Twigs and windfall branches everywhere, but all too wet to crack, thank Christ, as I creep crabwise to a place where I can see bare sky between the branches.

A snort. A white smouldering of smoke in the dark and a huge head up-reared, black as a raised hammer on that moony sky. My heart stops, and my bladder empties, drizzling warm piss down my legs into the puddle I'm crouched in. But then, as the thing swings towards me and shambles into a spill of moonshine, I let out my pent breath. I even manage a shuddery laugh.

For it's my own Dewi. Of course, the Irishman's boys who ran off the rest of our horses wouldn't have wanted a stocky old plodder like him. His dangling harness drags over another rock, making that dragony clitter and chink that had sounded so fearful a half-minute before. But I'm not scared now. "Dewi," I say, and I go forward gently, shushing and calming him, hands out to catch his long head, rubbing his nose, laying my face against his face. It's a stroke of good luck, plain and simple, but in my nervy state it's hard not to see it as more. Maybe it's a sign that God or the lake-lady is looking after me, and has sent Dewi into my way.

I lead him to a place where the trees grow dense. Knot

his broken reins around a birch-bole. Whisper goodbye and promise I'll be back soon. Then, feeling braver and luckier than before, I go fast as I can to the river. Fight my way out of the clutch of the birches a quarter-mile shy of the homestead I was birthed in.

My first idea, when I left Peredur, was to climb to the hall on the hill-top. My lady Nonnita has a bowl there, which I filled often and often for her with water from the spring, and sprinkled rose-petals in for her to wash herself. An old, gold bowl from Rome or Syria or somewhere fine like that, leopards and hares chasing round its rim. Peredur would easily believe a bowl like that was the lake-lady's magic cauldron, and even if he didn't, it would be fine tribute to carry home to Arthur.

But now I'm here, my mind's changed. My fright on the hillside and my meeting with Dewi have left me feeling thin on strength. The hill looks steep, and at the top there's a ditch and a rampart and a wall of logs to get through before I can even start creeping into the hall to find Nonnita's bowl. I'm not Odysseus. I decide to set my aim on something I can maybe reach.

I cross the first big field. Cattle stand sleeping, hairy backs steaming in the night cold, breath smelling of sweet grass. Over the turf wall into the yard. Pigs snuffling in their enclosure. The dwelling-place quiet under its loaf of thatch. Moonlight pales the crossed paws of a dog asleep in its kennel by the door. I creep round to the back, to the place where the spring purls up. Good luck offerings are balanced on the stones around it, to show the people here aren't yet so Christian they're ready to forget the older gods. And next to the spring, just where it stood in my childhood, a wooden cup, waiting there ready for any weary one who needs a drink. I pick it up. It's carved from cherry-wood, worn smooth by many hands.

I stuff it inside my tunic. At the front of the house the dog starts to bark, woken by some small sound I've made. But I'm over the wall, running along the field-boundary, into the eaves of the wood where the soot-black shadows lie beneath the trees like hides pegged out to dry in the moonlight.

Peredur slept. Fevery dreams of home drifted inside his head like smoke. The arrow-wound in his shoulder was a sick throbbing. Sometimes he thought Gwyn was with him, and sometimes he remembered that Gwyn had gone. He hoped he would come back soon. He was afraid, alone here. The bracken rustled and the stream belled. The night wind whispered words he couldn't catch.

Then, in the grey of early morning, he came dimly awake. He was not alone.

She stood on the far side of the little fire that Gwyn had made the day before. She was quite naked, and her limbs and her body were white as milk against the dull rusty colours of the autumn bracken. Behind her the hillsides were ghostly with mist, and she herself seemed ghostly, her shape wavering in the shimmer of heat from the smouldering fire. Sometimes the thin trickle of smoke veiled her completely.

Peredur started to move, to pull himself upright. He

tried to remember his prayers, but his mind was empty. Pain poked through his shoulder and his chest like another arrow hitting.

She came towards him. Her white body dripped river-water. Her face was half hidden by the hanging-down strands of her wet hair, but he felt he knew her and he was suddenly not scared.

In her hands she held a little bowl. Just a cup, really. Made of wood. Dark, and much used. Clear water filled it to the brim. He held his breath as she crouched in front of him. The water in the cup was a trembling oval of light. He glanced past it at her white breasts, her nipples dark against the white, like old coins. He started to raise his eyes to her face, but she pushed the cup towards him and said, "Drink from the cup, and you will be healed."

So he drank. The water was cold going down. The rim of the cup jarred against his teeth. It trembled with the steady trembling of the hands that held it.

"Shut your eyes," she said.

He didn't want to. He wanted to look at her some more. But he knew from stories that the creatures of the otherworld are fickle. If he didn't obey she might turn him into an owl or a log. He shut his eyes tight.

Her wet hair tickled his face. Her cool mouth touched his. He heard her shivery breath; felt it against his face.

Nothing else. The bracken rustled. He opened one eye. She was gone. On the grass at his side lay the empty cup.

Peredur stood up. He was giddy and his wound seared him, but he didn't care. He stumbled through the bracken and looked down into the stream. There was a deep pool overhung with trees. She crouched at the edge among mossy rocks, and though he called out she did not look at him. Just tilted forward and went in with a splash. He saw the white shape of her flatten and dim as she went down deep. Autumn leaves were scattered on the water. The leaves bobbed on the ripples that she'd made. They turned like fish, beneath the surface. Red-golden beech leaves and the paler leaves of oak. Peredur waited and waited, thinking that she'd come up for air. But she did not come up.

At last a noise behind him made him turn. There was Gwyn, coming down a path behind the old shelter, leading Dewi.

"Gwyn!" he shouted. "Gwyn!" Crashing through the bracken, forgetful of his pain. Waving. "Gwyn! She was here! The lake-woman! She was beautiful! She. . ."

"You've been dreaming." Gwyn was looking oddly at him. A flush of colour on that flat, honest face. A straggle of dew-damp hair hanging down from under his felt cap.

"No, no," said Peredur, eager to share the good news. He snatched up the cup. "Look! Look! She left this! The water in it, Gwyn, it tasted better than wine. It made me better, Gwyn. I feel strong again!"

He swayed, light-headed. Gwyn dropped the pony's reins and ran to catch him as he fell. He had been going to tell Gwyn about the lake-woman's kiss, but, falling, he decided not to. It would be his secret. He sat in the wet grass, laughing. "It wasn't like you said, Gwyn. It wasn't a golden cauldron. Just a wooden cup."

And Gwyn shrugged and said, "Well, you can't believe everything you hear in stories."

It was only river water, really.

I was afraid he'd guess. I thought he'd think back to Saint Porroc's miracle and guess his lake-lady was only me, up to my old tricks again. I planned to leave the cup upon a river stone, and work out a way for him to find it there.

But when I got back to the ruin before dawn I found him sleeping, a little feverish still, and I thought he'd be weak and dreamy enough when he woke to believe whatever I wanted him to. So I tethered Dewi in a holly-clump uphill, and left my clothes there too. Crept to the stream and ducked under water. My hair would look longer and straighter and darker wet. I combed it with my fingers, tugging it forward to hide my face. There wasn't enough to really hide behind, but I wasn't worried. I had spent enough time around boys to know it wouldn't be my face he'd be looking at.

The dawn air was chill on my wet skin. I had gathered some birch bark and some of the thin red twigs from the branches' tips, and I stooped and cast them on the half-dead fire without waking him. Added some wet oak leaves to make a smoulder. I put the fire between myself and him. The wind blew the thin smoke in his face and he woke.

"Drink from the cup, and you will be healed." I whispered it, so he wouldn't know my voice. And when he'd drunk I made him shut his eyes and left quick as I could. I hadn't planned on him coming after me, but I was glad to see he had enough life in him, even if it did mean I had to take another bath in that corpse-cold stream. From under the water I could see him, all ripply-looking, black against the sky. I let the water pull me away from him. Branches hid me as I slipped down into the next pool, and the next, and then I was out and haring round between the trees to find the place where I'd left my clothes and Dewi.

As for the kiss, you can't blame me for that, can you? He was so lovely, and so easy to fool. Sitting there with his eyes shut, all surprised. Just a quick warm touch of our mouths together, over in a heartbeat, but I felt glad to have the memory of it.

All the way back to Sulis he talked of nothing but the lake-woman. And every time he spoke of her she grew more beautiful, and her speech to him grew prettier. He wasn't lying. He really thought he remembered her dark blue eyes and her lips as red as rowan berries. Sometimes he filled the wooden cup at a spring or a well, but the water never tasted as good as the water *she* had filled it with.

I tried telling him my own tale; how I'd found Dewi wandering in the woods. But it couldn't compete with his miracle.

We found our way home along back-roads. Down drift-lanes and sheep-paths and half-forgotten tracks through the deep woods. Slow going, mostly, for the ways were poor, and Peredur still weak. His wound hurt him, and his fever rose and fell but never quite left him. I made him ride, and trudged along at Dewi's side until my feet wore through the bottoms of my boots. I listened out always for the Irishmen's riders coming after us, but they never did. Sometimes we passed small settlements where the men looked slantwise at us, but we had knives in our belts and nothing else worth stealing, and they let us go by.

Around first frost we crossed into Arthur's territory, and reached Din Branoc. The people were surprised to see me back, with only one companion. I asked if any others from Cei's war-band had passed that way, and they just stared. Save me and Peredur, none had returned from the Irishman's hills. The only traveller they'd seen since I stopped there was a messenger from the Irishman himself, who passed through like thunder, pausing just long enough to ask the way to Aquae Sulis.

"We offered him shelter," said the headman, as he welcomed us to his fireside, "but he would not stop. Said he was carrying news Arthur would be glad to hear. Said he'd eat well in Sulis that night."

That threw me. What word could the Irishman have sent that Arthur would be glad of? I wondered for a moment if Cei was alive after all, and the Irishman wanted Arthur to pay ransom for him. But my own eyes had seen the Irishman kill Cei. His messenger would not have been so sure of a welcome at Arthur's fireside if the message he had carried was only, "Your brother and his companions are all dead."

Would he?

I tried to think like Myrddin, remembering the reasons he had given for sending Cei and Cei's closest followers west. Some may not return at all, he'd said. As if that was a good thing.

So wouldn't it be an even better thing if none returned?

I imagined a messenger leaving Aquae Sulis, two days after Bedwyr died. Speeding west, outpacing Cei's war-band. One of Arthur's trusted companions, Owain or Gwri, with a message from Arthur for the Irishman. "Twenty warriors are riding to your hall. Meet them on the road. Kill them all."

I told myself I was wrong. I told myself I'd lived too long with Myrddin, and it had made me see tricks where there were none. But I still could think of no other reason for the Irishman's messenger to be riding up to Arthur's hall.

And if I was right, and Cei and his men had been meant to die in the Irishman's hills, what would Arthur make of me and Peredur coming home, with our tale of wonder and our wooden cup? We'd be dead within a day, I reckoned. Arthur would have us snuffed out, for fear we knew the truth about the others.

While I stood there, silent, thinking those thoughts,

Peredur had fetched the cup out. The men of Din Branoc passed it around reverently while he told them how he came by it. "It's a sign from the lady of the waters. Just like the sword she gave him. She's on his side still. She gave me this cup, and I'll give it to Arthur."

"May it change his luck," said the headman, shaking his head. "Arthur's fortune's turned foul. A score or more of his companions have sneaked off to join Medrawt."

"Medrawt's raising himself an army down in the Summer Country," another said. "We heard Maelwas has promised him lordship of Aquae Sulis if he'll rid the place of Arthur."

"What about Myrddin?" I asked. "What news of him?"

The men looked sour. I saw a couple cross themselves at the mention of Myrddin's name. One said, "That old heathen."

"Myrddin was took bad, a month back or more," said the headman, and leaned over to spit into the fire.

"There was a girl at his place," explained one of the others, pleased to be sharing good gossip with one who'd not heard it yet. "She was some kinswoman of his, who'd been Gwenhwyfar's handmaiden, and after Gwenhwyfar ran off she got took in by Myrddin. I reckon she must have turned his head, for when she left him he fell down in a fit, and now he can't walk nor talk. He keeps to that place of his, with just a boy to look after him."

"Nothing so foolish as an old man running after a girl," said the headman.

"She enchanted him's what I heard," put in another man. "She wove spells round him to make him love her, so she could learn his secrets."

I let them talk. It was strange, meeting my story-self in their tales. How much of what they'd said was true? Was Myrddin really ailing? If he was, it was no more than he deserved. Yet I felt troubled at the thought of him sick, and none but the boy Cadwy to look after him. And I thought, if I could see him, talk to him, he'd tell me whether what I feared was true, and whether it would be safe or not for Peredur to go back to Sulis.

Lulled by the voices and the fire's warmth Peredur fell asleep, leaning against me, his head on my shoulder. I lowered him gently on to the straw-covered boards, and brushed away a strand of hair that had fallen across his angel face. His brow was hot. His fever was worse again.

"Can you care for him?" I asked the headman. "He needs food and warmth and shelter till he's mended."

The headman nodded, the others too. They were good people. The headman's wife, who'd sat silent till then, said, "I'll nurse him. You've done your best, but nursing's woman's work."

"You leaving us, Gwyn?" someone asked, as I stood and pulled my cloak about me.

I nodded; told them I'd be back in a day or so with a horse for Peredur and not to let him leave before I came.

"It's an ill night for travelling," the headman said. "Snow on the way, maybe."

"Myrddin's my kin," I said. "If he's sick, I must go to him."

259

And if he isn't sick, I thought, going out into the cold to saddle Dewi, I shall have some hard things to say to him.

I reached my master's house soon after sunrise. Tethered
Dewi outside in the slanting, orange light. Quiet as a
grave it felt, as I pushed in past the dangling talismans.
Dead birds and knotted twine. An armour of hoar-frost
on everything. When I spoke into the silence my breath
made steam in the cold air.

"Master?"

The boy Cadwy was curled on the floor by the
embers of the kitchen fire. I left him sleeping and
went into Myrddin's bed-space. A sickroom stink
came out at me as I lifted the curtain at the doorway.
My nose told me the story I'd heard at Din Branoc
was true, even before my eyes got used to the
curtained gloom and I made out Myrddin lying on the
bed.

I couldn't believe a man could have shrunk so, aged
so, in the time I'd been away. I felt like the prince in the
story, the one who sails away to see the Blessed Isles,
and comes home after a month at sea to find a hundred

years have passed on land and everyone he knows is gone to bones and ashes.

Myrddin wasn't quite a corpse yet. He looked like one, shrunk as he was, yellowish, with his mouth twisted sideways and his eyes sunk deep. But he was breathing, and when I leaned closer he grunted and his eyes came open.

I don't think he knew me. I pulled off my cap, let my dead-bracken hair hang down. "It's me, master."

He frowned. His breath came harsh and rusty. It sounded like fate sawing at the thread of his life with a blunt knife. When he spoke, he didn't make words, just grunts and growlings. It took me a while to understand that he was trying to say my name. One hand flapped on top of his blankets, trying to reach for me. The angry questions I'd been saving up for him all night drained out of me and I sat down on the edge of the bed and pressed his hand against my face.

"Gwyna?" he asked.

Cadwy appeared in the doorway, his hair flat on one side where he'd lain pressed against the warm tiles by the fire.

"It's just me," I said. "Gwyna. I'm back."

I washed Myrddin's blankets and changed the straw in his mattress. With Cadwy's help I scrubbed down the walls of his chamber, trying to get rid of that stale sickroom smell. I fed him bread softened in goat's milk. The day deepened round us, fat snowflakes dithering past the windows like goose-down. Myrddin talked, and slowly I learned to fish words out of the badgery growls and owlish hoots he made.

He said, "That fool Arthur came here. Said I should go into Sulis, to the surgeons' care. As if I'd trust those butchers, bleeding and poisoning me."

He said, "Arthur wanted some trick that would defeat Medrawt. I told him I'm too old for tricks. No more tricks. When the time comes, he'll have to fight Medrawt the old way."

He said, "Ah, but you remember the sword, Gwyna? The sword from the water. That was a thing! What a tale!"

It was time to be a girl again. I itched to be gone, to ride back to Peredur. But Peredur would be safe at Din Branoc, and someone had to nurse the old man. Cadwy had done his best, but nursing is woman's work.

I looked in the chest I'd found my man's gear in, and there I found my old dress laid, pressed between sheets of linen and sprinkled with dried lavender.

"Master done that," said Cadwy, watching me take it out and hold it up against myself. "That morning we woke up and you were gone, he went chasing off to Sulis to bring you home. When he came back, it was liked he'd aged ten years. He said you'd not been seen there. Said you'd ridden to join Cei's war-band, and would be killed for sure. Said he had to go after you. Said it would be his fault if you died. He sent me outside to saddle his horse, and set about folding up your things neat. When I came back in I found him lying on the floor there by the chest. All he could say was Gwyna at first. Not even that very clear."

I felt like I was dreaming. Had Myrddin really cared about me so much my running off could strike him dumb and cripple him? Or had he just been angry that I'd disobeyed him? It was easier to believe that. But when I sat by him he didn't seem angry. He held my hand and said, "Gwyna."

All that night and the next and the one after I sat by Myrddin's bed. Sometimes he slept, but mostly he talked. He talked and I listened. By the end, his voice was almost the last thing left of him.

"You shouldn't have gone with them, Gwyna. When I thought of you riding off with Cei's band, and death waiting for you in the hills, something in me broke."

I didn't like that. What did he expect? Pity? I'd used up all my pity on Cei and Gwenhwyfar and Bedwyr. I pushed myself backwards, away from the stench of his breath. "And how did you know death was waiting for me? You'd had Arthur tell the Irishman to betray us, that's how!"

Myrddin turned his head a little, looking at me. "You were always sharp, Gwyn."

"Not sharp enough, or I'd have guessed your plan and warned Cei what he was riding to!" My shadow was huge on the wall behind his bed. It raised its fists, like it was getting ready to smash his eggshell skull.

He said, "It had to be done. Men were talking of Cei as a rival to Arthur. He had to be removed. At least if the Irishman did it Arthur wouldn't be left with the blood of another kinsman on his hands. Arthur's our hope, Gwyna. He's the hope of Britain."

I spat on him. I turned my back and flung myself to the far side of the room and hit the wall hard with both my hands. "Some hope!" I shouted. "Arthur? You've wasted your life building him high and wrapping him up in stories, but Arthur hasn't cleaned the Saxons away. They're still sitting on their stolen lands, growing stronger and stronger, and laughing at us while we fight among ourselves. Arthur doesn't care about anything but making his own self fat and rich, and he hasn't even managed to do that very well. And all you can do is make up stories, make up lies, try and turn him into something that he isn't. And your stories won't last any longer than Arthur does. When he dies, the stories will die with him, and he'll be forgotten. And so will you. And so will all of it."

Long silence after that. Wind lifting the roof-tiles. I wouldn't look at Myrddin for a time. When I did I saw a silvery line, like the trail of a snail, shining on his face. I looked closer. His eyes were tight shut, the yellowish eyelids wrinkly like the skin of an old apple. Tears seeped out from under them. He was weeping.

"Master?" I asked, softer. "Why did you keep me? After the waterfall, I mean."

He didn't answer. I thought he'd fallen asleep. His eyes stayed shut and the tears kept coming. But after a minute he spoke again. Still not an answer, exactly. Just another story. But at least it was one I hadn't heard before.

Out east somewhere. Out in the round green downs behind Noviomagus. So many years back the Saxons hadn't quite settled there yet. But this summer night one of their war-keels has slid out of its shelter in the coves of Vectis and come to drop its crew of fighters in the riverside woods. They come fast up the white roads in the moonlight. Flames leap from kindled villas.

And suddenly a boy is running and running, with the smoke of his home going up into the sky behind him. And behind him, running faster, comes a Saxon raider, reaching for him, catching him, flinging him at the chalk ground.

"I grew up a slave," said Myrddin. "I grew up like a beast, shoving a plough for my Saxon master through some piece of Britain that he'd stolen. But I listened to my fellow slaves telling stories, about how the Saxons had come, and how it had been before, back in the days of Rome-in-Britain. Civilization. Peace."

And as soon as he was old and strong enough, he

started planning his escape. He watched the men and women around him, Saxon and slave alike, and learned the ways their eyes and minds and hearts worked, till he knew how to deceive them. He watched the seasons and the skies, making himself weather-wise. One night, when he knew a fog would rise, he ran off, leaving behind him a litter of clues that set his Saxon owners searching for him in every direction but the one he'd really gone. They hunted for him for a night and day, and then decided that he'd been a magician, and had turned himself into a vapour and blown away on the wind.

Safe in the ancient forests, he fled west, always west, keeping the sunset ahead of him till he reached country where there were no Saxons. He'd picked up a few handy conjuring tricks from travelling men he met upon the road, and he remembered stories he'd heard, and spun better ones of his own. Tall tales and hedge-magic paid his way from town to town, until at last he came to Urbs Legionis, where Ambrosius had his headquarters that year. He wasn't a fighter, but he hung around the fringes of the army, sure that Ambrosius was the man who'd smash the Saxons and bring back the light of better days. And when Ambrosius died and the war-bands of Britain took to fighting each other instead of Saxons, he chose the one he thought the strongest, the armoured cavalry of Arthur, Uthr's son. Oh, he wasn't stupid; he could see that Arthur only wanted what the others wanted: power and land. But maybe, if Arthur could be made strong enough, that wouldn't matter. The Romans only wanted power and land, and they ended up uniting half the world. So he tried to use his wits and stories to make Arthur great, in the hope he'd finish what Ambrosius began.

And all those years he never had a wife. Never had children. Never wanted any. Said he was too busy. Said they'd have slowed him down when he was travelling. He'd already lost one family. He couldn't live with the fear of losing another. He still remembered the night the raiders came, and how the screams of his mother and sisters had sounded among the dark downs, calling out to God, who took no more notice of them than of the cries of the owls in the woods.

And then, one wintry night, out in the wild western hills, below a place that Arthur's men were burning, he stopped beside a river-pool to watch a girl claw her way out of the water. He'd learned not to let himself feel pity for the waifs that Arthur's wars left homeless. He told himself, as he watched her dry out beside his campfire, that he had only rescued her because she would be useful. But something about her touched his heart. Afraid and all alone, she put him in mind of himself.

He meant to let her play her part, then leave her be. But afterwards, riding away from the river with Arthur's band while they talked about the miracle of the sword from the water he found that he could not forget the girl. How bright she was. How brave. Just the same age as he'd been when the Saxons took him. Abandoning her was like leaving his own self behind. As soon as he could he crept away from Arthur's victory feast and went back to the waterfall, and found her.

At first she'd been a worry to him. He'd dressed her as a boy and called her Gwyn, but there was always a fear she'd be discovered, that the truth would come out, and Arthur would smell some insult in what he'd done. But months went by, and the girl seemed well able to play the role he'd put her in.

He started to enjoy travelling with her. Liked waking to her tuneless singing as she made up his fire, or readied his breakfast. Liked answering her endless questions. Teaching her things. Watching her learn, and grow. Her high seriousness as she picked the yellow-white specks of flies' eggs from her pony's coat. He started to feel proud of her. The way she'd exposed that old fraudulent so-called saint down on the sea-coast that time! And kept quiet about it after, as if she'd thought Myrddin hadn't the wit to go and ask among the monks and work out for himself what she had done. . .

He started to see why even hard, strong-headed men like Cei went soft when they spoke about their children.

And when she grew older, and he couldn't keep up the pretence that she was a boy, he made a girl of her again. It had cost him dear, to go away that year and stay away while she learned women's ways. If he'd been in Aquae Sulis to keep Arthur in check, things might have gone better afterwards. But at the time, the girl had seemed more important. He was starting to fear that Arthur was not the man he'd hoped. Arthur couldn't unite the greedy, squabbling Britons, and maybe no one could. But if the girl could grow up happy maybe that would be enough. Enough reward for one life's work.

He found her a place in the household of Arthur's

wife. He was startled by how much it hurt him to let her go. When she stood weeping on that road in the west and said, "I don't want to leave you," he had had to hide his face from her in case she saw his tears. It would have been so easy to give in to her and let her stay. But she deserved better than a life used up in serving an old man. He wanted her to have the company of other girls, and the hope of a good marriage one day, and children of her own. So he made up a story to save her pride, and to give him a reason to see her sometimes. Told her she'd be his spy in Gwenhwyfar's house.

He half hoped Bedwyr might take the girl, after Bedwyr was wounded. No man could have asked for a better wife, and he knew the girl's upbringing had made her impatient with the settled, cow-ish ways of women. She would be happier with a husband who needed her help.

Then she told him of Gwenhwyfar's betrayal. A double betrayal, it seemed to him, for not only was Gwenhwyfar deceiving Arthur, she was making the girl part of her deception. What would happen when Arthur learned of it? What would he do to a girl who had helped his wife insult him?

He'd had to tell Arthur, of course, before Arthur found out for himself. He'd thought he'd be able to control Arthur's temper. Thought he'd snatch the girl safe out of the storm that followed. But she'd grown headstrong. He'd *taught* her to be headstrong, and he felt sorry for it, for it made her put herself in danger's path. Made her go riding off to her death.

He had folded her dress with his own trembling

hands. Folded and smoothed it and pressed it in linen, and scattered lavender on it to keep the moths and mould away. And all the weeks since, in his sickness, he had prayed to the God he did not believe in to send her back to him. And now, at the very end, here she was, leaning over his bed, watching him talk, a little small frown between her eyebrows, and her hand holding his.

"Gwyna," he said. "You've been a good daughter to me. And a good son, too."

Well, I didn't feel like a good daughter. I felt angry at him. If he loved me so, why had he never said? Why had he never said something till now? Why had he never told me till it was too late? I could have done with a father, but I'd always thought him just my master. I'd thought I was a servant, and a feckless one at that. I hadn't realized that love was part of the arrangement.

I wasn't even sure I believed his tale. I wanted to. But what if it was just another story, one to make sure I stayed by him, nursing him? That's the trouble with a story-spinner. You never know what's real and what's made up. Even when they are telling the truth, they can't stop themselves from spinning it into something better; something prettier, with more of a pattern to it.

And as I sat there, thinking on all this, I started to notice how quiet it was in the room. How even the rusty saw of Myrddin's breath had stopped. And I looked at him, and I saw that death had stolen him away from me.

I felt flat and quiet as the sand when the tide goes

out. I knelt beside Myrddin and held his hand until it was quite cold, wishing my hard words of earlier could be unsaid. "I didn't mean it," I told him. "About the stories. They'll last, even if nothing else does. They'll be like a light in the dark, and they'll burn as long as the dark lasts and go on out the far side of it into the morning."

Which I didn't believe, but I thought his ghost might be lingering close by, and I didn't want it to linger in a foul mood.

Morning came. Snow on the hill-tops. I woke the boy Cadwy and told him what had happened, and together we set out to dig a grave for our master. In the overgrown gardens the dead grass was grey with frost, matted and shaggy like an old badger. The ground beneath was frozen stone-hard. I broke a spade on it, and blistered my hands on a mattock shaft, and didn't make a scratch.

So I carried Myrddin to the woods, which clustered closer to the house each year. Light as a linnet he was, with all the words gone out of him. I took him to the great old oak, the ancient oak which had stood outside his house before it *was* a house, before the Romans even came to Britain. Its trunk was hollow, and the deep loam inside had been sheltered from the winter winds and had not frozen. I used my hands and the broken spade to shovel it out. While Cadwy watched, I laid Myrddin inside, and wrapped my own cloak round him, and I piled the loam back over him, heaping it over him with my hands and whispering what prayers I knew.

And there I left him, in the hollow oak. Littler trees will have grown up round it now, and the brambles tangled thick, and the nettles and the dock grown deep and green. And I suppose he lies there still, and will for ever.

XLVIII

That was the last I saw of Cadwy. He went home to his own people, to tell them about the girl who'd buried his master in a tree. Alone, I haunted that empty house like a ghost. The day was already dying. I hadn't the heart to start out for Din Branoc. I found Myrddin's old harp, and rubbed the mildew off it, and carved new pegs to replace the ones which had broken, and tuned the strings as best I could, and made it sing again, after its own crack-throated fashion. And that night, which was long and lonely and full of strange, small noises, I told over the songs and stories I'd heard Myrddin tell, making sure each one was fixed firm in my memory like a stone in a wall. It was something to do, and at the sound of my voice and the harp the ghosts of the place drew back and left me safe.

"Myrddin!"

I came awake thinking the voice was in my head. Just my dreams forming words out of the roaring rush of the

275

trees. The creak of branches. It was full daylight. I'd fallen asleep with the harp on my knees by the dying-down fire.

"Myrddin!" A shout outside, louder than the wind in the oak-tops. Other sounds too. Harness-jingle. Putter-thud of hooves, like fingers tapped on the drum-skin of the earth. I stumbled to the gateway, rubbing sleep from my eyes. Arthur and a half-dozen of his men waited outside the house on their white horses, looking warily at the talismans and spells Myrddin had hung about the entrance. Strange, I thought; these men would charge shield-walls, but not one would venture in through Myrddin's flimsy fence of charms.

Arthur rode closer when he saw me. Came and looked down at me through a smoke of hot horse-breath. He was all in armour, fish-scales gleaming, Caliburn at his side. His eyes considered me through the gap between the cheek-guards of his helmet. Either he didn't recognize me as his wife's companion or he didn't care. He said, "Where's Myrddin, girl?"

"Myrddin is gone, my lord," I said.

"Gone? I need him."

"He is dead."

Arthur looked hard at me a moment, then sniffed and started to turn his horse away. "I was afraid so."

Beyond him, on the road, a whole line of riders was passing. Spear-points and shield-fittings shining like candle-flames as the sun came up out of the bare woods. Arthur started to ride back to them, and the men who'd left the road with him turned their horses and galloped away to join the rest. But Arthur, maybe thinking I had some of my master's magic about me, hesitated, and looked back at me while his horse danced nervously.

"Medrawt is coming," he said. "We had word last night. We ride out to meet him."

I said nothing. It seemed to me that this was a strange time of year to make a war, with winter just closing its grip on the world. In Din Branoc they'd spoken as if Medrawt was raising an army and would wait till spring before he tried to overthrow his uncle. But then Medrawt had always been impatient. Medrawt couldn't wait the months it would take to gather a proper warband round him. He'd attack with whatever men he could muster. I imagined him hurrying them towards Sulis, his face set in that look of furious longing I'd seen on it the night I first met him.

If Arthur had been hoping for me to tell his fortune or weave a spell to help him, I disappointed him. He sniffed again – I think he had a cold – and kicked his horse and went off quick towards the road, galloping to the head of the passing column.

I watched them go. I watched their banners swim through the morning mist and pass into the west. And then I ran back inside and hunted out my travelling clothes. Because I'd worked out, see, that if Medrawt's band was coming to Sulis and Arthur's band was riding out to meet him, one or other of them would be passing Din Branoc. And if Arthur found Peredur there he'd want him silenced before he could tell of Cei's betrayal, and if Medrawt found him he'd press him to join his war-band, and either way it would end up with Peredur dead.

Which is how people mostly seem to end up when I try to look after them.

So I wasn't going to let it happen this time.

I put away Gwyna's dress for the last time, and pulled on my worn old breeks and tunic and my master's cloak, and saddled poor, patient Dewi and set off after Arthur's band. It was midday. The sun had gone, hidden behind a lot of lead-grey clouds. More snow started falling, whitening the road and making the winter trees look even starker. It was bad weather for fighting in. I thought that if Arthur had had Myrddin with him Myrddin would have read the sky-signs and told him snow was coming, and he'd not have gone.

Aiming to outpace the war-band, I turned Dewi off the miry roads and went over the heads of the downs. But I'd not gone more than halfway to Din Branoc when I heard a sound like a great wind down to my right where the road lay. I knew it too well, that sound, though I'd heard it only three times in my life. The bellowing of men, the clash and thud of weapons. The scream of a horse rising clear above it made Dewi's ears go up like two knives.

I reined him in and sat listening to the noise as it rose and fell, surging between the hills. Whatever was happening was happening out of my sight, beyond a spur of downland. I remembered the place: a ford in a gorse-speckled valley where the road from Sulis crossed a river. If Medrawt's army had reached it then they must have passed through Din Branoc the day before. I hoped that Peredur had had the good sense to hide from them. But good sense and Peredur were not things that went together. I could see him taking on Medrawt's whole war-band, sure that the lake-lady's cup would protect him.

I went west. A river barred my way, fat with autumn rain. I went north. A bog stretched across my path, too wet to pass. I wasted a while, searching for a crossing place. Itchy with worry. The battle noises grew fainter, rose up, died away. There was nothing for it but to risk the ford. Hope the battle there had finished, or at least moved off.

I followed the line of the river, crashing through dead bracken, alders, seeking paths through masses of gorse. After a time I started to pass wounded men dragging themselves away from the fight. Some lay moveless, dying or already dead. Others sat with their heads hanging down, too hurt to even bother glancing up as I went by. One shouted out to me, challenging me or begging help, but I kicked Dewi to a canter and went past. Then there was only silence, and my own sharp breathing, and the beat of Dewi's hooves. Snow coming down again. White patches on those drab ochre tangles of winter grass between the gorse. On the red sky, ravens wheeling.

And me on my tired pony coming around that shoulder of the hills at last and riding out on to the battle-place of Camlann.

XLIX

The river made a turn there, bent round a low hillock that stood above the ford. All the land from the river to the hillock's crown was sewn with spears and swords and fallen horses and dead men. Over my head the ravens went, their wings' black fingers combing sighs out of the air. Others hopped about among the dead, walking with careful, prissy steps. Arrows jutted out of the grass at all angles, like last year's thistles. On the slope of the hill a dying horse was struggling to stand up and falling back and struggling to stand up and falling back. . .

I brought Dewi to a halt and climbed down off him. Don't ask me why. It was a place that needed looking at, however much I didn't want to. I went along the riverside, then up the hill, setting my boots down carefully on the patches of bare ground between the dead The further I went, the harder it was to find ground that wasn't squelchy with blood or covered with heaped-up bodies and fallen shields. Here and there men stirred, or moaned, or called out for God, or for their mothers. There was that shit-smell of ripped open bodies. Two jackdaws squabbled over a drabble of gut, so blind with greed they didn't see me till I was almost on them, when they took off with flat tearing wing-beats and indignant cries. Arthur's dragon banner slapped at its staff, which poked sideways out of a snow-drift of dead white horses.

"Myrddin!"

It was the second time that day that voice had hailed me.

"Myrddin!"

Right at the hill's top he was. Arthur himself. As soon as I saw him I knew that it was him I'd come here looking for. I'd wanted to see him dead. But he wasn't. He was dragging himself across the smeared grass, reaching out towards me with one hand, parched voice cracking as he shouted at me.

"Myrddin!"

I suppose it was the cloak. The black hood I'd pulled up against the wind. And he probably couldn't see me too well. One of his eyes was gone, and the other was covered with blood that had spilled out of a gash in his head. There wasn't an inch of him had not been splashed with his own blood or some other man's, and where a gleam of his fine scale armour did show through that showed red too, reflecting the fat red sun that was going down into the mists and flood-waters of the levels westward. There was a great ragged hole punched right through that armour of his. An ordinary man would have been dead long before, and even the

Bear was failing, his strength slopping out of him into the grass.

I went closer.

"That girl," he said. "She told me you were gone."

I swallowed, and wondered about making a run for it, back down the hill to Dewi. Arthur looked finished, but there was no telling with a man like him. He might take it amiss if I deserted him, or explained I wasn't Myrddin. There was no shortage of spiky things laid round about that he might snatch up and hurl at me with his last strength.

So I said, "I have come back."

He beckoned me close so I could hear the words that he hissed out through his clenched teeth. "Take Caliburn. Cast it into the waters."

The sword was in his hand. I took it from him. After all, it's a woman's job to tidy up after the men. Caliburn felt smaller than I'd remembered. Stickier, too. Arthur grunted at me to hurry.

I've regretted it since. The gold on that sword would have kept me for a year. But there in the dusk with the mist rising round me, I felt the tug of a story. Arthur was right, for once. Things needed finishing.

I went slither-scrambling down the steep west slope of the hill, scattering the carrion birds. At the hill's foot were reeds and alders and the dark swirl of the river. The sun was wedged in the bare branches of the trees on the far bank. I paused and steadied myself and drew back my arm, and I flung Caliburn as far as I could out across the shining water.

Which wasn't very far. A sword is a heavy thing. It fell

a few feet from the bank. Hit the water with a flat splat like the sound a collop of dung makes dropping from a cow's arse. Went under with barely a ripple, and the river rolled over it.

Back up the hill I went, cursing its steepness, grabbing at tussocks of stiff grass for handholds. Arthur was watching me as I picked my way through the corpse-field to him. Not moving any more, but still not dead.

"Did you see her?" he asked, when I sat down beside him.

I could have told him a lie, but I was sick of them. So I shook my head, and said, "I saw nothing. Just the wind on the water."

People will tell you Arthur isn't dead. They'll tell you how he was borne away to lie in enchanted sleep under a hill, or on the Isle of Glass. But don't you believe them. I heard his last breath rattle up his throat. I watched his thick fingers dig into the soil as if he was clinging on to the world with all his might. And when he'd finished dying it was me who helped myself to his rings and his belt and his boots and the old gold cross he wore round his neck. I thought I'd earned them.

I left that place, and I rode hard, and I came to Din Branoc under a bleached-skull moon. A door banged in the wind. I walked Dewi up the muddy track, expecting to find more dead men. But I found no men at all. In the hall the women waited, cautious, wary, the way women wait when their husbands and their sons have gone to war. Medrawt had come through the day before, and made the men of fighting age join his war-band. By now they were either dead in the mud of Camlann-ford or in Aquae Sulis, taking for themselves the things that had been Arthur's.

"What, even Peredur?"

Not Peredur. When he heard word that Medrawt's crowd were coming the headman told Peredur to run and hide in the deep woods, for fear they'd know him as Arthur's man and do him harm. But Peredur had been too weak to run, and so the headman's wife had hidden him instead at her own fireside, among the women. Thin as he was from his long fever, pale and big-eyed, he made a pretty girl.

He wouldn't meet my eye when they took me to him. He hung his head, face down-cast, like a shy young maiden. He felt ashamed. He thought I'd laugh at him. But if I laughed, it was the laughter of relief, at finding him alive still. And when the women let us be I went to him, and hugged him, and whispered him my secret.

It felt good to tell it. People had sometimes found me out – Maelwas, and Gwenhwyfar – but I'd never *told* anyone before, "Gwyn and Gwyna, we're one and the same."

How he stared, when he began to understand me. I thought his understanding would carry him further and he'd work out it had been me beside the river, giving him that cup. But he never thought to. In his memory, the lake-lady was beautiful, and I was hardly that, with my flat round face like a barley bannock, and dressed up as a boy. I had to explain that, too.

"But I *saw* her," he said, struggling to make my face fit his remembering.

"You saw *me*. You were fevery. Half in a dream. . ."

"She kissed me."

"Yes," I said. I suppose I should have been shy about it. Maidenly. But I didn't feel maidenly. I felt like I'd ridden a long way, through battles and bad country, and he was my girl, waiting for me at journey's end. "Yes," I said, "she did." And I kissed him again. And we held each other, and it seemed to me he was pleased to find his old friend Gwyn was Gwyna after all.

"And if there's no lake-lady," he said, "is there really no magic? Is there nothing but tricks?"

"All tricks and stories, angel," I told him. "But that story's over now. It's time to start another."

Time to go, before winter tightened its grip so hard we could not go at all. We kept off the roads. Stuck to the woods and the quiet places. Just a young harper and his travelling-companion heading west, taking turns to ride our single pony. Soon we were across Tamar, out of the lands where Arthur had been known, and riding into country where he was just a story.

I paid our way with that story. It bought us food and warm beds and shelter from the winter's snow. All down the long tongue of Kernyw, where Britain narrows south and west into the grey ocean, in high halls and cow-warm herdsman's huts I told my tales of Arthur. For was I not Gwyn, son of Myrddin? And didn't I alone know the truth of it? And couldn't my beautiful young friend coax such songs from that cracked old harp that my words took flight upon the music, and wheeled about like swifts under the roof-beams?

I didn't tell what really happened, of course. At first I felt ashamed to be telling lies for a living, and it stung me that I could not tell the truth. But as the year ripened and our road wound west I came to see it didn't matter any longer what the truth had been. The real Arthur had been just a little tyrant in an age of tyrants. What mattered about him was the stories.

So I told stories of the high deeds of Arthur, and that last great battle where he and the traitor Medrawt fell. I put Cei in that fight, too, at Arthur's side. And I told how Arthur, as he lay dying, commanded Bedwyr, the last and bravest of his men, to take his sword Caliburn and throw it into a pool of still, clear water. But when he reached the water's edge Bedwyr could not bring himself to cast the sword away, so he hid it there among the reeds and went back to Arthur. And Arthur asked him, "What did you see?" And Bedwyr said, "I saw nothing but the wind on the water."

And then Arthur knew that he was lying, and he lifted himself up in that last red of the dying day and said, "Do as I ask, Bedwyr."

So back went Bedwyr to the water's side, and he took Caliburn and threw it out far, far across the mere. And a white hand, jewelled with water-drops, reached up out of its own reflection and caught the sword, and held it for a moment, and then drew it down beneath the waters.

And always at the end someone would ask, "Is it true he's not dead? Not really dead? Will Arthur return?" And I'd think, "Christ, I hope not!"

But they weren't thinking of the Arthur I'd known. It was Myrddin's Arthur they wanted back, the story-Arthur, the wisest and fairest and best king they had ever heard of. You can't blame people for wanting to believe there'd been a man like that once, and might be again.

So I'd say, "A ship came for Arthur as he lay on the field of Camlann. Away downriver it took him, to the sea. And on an island in the west he lies sleeping, healed of all his wounds. And he'll wake one day, when our need of him is bad enough, and he'll come back to us."

Then, if the hall was rich, and the listeners friendly, I'd unwrap the things I carried in my pack and say, "Here. This ring was Arthur's. This cross was the one he wore through all his battles." And I got enough in exchange for those relics that by the time we found our way to Din Tagyll in the springtime, my Peri and I, we had enough to buy passage with a trader, outbound for somewhere better.

So I'll end my story the way stories of Arthur always end. A little ship is setting out on the evening tide. Further and further from the land she goes, out beyond the breaking surf, out away from the cliff's lee and the chough's cry and the deepening shadows of the land, out to where the sun lies silver on the western sea. And the ship gets smaller and smaller as she goes away, until at last the faint square of her sail fades altogether into the mist of light where the waters meet the sky.

And the name of that ship, the name of that ship is called, *Hope*.

AUTHOR'S NOTE

Here Lies Arthur is not a historical novel, and in writing it I did not set out to portray "the real King Arthur", only to add my own little thimbleful to the sea of stories which surrounds him.

Very little historical evidence survives from fifth and sixth century Britain. The last Roman legions left around AD 410, but we don't know how long a Roman-style government went on operating after that, or who took power as it collapsed. There are references to states like Dumnonia and Calchvynydd, but we can't be sure where their borders lay, or who their rulers were. Nor do we know whether there was a major war between the Saxons and the native British, or whether Saxon settlement was a more gradual and peaceful process.

As for Arthur, we know only that he is mentioned as a war-leader in records compiled some centuries later. He is associated with a British victory at the battle of Mount Badon, which some traditions place near Bath (though dozens of alternative sites have been suggested). Some historians have seen him as a

Romano-British general fighting against the Saxons, some as a sort of emperor of Britain, and some claim he lived much earlier. Many would argue that he never existed at all.

The names of Bedwyr and Cei are associated with Arthur from some of the earliest stories. Bedwyr is remembered as Sir Bedivere, but his strength and heroism seem to be transferred to Lancelot in the later tales. Cei becomes Sir Kay, Arthur's brother or step-brother, who is often presented as a rather rude, boorish customer.

Peredur is the hero of one of the stories in *The Mabinogion*, a collection of Welsh myths and legends. In later mediaeval romances he becomes Perceval, the most human of Arthur's knights, and finds the Holy Grail. (And, yes, he really does spend his childhood dressed as a girl in several versions.)

Myrddin, the prototype for the Merlin of later stories, may actually have existed; there seem to have been two poets of that name in the late sixth century.

Gwyna, like Saint Porroc, is my own invention.

Anyone interested in learning more about the historical background and the development of the Arthurian legend will find that there is a vast array of books on the subject. Paul White's *King Arthur – Man or Myth?* (available from www.bossineybooks.com) might be a useful starting place, as it's fair, thorough, well written and only forty pages long! Kevin Crossley-Holland's *Arthur* trilogy, published by Orion, is a great modern reworking of the mediaeval Arthurian romances.

As usual, I'm indebted to my editors at Scholastic, Kirsten Stansfield, Amanda Punter and Katy Moran (who also came up with the title). Tim Wright, whose knowledge of the subject (and most others) is far deeper than my own, was a source of much useful information, as was George Southcombe. Lu and Tizzy Palmes helped me with the horses. Needless to say, any mistakes are my own silly fault.

My interest in Arthur began on 5 July 1981 at about two o'clock in the afternoon, when I wandered into the ABC cinema in Brighton to watch John Boorman's film *Excalibur* (cert. 15). Brilliant, beautiful and barking mad, it's still my favourite modern retelling of the legends.

Philip Reeve, Dartmoor
2006

NOTE ON PRONUNCIATION

Due to the very different sound systems of English and Welsh, many of these are approximate rather than exact representations of the Welsh pronunciations. Italics show that the syllable is stressed.

NAME	PRONUNCIATION
Bannawg	*ban*-owg
Bedwyr	*bed*wirr
Cadwy	*kad*wi
Calchvynydd	kalck*va*nith*
Cei	kay
Celemon	*ke*lemon
Celliwic	keth*lee*wick
Cunaide	*koon*-eyed
Dewi	deh-wee
Din Branoc	deen *bra*nnock
Din Tagyll	deen *ta*gihl
Greidawl	*grayd*-owl
Gwenhwyfar	gooenn*hooee*varr
Gworthigern	goo-or*thee*gern**
Gwri	*goo*ree
Gwyn	goo*inn*
Gwyna	goo*inn*ah
Gwynedd	goo*inn*eth*
Kernyw	*ker*nioo
Maelwas	*maee*lwahss
Medrawt	*medd*r-out
Myrddin	*mar*thinn*
Peredur	per*re*dirr
Powys	*poh*wiss
Rheged	*hreh*gedd
Rhiannedd	hrree*ann*eth*
Tewdric	*tao*-drick
Trwch Trwyth	toorckh *troith*
Uthr	*ith*irr**
Ygerna	ee*ger*rna
Ynys Wydryn	*un*-niss *wid*rinn
Ysbaddaden	uss-bad*ath*enn*

* In these words, "th" is pronounced as it is in the English word "then"
** In these words, "th" is pronounced as it is in the English word "thin"

With thanks to Dr Mari Jones of the University of Cambridge